AS-Lev
Biology

The Revision Guide

Exam Board: OCR

Published by Coordination Group Publications Ltd.

Editors:
Amy Boutal, Ellen Bowness, Joe Brazier, Charlotte Burrows, Tom Cain, Katherine Craig, Laurence Stamford, Jane Towle.

Contributors:
Gloria Barnett, James Foster, Barbara Green, Liz Masters, Richard Parsons, Stephen Phillips, Adrian Schmit, Sophie Watkins, Anna-fe Williamson.

Proofreaders:
Sue Hocking, Glenn Rogers.

ISBN: 978 1 84762 122 1

With thanks to Jan Greenway for the copyright research.

With thanks to Science Photo Library for permission to reproduce the photograph used on page 21.

Data used to construct the graph on page 87 from R. Doll, R. Peto, J. Boreham, I Sutherland. Mortality in relation to smoking: 50 years' observations on male British doctors. BMJ 2004; 328:1519.

Exam question graph on page 91 © 2006 WWF (panda.org). Some rights reserved.

Groovy website: www.cgpbooks.co.uk
Jolly bits of clipart from CorelDRAW®
Printed by Elanders Hindson Ltd, Newcastle upon Tyne.

Contents

The Scientific Process

'How Science Works' is all about the scientific process — how we develop and test scientific ideas. It's what scientists do all day, every day (well, except at coffee time — never come between a scientist and their coffee).

Scientists Come Up with **Theories** — Then **Test Them**...

Science tries to explain **how** and **why** things happen — it **answers questions**. It's all about seeking and gaining **knowledge** about the world around us. Scientists do this by **asking** questions and **suggesting** answers and then **testing** them, to see if they're correct — this is the **scientific process**.

1) **Ask** a question — make an **observation** and ask **why or how** it happens. E.g. why is trypsin (an enzyme) found in the small intestine but not in the stomach?
2) **Suggest** an answer, or part of an answer, by forming a **theory** (a possible **explanation** of the observations) e.g. pH affects the activity of enzymes. (Scientists also sometimes form a **model** too — a **simplified picture** of what's physically going on.)
3) Make a **prediction** or **hypothesis** — a **specific testable statement**, based on the theory, about what will happen in a test situation. E.g. trypsin will be active at pH 8 (the pH of the small intestine) but inactive at pH 2 (the pH of the stomach).
4) Carry out a **test** — to provide **evidence** that will support the prediction (or help to disprove it). E.g. measure the rate of reaction of trypsin at various pH levels.

The evidence supported Quentin's Theory of Flammable Burps.

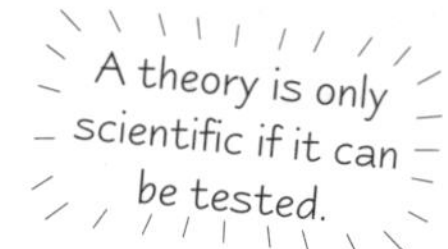

...Then They **Tell** Everyone About Their **Results**...

The results are **published** — scientists need to let others know about their work. Scientists publish their results in **scientific journals**. These are just like normal magazines, only they contain **scientific reports** (called papers) instead of the latest celebrity gossip.

1) Scientific reports are similar to the **lab write-ups** you do in school. And just as a lab write-up is **reviewed** (marked) by your teacher, reports in scientific journals undergo **peer review** before they're published.
2) The report is sent out to **peers** — other scientists that are experts in the **same area**. They examine the data and results, and if they think that the conclusion is reasonable it's **published**. This makes sure that work published in scientific journals is of a **good standard**.
3) But peer review **can't guarantee** the science is **correct** — other scientists still need to **reproduce** it.
4) Sometimes **mistakes** are made and bad work is published. Peer review **isn't perfect** but it's probably the best way for scientists to self-regulate their work and to publish **quality reports**.

...Then **Other Scientists** Will **Test** the Theory Too

Other scientists read the published theories and results, and try to **test the theory** themselves. This involves:

- Repeating the **exact same experiments**.
- Using the theory to make **new predictions** and then testing them with **new experiments**.

If the **Evidence** Supports a Theory, It's **Accepted** — **for Now**

1) If all the experiments in all the world provide good evidence to back it up, the theory is thought of as **scientific 'fact'** (for now).
2) But it will never become **totally indisputable** fact. Scientific **breakthroughs or advances** could provide new ways to question and test the theory, which could lead to **new evidence** that **conflicts** with the current evidence. Then the testing starts all over again...

And this, my friend, is the **tentative nature of scientific knowledge** — it's always **changing** and **evolving**.

The Scientific Process

So scientists need evidence to back up their theories. They get it by carrying out experiments, and when that's not possible they carry out studies. But why bother with science at all? We want to know as much as possible so we can use it to try and improve our lives (and because we're nosy).

Evidence Comes from *Lab Experiments*...

1) Results from **controlled experiments** in **laboratories** are **great**.
2) A lab is the easiest place to **control variables** so that they're all **kept constant** (except for the one you're investigating).
3) This means you can draw meaningful **conclusions**.

For example, if you're investigating how temperature affects the rate of an enzyme-controlled reaction you need to keep everything but the temperature constant, e.g. the pH of the solution, the concentration of the solution etc.

...and *Well-Designed Studies*

1) There are things you **can't** investigate in a lab, e.g. whether stress causes heart attacks. You have to do a study instead.
2) You still need to try and make the study as controlled as possible to make it **more reliable**. But in reality it's **very hard** to control **all the variables** that **might** be having an effect.
3) You can do things to help, e.g. have **matched groups** — **choose two groups** of people (those who have quite stressful jobs and those who don't) who are **as similar as possible** (same mix of ages, same mix of diets etc.). But you can't easily rule out every possibility.

Samantha thought her study was very well designed — especially the fitted bookshelf.

Society *Makes Decisions* Based on *Scientific Evidence*

1) Lots of scientific work eventually leads to **important discoveries** or breakthroughs that could **benefit humankind**.
2) These results are **used by society** (that's you, me and everyone else) to **make decisions** — about the way we live, what we eat, what we drive, etc.
3) All sections of society use scientific evidence to make decisions, e.g. politicians use it to devise policies and individuals use science to make decisions about their own lives.

Other factors can **influence** decisions about science or the way science is used:

Economic factors

- Society has to consider the **cost** of implementing changes based on scientific conclusions — e.g. the **NHS** can't afford the most expensive drugs without **sacrificing** something else.
- Scientific research is **expensive** so companies won't always develop new ideas — e.g. developing new drugs is costly, so pharmaceutical companies often only invest in drugs that are likely to make them **money**.

Social factors

- **Decisions** affect **people's lives** — E.g. scientists may suggest **banning smoking** and **alcohol** to prevent health problems, but shouldn't **we** be able to **choose** whether **we** want to smoke and drink or not?

Environmental factors

- Scientists believe **unexplored regions** like remote parts of rainforests might contain **untapped drug** resources. But some people think we shouldn't **exploit** these regions because any interesting finds may lead to **deforestation** and **reduced biodiversity** in these areas.

So there you have it — how science works...

Hopefully these pages have given you a nice intro to how science works, e.g. what scientists do to provide you with 'facts'. You need to understand this, as you're expected to know how science works — for the exam and for life.

Eukaryotic Cells and Organelles

Cells — what an original way to start a biology book... Oh well. There are two types of cell — prokaryotic and eukaryotic. Eukaryotic cells are stuffed full of organelles (all the tiny bits and bobs that you can only see in detail with a fancy microscope), and you need to know about all of them...

Organisms can be **Prokaryotes** or **Eukaryotes**

1) Prokaryotic organisms are **prokaryotic cells** (i.e. they're single-celled organisms) and eukaryotic organisms are made up of **eukaryotic cells**.
2) Both types of cells contain **organelles**. Organelles are **parts** of cells — each one has a **specific function**.

1) Eukaryotic cells are **complex** and include all **animal** and **plant cells**.
2) Prokaryotic cells are **smaller** and **simpler**, e.g. bacteria.

Plant *and* ***Animal*** *Cells are Both* ***Eukaryotic***

Eukaryotic cells are generally a **bit more complicated** than prokaryotic cells. You've probably been looking at **animal** and **plant cell** diagrams for years, so hopefully you'll be familiar with some of the bits and pieces...

Animal Cell

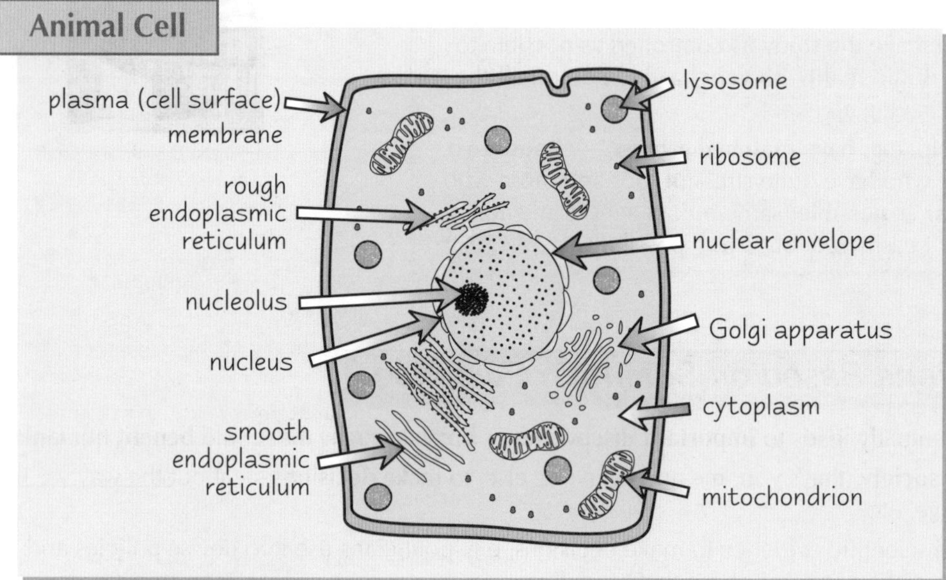

The new head of department was insane in the membrane.

Plant Cell

Plant cells have all the **same organelles** as animal cells, but with a few **added extras**:

- a **cell wall** with **plasmodesmata** ('holes' for exchanging substances with adjacent cells),
- a **vacuole** (compartment that contains cell sap),
- and of course good old **chloroplasts**.

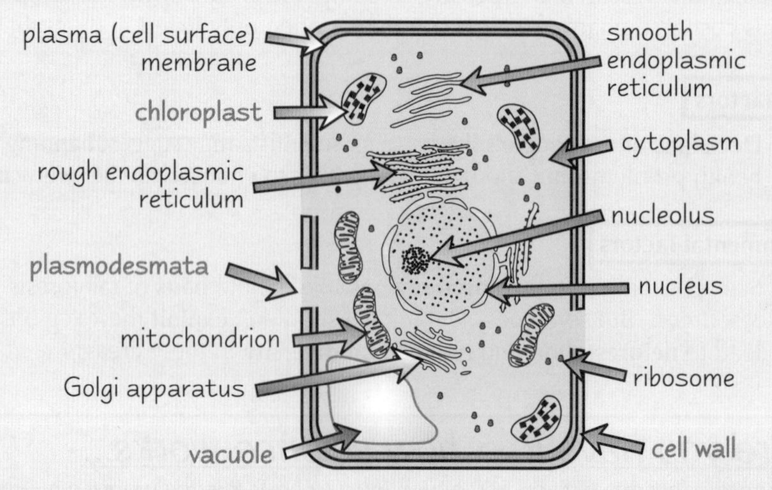

Eukaryotic Cells and Organelles

Different Organelles have Different Functions

This giant table contains a big list of organelles — you need to know the **structure** and **function** of them all. Sorry. Most organelles are surrounded by **membranes**, which sometimes causes confusion — don't make the mistake of thinking that a diagram of an organelle is a diagram of a whole cell. They're not cells — they're **parts of** cells.

ORGANELLE	DIAGRAM	DESCRIPTION	FUNCTION
Plasma (cell surface) membrane	plasma membrane cytoplasm	The membrane found on the **surface** of **animal cells** and just inside the cell wall of **plant cells** and **prokaryotic cells**. It's made mainly of **lipids** and **protein**.	**Regulates the movement** of substances into and out of the cell. It also has **receptor molecules** on it, which allow it to respond to chemicals like hormones.
Cell wall	plasma membrane cell wall cytoplasm	A rigid structure that surrounds **plant cells**. It's made mainly of the carbohydrate **cellulose**.	**Supports** plant cells.
Nucleus	nuclear envelope nucleolus nuclear pore chromatin	A large organelle surrounded by a **nuclear envelope** (double membrane), which contains many **pores**. The nucleus contains **chromatin** and often a structure called the **nucleolus**.	**Chromatin** is made from proteins and DNA (DNA **controls the cell's activities**). The pores allow substances (e.g. RNA) to move between the nucleus and the cytoplasm. The **nucleolus** makes **ribosomes** (see below).
Lysosome		A **round organelle** surrounded by a **membrane**, with no clear internal structure.	Contains **digestive enzymes**. These are kept separate from the cytoplasm by the surrounding membrane, and can be used to **digest invading cells** or to **break down** worn out components of the cell.
Ribosome	small subunit large subunit	A **very small organelle** that either **floats free** in the cytoplasm or is attached to the **rough endoplasmic reticulum**.	The **site** where **proteins** are made.

Eukaryotic Cells and Organelles

ORGANELLE	DIAGRAM	DESCRIPTION	FUNCTION
Rough Endoplasmic Reticulum (RER)	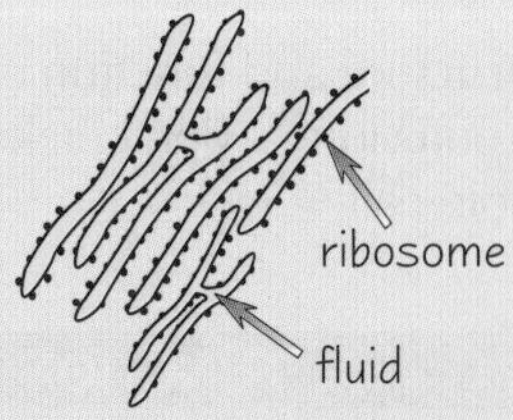 ribosome fluid	A system of membranes enclosing a fluid-filled space. The surface is **covered with ribosomes.**	**Folds** and **processes proteins** that have been made at the ribosomes.
Smooth Endoplasmic Reticulum	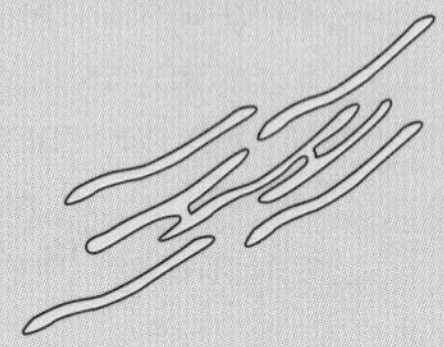	Similar to rough endoplasmic reticulum, but with no **ribosomes.**	**Synthesises** and **processes lipids.**
Vesicle	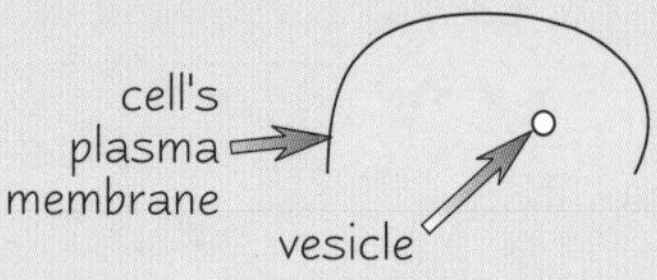 cell's plasma membrane vesicle	A small **fluid-filled sac** in the cytoplasm, surrounded by a membrane.	**Transports substances** in and out of the cell (via the plasma membrane) and between organelles. Some are formed by the Golgi apparatus or the endoplasmic reticulum, while others are formed at the cell surface.
Golgi Apparatus	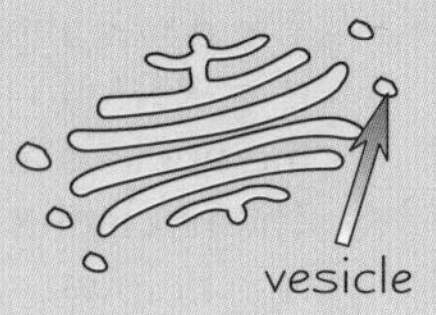 vesicle	A group of fluid-filled **flattened sacs.** Vesicles are often seen at the edges of the sacs.	It **processes** and **packages** new lipids and proteins. It also **makes lysosomes.**
Mitochondrion	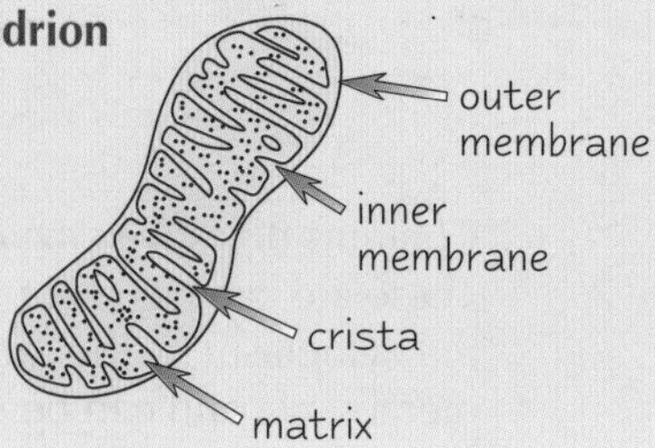 outer membrane inner membrane crista matrix	They're usually oval-shaped. They have a **double membrane** — the inner one is folded to form structures called **cristae.** Inside is the **matrix,** which contains enzymes involved in respiration (but, sadly, no Keanu Reeves).	The **site of aerobic respiration,** where **ATP** is produced. They're found in large numbers in cells that are very **active** and require a lot of **energy.**
Chloroplast	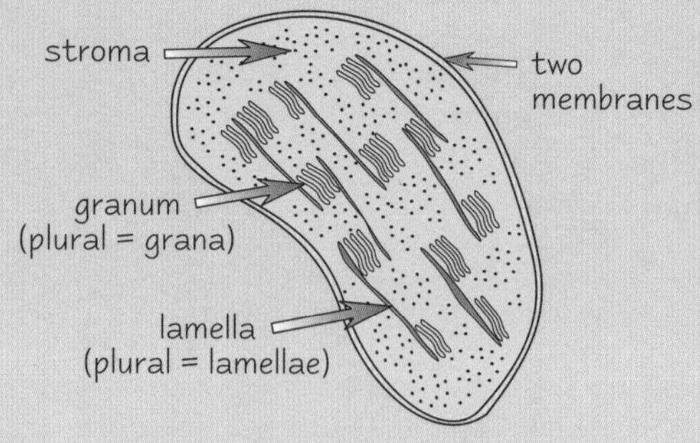 stroma two membranes granum (plural = grana) lamella (plural = lamellae)	A small, **flattened** structure found in **plant cells.** It's surrounded by a **double membrane,** and also has membranes inside called **thylakoid membranes.** These membranes are stacked up in some parts of the chloroplast to form **grana.** Grana are linked together by lamellae — thin, flat pieces of thylakoid membrane.	The **site** where **photosynthesis** takes place. Some parts of photosynthesis happen in the **grana,** and other parts happen in the **stroma** (a thick fluid found in chloroplasts).

Eukaryotic Cells and Organelles

ORGANELLE	DIAGRAM	DESCRIPTION	FUNCTION
Centriole		Small, **hollow cylinders**, containing a ring of microtubules (tiny protein cylinders).	Involved with the **separation of chromosomes** during cell division (see p. 20).
Cilia	side / cross-section	Small, **hair-like structures** found on the surface membrane of some **animal cells**. In cross-section, they have an outer membrane and a ring of nine pairs of **protein microtubules** inside, with a single pair of microtubules in the middle.	The microtubules allow the cilia to **move**. This movement is used by the cell to **move substances along the cell surface**.
Flagellum		Flagella on eukaryotic cells are **like cilia** but longer. They **stick out** from the cell surface and are surrounded by the plasma membrane. Inside they're like cilia too — two **microtubules** in the centre and nine pairs around the edge.	The microtubules **contract** to make the flagellum **move**. Flagella are used like **outboard motors** to propel cells forward (e.g. when a **sperm cell** swims).

Practice Questions

Q1 Describe the function of vesicles.

Q2 How does the structure of rough endoplasmic reticulum differ from that of smooth endoplasmic reticulum?

Q3 What is the function of chloroplasts?

Q4 What is the function of the centrioles?

Q5 Name one organelle found only in animal cells.

Exam Questions

Q1 Give four things commonly found in plant cells but not in animal cells. [4 marks]

Q2 a) Identify these two organelles from their descriptions as seen in an electron micrograph.

i) An oval-shaped organelle surrounded by a double membrane. The inner membrane is folded and projects into the inner space, which is filled with a grainy material. [1 mark]

ii) A collection of flattened membrane 'sacs' arranged roughly parallel to one another. Small, circular structures are seen at the edges of these 'sacs'. [1 mark]

b) State the function of the two organelles that you have identified. [2 marks]

That's enough talk of fluid-filled sacs for my liking. Scientists these days...

'Organelle' is a very pretty-sounding name for all those blobs. Actually, under a microscope some of them are really quite fetching — well I think so anyway, but then my mate finds sheep fetching, so there's no accounting for taste. Anyway, you need to know the names and functions of all the organelles and also what they look like.

Organelles Working Together

After that endless list of organelles, you might need a few minutes to regain consciousness... Then you can read this lovely page about how they work together to produce proteins. And there's some stuff on cytoskeletons too... Whoop!

Organelles are Involved in Protein Production

1) Proteins are made at the **ribosomes**.
2) The ribosomes on the **rough endoplasmic reticulum (ER)** make proteins that are **excreted** or attached to the **cell membrane**. The free ribosomes in the **cytoplasm** make proteins that **stay in the cytoplasm**.
3) New proteins produced at the rough ER are **folded** and **processed** (e.g. sugar chains are added) in the rough ER.
4) Then they're **transported** from the ER to the **Golgi apparatus** in **vesicles**.
5) At the Golgi apparatus, the proteins may undergo **further processing** (e.g. sugar chains are trimmed or more are added).
6) The proteins enter more **vesicles** to be transported around the cell. E.g. glycoproteins (found in **mucus**) move to the cell surface and are **secreted**.

Protein Production in a Cell

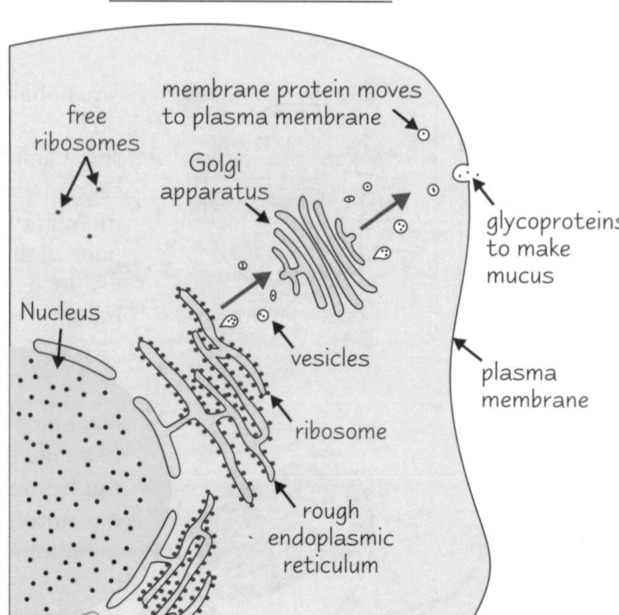

The Cytoskeleton has Several Functions

1) The organelles in cells are surrounded by the **cytoplasm**. The cytoplasm is more than just a solution of chemicals though — it's got a **network of protein threads** running through it. These protein threads are called the **cytoskeleton**.
2) In eukaryotic cells the protein threads are arranged as **microfilaments** (small solid strands) and **microtubules** (tiny protein cylinders).

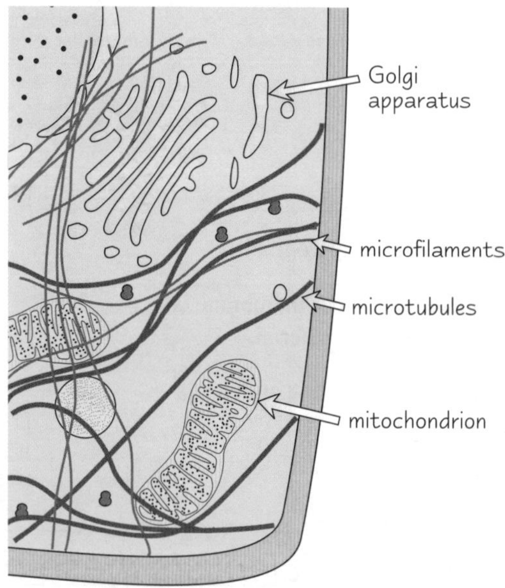

The cytoskeleton has **four main functions**:

1) The microtubules and microfilaments **support** the cell's organelles, keeping them **in position**.
2) They also help to **strengthen** the cell and **maintain its shape**.
3) As well as this, they're responsible for the **transport of materials** within the cell. For example, the movement of **chromosomes** when they separate during cell division depends on contraction of microtubules in the spindle (see page 20 for more on cell division).
4) The proteins of the cytoskeleton can also cause the cell to **move**. For example, the movement of **cilia** and **flagella** is caused by the cytoskeletal protein filaments that run through them. So in the case of single cells that have a flagellum (e.g. sperm cells), the cytoskeleton propels the **whole cell**.

Prokaryotic Cells

Prokaryotes are a Different Kind of Cell

You need to be able to compare and contrast prokaryotic and eukaryotic cells. This big orange table should help...

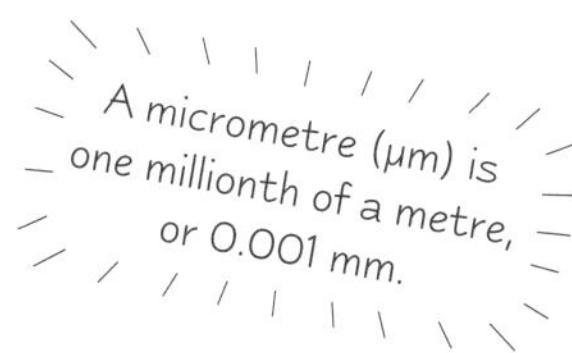

PROKARYOTES	EUKARYOTES
Extremely small cells (less than 2 μm diameter)	Larger cells (2-200 μm diameter)
DNA is circular	DNA is linear
No nucleus — DNA free in cytoplasm	Nucleus present — DNA is inside nucleus
Cell wall made of a polysaccharide, but not cellulose or chitin	No cell wall (in animals), cellulose cell wall (in plants) or chitin cell wall (in fungi)
Few organelles, no mitochondria	Many organelles, mitochondria present
Small ribosomes	Larger ribosomes
Example: *E. coli* bacterium	**Example:** Human liver cell

Bacterial Cells are Prokaryotic

1) Prokaryotes like bacteria are roughly a **tenth the size** of eukaryotic cells.
2) This means that normal microscopes aren't really powerful enough to look at their **internal structure**.
3) The diagram shows a bacterial cell as seen under an **electron microscope** (see next page).

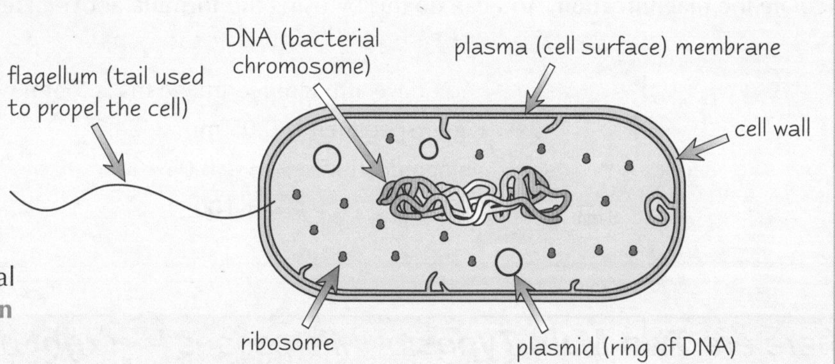

Practice Questions

Q1 Give two structures that you might find in a prokaryotic cell but not in an animal cell.

Q2 An unidentified cell is found to contain mitochondria. Is it prokaryotic or eukaryotic?

Exam Questions

Q1 Some mucus-secreting cells were immersed in a solution of radioactive amino acids. Every five seconds, some of the cells were removed and their organelles were separated and analysed. The radioactivity in the different organelles was measured for each five second interval.

When answering the first two questions below, use organelles from this list —
Golgi apparatus, ribosomes, rough endoplasmic reticulum, vesicles.

a) In which of these organelles would you expect radioactivity to appear first? Explain your answer. [2 marks]

b) After 5 minutes, the Golgi apparatus had become radioactive.
Which other organelle(s) would be radioactive by this time? [3 marks]

c) The researchers were particularly interested in the cells' vesicles. What is the function of vesicles? [1 mark]

Q2 Give three functions of a cell's cytoskeleton. [3 marks]

A cell without a nucleus — that can't be right... it's like Posh without Becks...

Prokaryotes are way, way older than eukaryotes. In fact, most cellular biologists think that mitochondria and chloroplasts are remnants of ancient prokaryotes that lived inside the first eukaryotes and eventually just became part of them... Mad.

Studying Cells — Microscopes

If you were born over a century ago then you wouldn't have had to learn all this stuff about organelles because people wouldn't have known anything about them. But then better microscopes were invented and here we are. Unlucky.

Magnification is *Size, Resolution* is *Detail*

We all know that microscopes produce a **magnified image** of a sample, but **resolution** is just as important...

1) MAGNIFICATION is how much **bigger** the image is than the specimen (the sample you're looking at). It's calculated using this formula:

$$\text{magnification} = \frac{\text{length of image}}{\text{length of specimen}}$$

2) RESOLUTION is how **detailed** the image is. More specifically, it's how well a microscope **distinguishes** between **two points** that are **close together**. If a microscope lens can't separate two objects, then increasing the magnification won't help.

You Need to be Able to Calculate *the* Linear Magnification *of an Image*

In the exam, you might be told the actual and magnified size of an object and then be asked to calculate the **magnification**. You can do this by using the **formula** above. Here's an example...

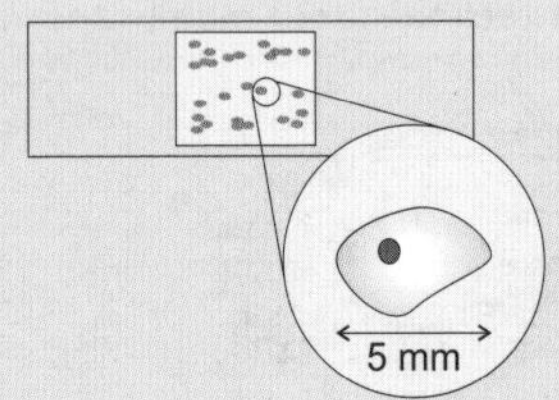

You have a magnified image that's 5 mm wide.
Your specimen is 0.05 mm wide.
magnification = 5 ÷ 0.05
= **× 100**.

Georgina didn't believe in the need for microscopes — she had her trusty varifocals.

There are Two Main Types *of Microscope —* Light *and* Electron

Light microscopes

1) **Light microscopes** use light (no surprises there).
2) They have a **lower resolution** than electron microscopes — they have a maximum resolution of about **0.2 micrometres** (μm).
3) The maximum useful **magnification** of a light microscope is about **× 1500**.

Electron microscopes

Electron microscopes use **electrons** instead of light to form an image. They have a **higher resolution** than light microscopes so give **more detailed images**. There are two kinds of electron microscope:

1) **Transmission electron microscope** (TEM) — use **electromagnets** to focus a **beam of electrons**, which is then transmitted **through** the specimen. **Denser** parts of the specimen absorb **more electrons**, which makes them look **darker** on the image you end up with. TEMs are good because they provide **high resolution images**, but they can only be used on **thin specimens**.
2) **Scanning electron microscope** (SEM) — **scan** a beam of electrons across the specimen. This **knocks off** electrons from the specimen, which are gathered in a **cathode ray tube** to form an **image**. The images produced show the **surface** of the specimen and can be **3-D**. But they give **lower resolution images** than TEMs.

There are quite a lot of facts and figures about microscopes here. You need to know about the **magnification** and **resolution** of light microscopes and both types of electron microscope. So I've put all the important numbers in this box 'cos I'm nice like that.

	light microscope	TEM	SEM
maximum resolution	0.2 μm	0.0001 μm	0.005 μm
maximum magnification	× 1500	more than × 1 000 000	less than × 1 000 000

Studying Cells — Microscopes

You Need to **Stain Your Samples**

1) In light microscopes and TEMs, the beam of light (or electrons) **passes through the object** being viewed. An image is produced because some parts of the object **absorb more light** (or electrons) than others.
2) Sometimes the object being viewed is completely **transparent**. This makes the whole thing look **white** because the light rays (or electrons) just pass **straight through**.
3) To get round this, the object can be **stained**:

- For the light microscope, this means using some kind of **dye**. Common stains are **methylene blue** and **eosin**. The stain is taken up by some parts of the object more than others — the **contrast** makes the different parts show up.
- For the electron microscope, objects are dipped in a solution of **heavy metals** (like **lead**). The metal ions scatter the electrons, again creating contrast.

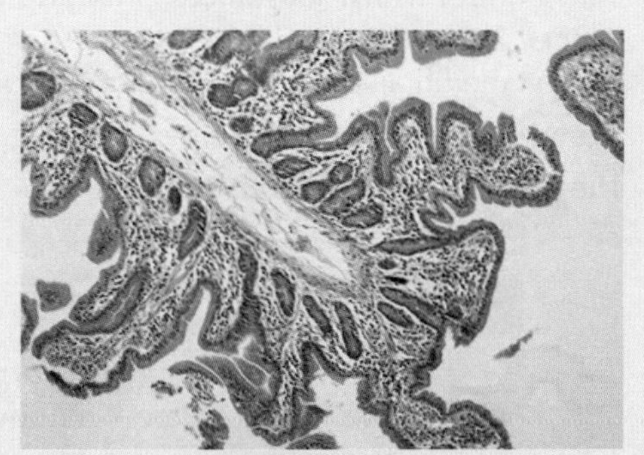

An eosin stained specimen, as seen through a light microscope.

Either way, an image is produced because some parts of the object show up **darker** than others.

Practice Questions

Q1 What is the formula for calculating the magnification of an image?

Q2 What is meant by a microscope's resolution?

Q3 Why is it sometimes necessary to stain an object before viewing it through a microscope?

Exam Questions

Q1 An insect is 0.5 mm long. In a book, a picture of the insect is 8 cm long.
Calculate the magnification of the image. [2 marks]

Q2 The table shows the dimensions of some different organelles found in animal cells.

organelle	diameter / μm
lysosome	0.1
mitochondrion	2
nucleus	5
ribosome	0.02
vesicle	0.05

a) Name those organelles in the table that would be visible using a good quality light microscope.
Explain your answer. [3 marks]

b) Which organelles would be visible using an SEM? Explain your answer. [2 marks]

'Staining your samples' — a common problem at the start of exams...

OK, there's quite a bit of info on these pages, but the whole magnification thing isn't all that bad once you've given it a go. Make sure you can define resolution — that's a bit trickier. You also need to have a good grasp of what TEMs and SEMs are, and how the resolution of their images compare to each other and to those of light microscopes. Happy memorising...

Cell Membranes — The Basics

You might remember a bit about cell membranes from that giant pink table of fun back in Section 1. Well now it's time to delve a little deeper and see exactly what they do — lucky you.

Membranes Control What **Passes Through** Them

Cells, and many of the **organelles** inside them, are surrounded by **membranes**, which have a **range of functions**:

Membranes at the surface of cells (PLASMA membranes)

1) They control **which substances enter and leave** the cell. They're **partially permeable** — they let some molecules through but not others. Substances can move across the plasma membrane by **diffusion**, **osmosis** or **active transport** (see pages 16-19).
2) They allow **recognition** by other cells, e.g. the cells of the **immune system** (see p. 81).
3) They allow **cell communication** (see p. 14 for more).

Partially permeable membranes can be useful at sea

Membranes within cells

1) The membranes around **organelles divide** the cell into different **compartments**. This makes different **functions more efficient**, e.g. the substances needed for **respiration** (like enzymes) are kept together inside **mitochondria**.
2) The membranes of some organelles are folded, increasing their **surface area** and making **chemical reactions more efficient**. E.g. the **inner membrane** of a mitochondrion contains **enzymes** needed for **respiration**. It has a large surface area, which **increases** the **number** of enzymes present and makes respiration more efficient.
3) They can form **vesicles** to **transport** substances between different areas of the cell (see p. 6).
4) They control **which substances enter and leave** the organelle, e.g. RNA (see p. 63) leaves the nucleus via the nuclear membrane. They are also **partially permeable**.

Cell Membranes have a **'Fluid Mosaic' Structure**

The **structure** of all membranes is basically the same. They're composed of **lipids** (mainly phospholipids), **proteins** and **carbohydrates** (usually attached to proteins or lipids).

1) In 1972, the **fluid mosaic model** was suggested to describe the **arrangement of molecules** in the membrane.
2) In the model, **phospholipid molecules** form a continuous, double layer (**bilayer**).
3) This bilayer is '**fluid**' because the phospholipids are **constantly moving**.
4) **Cholesterol** molecules are present within the bilayer (see next page).
5) **Protein molecules** are scattered through the bilayer, like tiles in a **mosaic**.
6) Some **proteins** have a **polysaccharide** (carbohydrate) **chain** attached — these are called **glycoproteins**.
7) Some **lipids** also have a **polysaccharide chain** attached — these are called **glycolipids**.

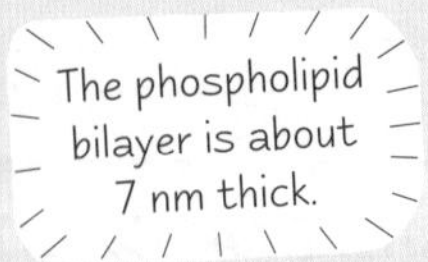

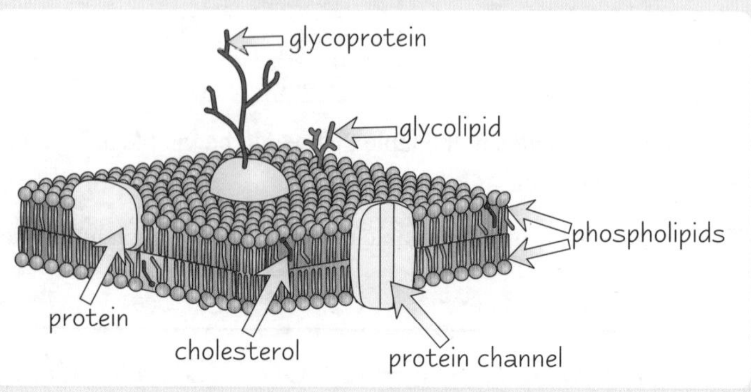

Cell Membranes — The Basics

The Different Components of Cell Membranes have Different Roles

Phospholipids Form a Barrier to Dissolved Substances

1) **Phospholipid molecules** have a 'head' and a 'tail'.
2) The **head** is **hydrophilic** — it **attracts water**.
3) The **tail** is **hydrophobic** — it **repels water**.
4) The molecules automatically **arrange** themselves into a **bilayer** — the **heads face out** towards the water on either side of the membrane.
5) The **centre** of the bilayer is **hydrophobic** so the membrane **doesn't** allow **water-soluble substances** (like ions) through it — it acts as a **barrier** to these dissolved substances.

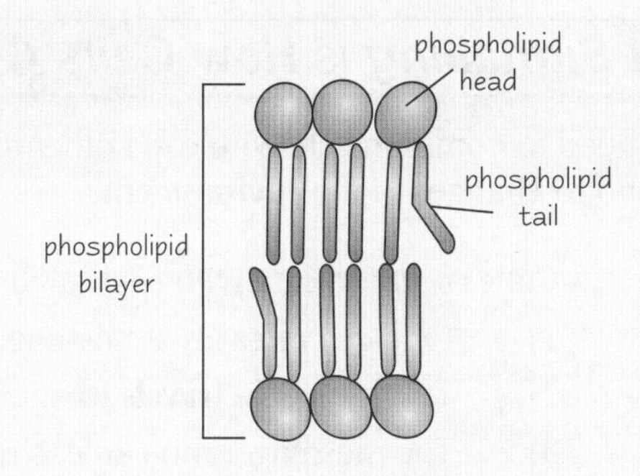

See p. 59 for more on phospholipids and cholesterol.

Cholesterol Gives the Membrane Stability

1) **Cholesterol** is a type of lipid (fat).
2) It's present in **all** cell membranes (except bacterial cell membranes).
3) Cholesterol molecules fit **between** the phospholipids. They bind to the hydrophobic tails of the phospholipids, causing them to pack **more closely together**. This makes the membrane **less fluid** and **more rigid**.

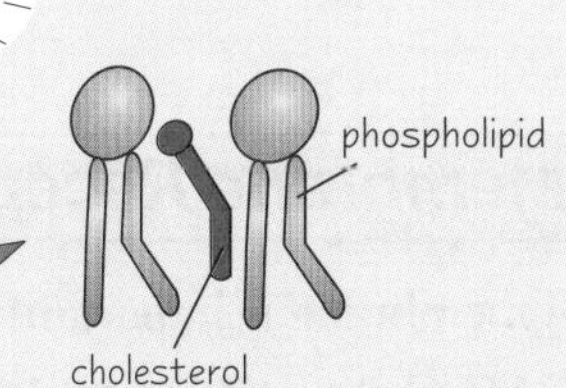

Proteins Control What Enters and Leaves the Cell

1) Some proteins form **channels** in the membrane (see p. 18) — these allow **small** or **charged** particles **through**.
2) Other proteins (called **carrier proteins**) **transport molecules** and **ions** across the membrane by **active transport** and **facilitated diffusion** (see page 18).
3) Proteins also act as **receptors** for molecules (e.g. hormones) in **cell signalling** (see next page). When a molecule **binds** to the protein, a **chemical reaction** is triggered inside the cell.

Glycolipids and Glycoproteins act as Receptors for Messenger Molecules

1) Glycolipids and glycoproteins **stabilise** the membrane by forming **hydrogen bonds** with surrounding **water molecules**.
2) They're also sites where **drugs**, **hormones** and **antibodies** bind.
3) They act as **receptors** for **cell signalling** (see next page).
4) They're also **antigens** — cell surface molecules involved in the immune response (see p. 80).

Practice Questions

Q1 Give two functions of membranes within the cell and two functions of membranes at the cell surface.

Q2 Give three molecules, other than proteins and cholesterol, that are present in animal cell membranes.

Exam Questions

Q1 Explain why the plasma membrane can be described as having a fluid-mosaic structure. [2 marks]

Q2 Describe the role of cholesterol in cell membranes. [1 mark]

Fluid Mosaic Model — think I saw one being sold at a craft fair...

It's weird to think that cells are surrounded by a layer that's 'fluid' — it's a good job it is though, 'cause if cell membranes were rigid a cell wouldn't be able to change shape or stretch without bursting, and that wouldn't be a pretty sight. It's also a good job that the membrane's partially permeable — so that it can let oxygen and carbon dioxide in and out of the cell.

Cell Membranes — The Basics

Cells like to have a good chat with one another every once in a while to make sure everything's going OK. To do this they use a process called cell signalling. The cell membrane is pretty important in cell signalling.

Cell Signalling is How Cells Communicate with Each Other

Cells need to communicate with each other to **control processes** inside the body and to **respond** to **changes** in the **environment**.

Cells communicate with each other using **messenger molecules**:

1) One cell **releases** a messenger molecule (e.g. a **hormone**).
2) This molecule **travels** to another cell (e.g. in the blood).
3) The messenger molecule is detected by the cell because it **binds** to a **receptor** on its **cell membrane**.

Emma was learning that communication with the opposite sex wasn't always easy...

Cell Membrane Receptors Play an Important Role in Cell Signalling

The **cell membrane** is **important** in the signalling process.

1) Membrane-bound **proteins** act as **receptors** for messenger molecules.
2) Receptor proteins have **specific shapes** — only **messenger molecules** with a **complementary shape** can **bind** to them.
3) **Different cells** have **different types** of receptors — they respond to **different messenger molecules**.
4) A cell that responds to a particular messenger molecule is called a **target cell**.

The diagram below shows how messenger molecules bind to target cells.

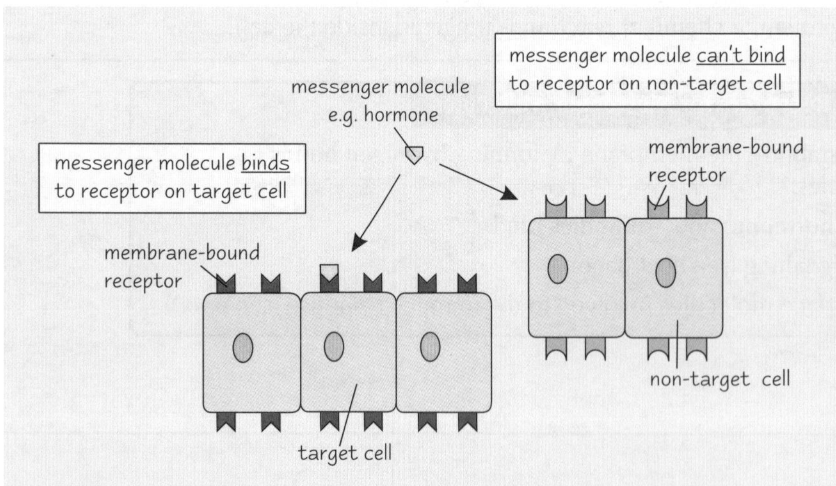

EXAMPLE: GLUCAGON

Glucagon is a **hormone** that's **released** when there **isn't enough glucose** in the **blood.** It **binds** to **receptors on liver cells,** causing the liver cells to **break down** stores of **glycogen** to glucose.

Drugs Also Bind to Cell Membrane Receptors

1) Many **drugs** work by **binding** to **receptors** in cell membranes.
2) They either to **trigger** a **response** in the cell, or **block** the receptor and **prevent** it from **working**.

EXAMPLE: ANTIHISTAMINES

Cell damage causes the release of **histamine.** Histamine binds to receptors on the surface of other cells and causes **inflammation.** **Antihistamines** work by **blocking histamine receptors** on cell surfaces. This **prevents** histamine from binding to the cell and **stops inflammation.**

Cell Membranes — The Basics

Membranes are Affected by Temperature

Temperature affects how much the phospholipids in the bilayer can move, which affects membrane structure.

1. **Temperatures below 0 °C**
   The phospholipids don't have much energy, so they can't move very much. They're **packed closely together** and the membrane is **rigid**. But **channel proteins** and **carrier proteins** in the membrane **denature** (see p. 68), **increasing** the **permeability** of the membrane. **Ice crystals** may form and **pierce** the membrane, making it **highly permeable** when it thaws.

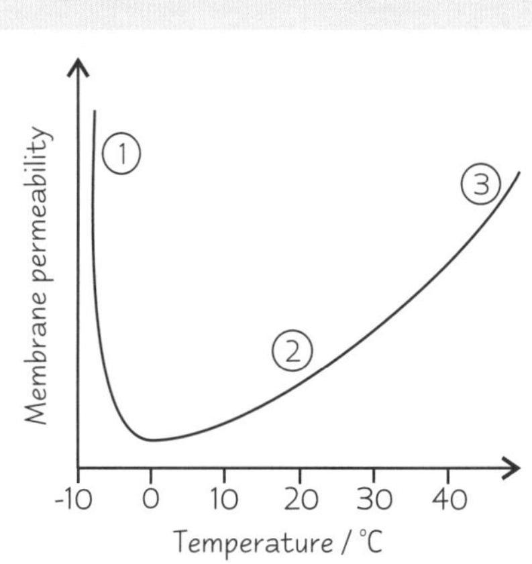

2. **Temperatures between 0 and 45 °C**
   The phospholipids can **move** around and **aren't** packed as tightly together — the membrane is **partially permeable**. As the temperature **increases** the phospholipids **move more** because they have more energy — this **increases** the **permeability** of the membrane.

3. **Temperatures above 45 °C**
   The phospholipid bilayer starts to **melt** (break down) and the membrane becomes more **permeable**. **Water** inside the cell **expands**, putting pressure on the membrane. **Channel proteins** and **carrier proteins** in the membrane **denature** so they can't control what enters or leaves the cell — this increases the **permeability** of the membrane.

Practice Questions

Q1 What is cell signalling?

Q2 What do messenger molecules bind to?

Exam Questions

Q1 Nicotine has an effect on nerve cells, but not on other types of cell in the body. Use your knowledge of cell membrane structure to explain why. [3 marks]

Q2 Beetroot cells contain a red pigment. In an experiment, four identical cubes of beetroot were washed and placed in four different test tubes of water. Each test tube was placed in a water bath at a different temperature, for 10 minutes. The water from each test tube was then placed in a colorimeter, to measure the concentration of pigment. A large absorbance value indicates a high concentration of pigment. The results are shown in the table on the right.

Tube number	Temperature / °C	Absorbance
1	10	1
2	30	5
3	50	43
4	70	56

a) Which tube contained the greatest concentration of beetroot pigment? [1 mark]

b) Describe and explain the difference between the results for tubes 1 and 2. [4 marks]

c) Describe and explain the difference between the results for tubes 2 and 3. [4 marks]

d) The experiment was repeated, with a test tube placed in the freezer for 10 minutes. The test tube was left to thaw before the absorbance reading was taken. Suggest whether the absorbance reading would have been high or low, and explain your answer. [4 marks]

Perm-eability — it's definitely decreased since the 80s...

Hopefully the mystery of cell signalling should now seem a bit clearer. At any one time, there are loads of messenger molecules being released by different cells in your body — travelling round and binding to receptors on other cells, causing some kind of response or another. This signalling fine-tunes all the body's processes and keeps us working properly.

Transport Across Cell Membranes

The beauty of cell membranes is that they're partially permeable — they'll only let certain substances enter and leave. Some substances move across cell membranes by passive transport, which means no energy is involved in the process. Passive transport processes include diffusion, osmosis and facilitated diffusion (see p. 18).

Diffusion is the Passive Movement of Particles

1) Diffusion is the net movement of particles (molecules or ions) from an area of **higher concentration** to an area of **lower concentration**.
2) Molecules will diffuse **both ways**, but the **net movement** will be to the area of **lower concentration**. This continues until particles are **evenly distributed** throughout the liquid or gas.
3) The **concentration gradient** is the path from an area of higher concentration to an area of lower concentration. Particles diffuse **down** a concentration gradient.
4) Diffusion is a **passive process** — **no energy** is needed for it to happen.
5) Particles can diffuse **across plasma membranes**, as long as they can **move freely** through the membrane. E.g. oxygen and carbon dioxide molecules are **small enough** to pass easily through spaces between phospholipids.

Diffusion — not good in a swimming pool.

The Rate of Diffusion Depends on Several Factors

1) The **concentration gradient** — the **higher** it is, the **faster** the rate of diffusion.
2) The **thickness** of the **exchange surface** — the **thinner** the exchange surface (i.e. the **shorter** the **distance** the particles have to travel), the **faster** the rate of diffusion.
3) The **surface area** — the **larger** the surface area (e.g. of a cell membrane), the **faster** the rate of diffusion.

Osmosis is Diffusion of Water Molecules

1) Osmosis is the **diffusion** of **water molecules** across a **partially permeable membrane**, from an area of **higher water potential** (i.e. higher concentration of water molecules) to an area of **lower water potential** (i.e. lower concentration of water molecules).
2) **Water potential** is the potential (likelihood) of water molecules to diffuse out of or into a solution.
3) **Pure water** has the **highest water potential**. All solutions have a **lower** water potential than pure water.

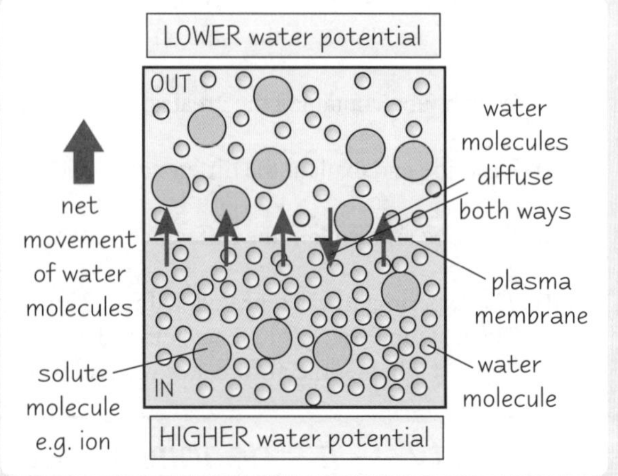

Transport Across Cell Membranes

Cells are Affected by the Water Potential of the Surrounding Solution

Water moves **in** or **out** of a cell by osmosis. **How much** moves in or out depends on the **water potential** of the **surrounding solution**. Animal and plant cells behave differently in different solutions.

ANIMAL CELL

Solution with a higher water potential than the cell (hypotonic solution).

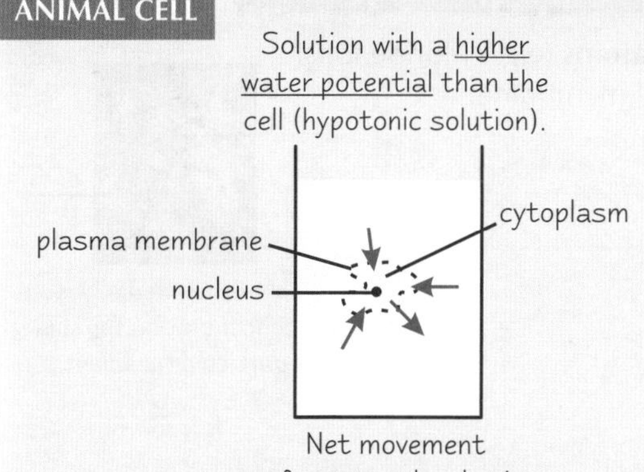

Net movement of water molecules is into the cell. Cell bursts.

Solution with the same water potential as the cell (isotonic solution).

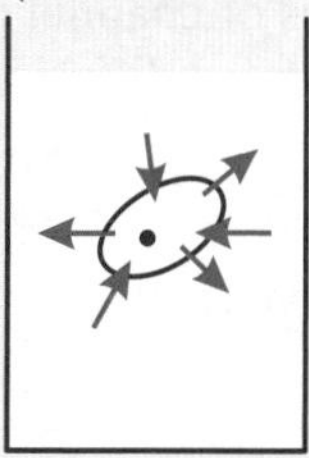

Water molecules pass into and out of the cell in equal amounts. The cell stays the same.

Solution with a lower water potential than the cell (hypertonic solution).

Net movement of water molecules is out of the cell. The cell shrinks.

PLANT CELL

Hypotonic solution

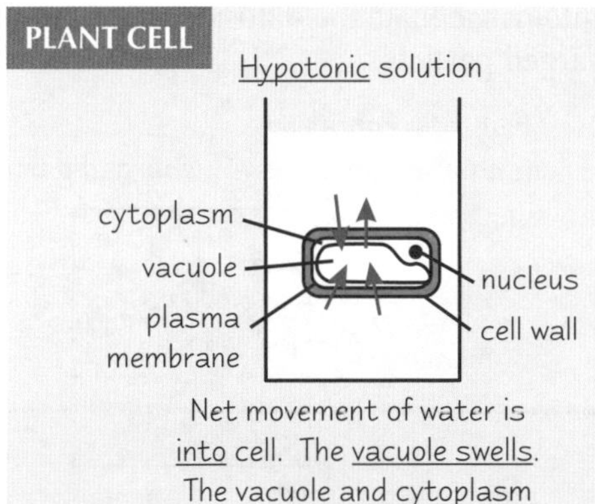

Net movement of water is into cell. The vacuole swells. The vacuole and cytoplasm push against the cell wall. The cell becomes turgid (swollen).

Isotonic solution

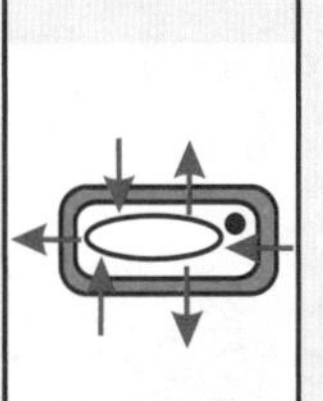

Water molecules move into and out of the cell in equal amounts. The cell stays the same.

Hypertonic solution

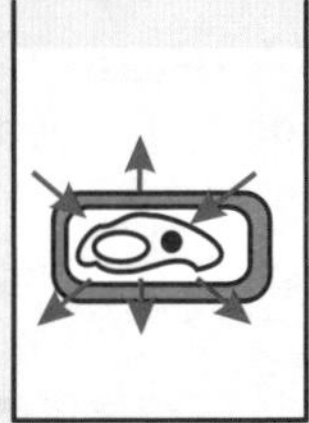

Net movement of water is out of the cell. The cell becomes flaccid (limp). The cytoplasm and the membrane pull away from the cell wall. This is called plasmolysis.

Practice Questions

Q1 Diffusion is a passive transport process. What does this mean?

Q2 What happens to an animal cell if it is placed in a solution with the same water potential as the cell?

Q3 What happens to a plant cell if it is placed in a solution with a higher water potential than the cell?

Exam Question

Q1 Pieces of potato of equal mass were put into different concentrations of sucrose solution for three days. The difference in mass for each is recorded in the table.

Concentration of sucrose / %	1	2	3	4
Mass difference / g	0.4	0.2	0	– 0.2

a) Explain why the pieces of potato in 1% and 2% sucrose solutions gained mass. [3 marks]

b) Suggest a reason why the mass of the piece of potato in 3% sucrose solution stayed the same. [1 mark]

c) What would you expect the mass difference for a potato in a 5% solution to be? Explain your answer. [4 marks]

Ginantonic solution — my gran's favourite...

Osmosis is just a fancy name for the diffusion of water molecules. But whether water moves in or out of a cell depends on the water potential of the surrounding solution. Water potential can be pretty confusing — if you can't make head nor tail of an exam question about it try replacing the word 'potential' with 'concentration' and it'll become clearer.

Transport Across Cell Membranes

Facilitated diffusion is another passive transport process, but there's also an active transport process, which is imaginatively named 'active transport'. Facilitated diffusion and active transport are actually quite similar though — they both involve proteins.

Facilitated Diffusion uses Carrier Proteins and Protein Channels

1) Some **larger molecules** (e.g. amino acids, glucose) and **charged atoms** (e.g. chloride ions) **can't diffuse directly through** the phospholipid bilayer of the cell membrane.
2) Instead they diffuse through **carrier proteins** or **channel proteins** in the cell membrane — this is called **facilitated diffusion**.
3) Like diffusion, facilitated diffusion moves particles **down** a **concentration gradient**, from a higher to a lower concentration.
4) It's also a passive process — it **doesn't** use **energy**.

Andy needed all his concentration for this particular gradient...

Carrier proteins move **large molecules** into or out of the cell, down their concentration gradient. **Different carrier proteins** facilitate the diffusion of **different molecules.**

1) First, a large molecule **attaches** to a carrier protein in the membrane.
2) Then, the protein **changes shape**.
3) This **releases** the molecule on the **opposite side** of the membrane.

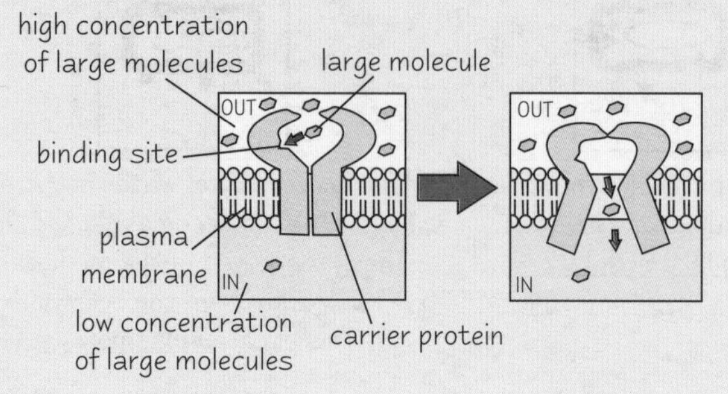

Channel proteins form **pores** in the membrane for **charged particles** to diffuse through (down their concentration gradient). **Different channel proteins** facilitate the diffusion of **different charged particles.**

Active Transport Moves Substances Against a Concentration Gradient

Active transport uses **energy** to move **molecules** and **ions** across plasma membranes, **against** a **concentration gradient.** This process involves **carrier proteins.**

1) The process is pretty similar to facilitated diffusion — a molecule **attaches** to the carrier protein, the protein **changes shape** and this moves the molecule **across** the membrane, **releasing it** on the other side.
2) The only difference is that **energy** is used (from **ATP** — a common source of energy used in the cell), to move the solute against its concentration gradient.
3) The diagram on the right shows the active transport of **calcium.**

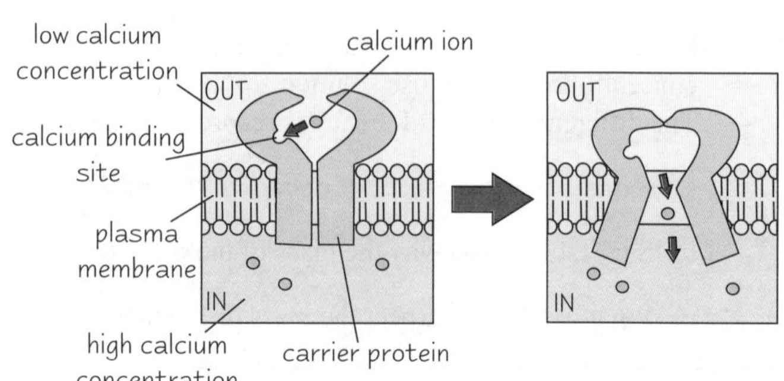

Transport Across Cell Membranes

Cells can **Take in** Substances by **Endocytosis**

1) Some molecules are way too **large** to be taken into a cell by carrier proteins, e.g. proteins, lipids and some carbohydrates.
2) Instead a cell can **surround** a substance with a **section** of its **plasma membrane**.
3) The membrane then **pinches off** to form a **vesicle** inside the cell containing the **ingested substance** — this is **endocytosis**.
4) Some cells also take in much **larger objects** by endocytosis — for example, some **white blood cells** (mainly phagocytes, see p. 80) use endocytosis to take in things like **microorganisms** and **dead cells** so that they can destroy them.

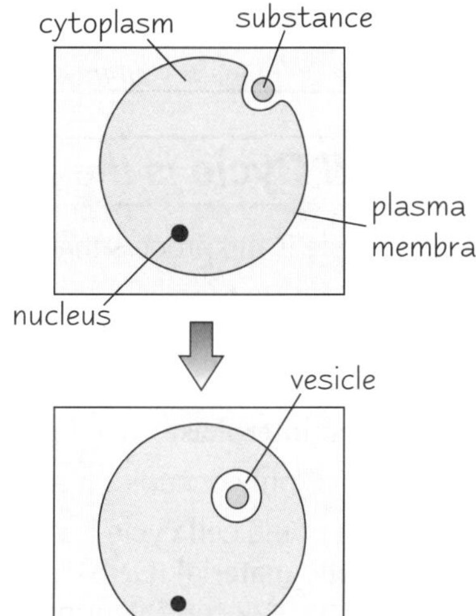

Cells can **Secrete** Substances by **Exocytosis**

1) Some substances **produced** by the cell (e.g. **digestive enzymes, hormones, lipids**) need to be **released** from the cell — this is done by **exocytosis**.
2) **Vesicles** containing these substances **pinch off** from the sacs of the **Golgi apparatus** (see p. 6) and **move towards** the plasma membrane.
3) The vesicles **fuse** with the **plasma membrane** and **release** their contents **outside** the cell.
4) Some substances (like membrane proteins) **aren't** released outside the cell — instead they are **inserted** straight into the plasma membrane.

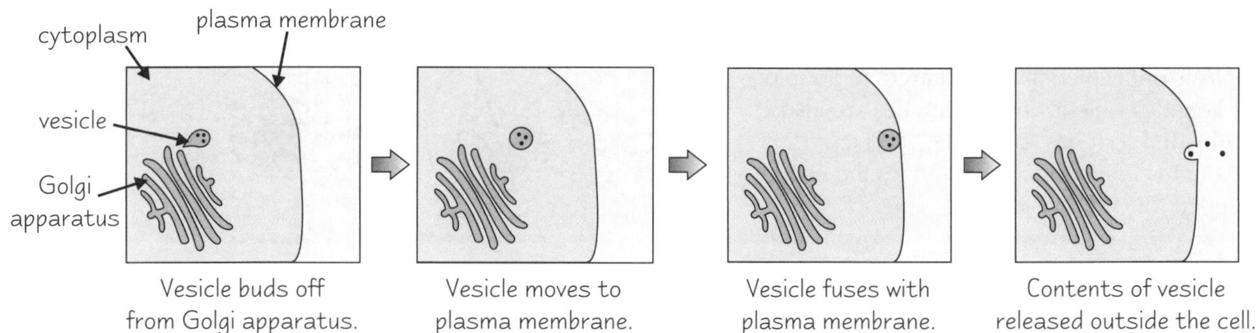

Practice Questions

Q1 What is active transport?

Q2 Which molecule provides the energy for active transport?

Exam Questions

Q1 Describe the role of membrane proteins in facilitated diffusion. [6 marks]

Q2 Explain the difference between endocytosis and exocytosis. [4 marks]

Revision — like working against a concentration gradient...

Wouldn't it be great if you could revise by endocytosis — you could just stick this book on your head and your brain would slowly surround it and take it in... actually when I put it like that it sounds a bit gross. Maybe just stick to good old 'closing the book and scribbling down the diagrams till you know them off by heart'.

Cell Division — Mitosis

I don't like cell division. There, I've said it. It's unfair of me, because if it wasn't for cell division I'd still only be one cell big. It's all those diagrams that look like worms nailed to bits of string that put me off.

The Cell Cycle is the Process of Cell Growth and Division

The **cell cycle** is the process that all body cells from **multicellular organisms** use to **grow** and **divide**.

1) The cell cycle **starts** when a cell has been produced by cell division and **ends** with the cell dividing to produce two identical cells.
2) The cell cycle consists of a period of **cell growth**, called **interphase**, and a period of **cell division**, called **mitosis**.
3) Mitosis only occupies a **small percentage** of the cell cycle.
4) Most of the cell cycle is taken up by **interphase**, during which the **genetic material** (DNA) is **copied** and **checked** for any errors that may have occurred during copying.
5) If errors in the genetic material are detected at this stage, the cell may **kill itself**. This prevents any **mutations** (errors) in the DNA from being passed on.

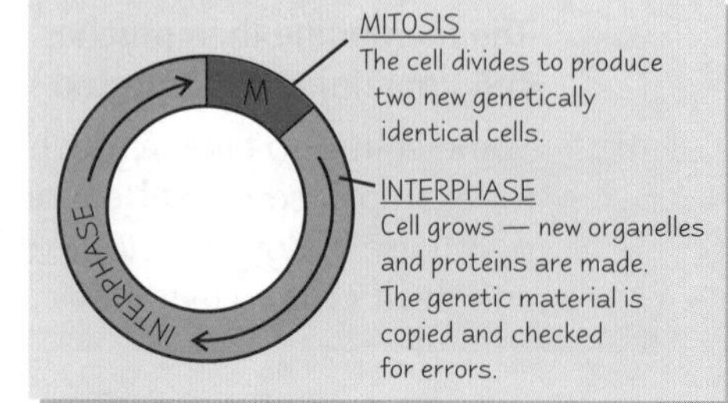

Mitosis has Four Division Stages

1) Mitosis is needed for the **growth** of multicellular organisms (like us) and for **repairing damaged tissues**.
2) Mitosis is really one **continuous process**, but it's described as a series of **division stages** — prophase, metaphase, anaphase and telophase.
3) **Interphase** comes **before** mitosis in the cell cycle — it's when cells grow and replicate their DNA ready for division.

Interphase — The cell carries out normal functions, but also prepares to divide. The cell's **DNA** is unravelled and **replicated**, to double its genetic content. The **organelles** are also **replicated** so it has spare ones, and its ATP content is increased (ATP provides the energy needed for cell division).

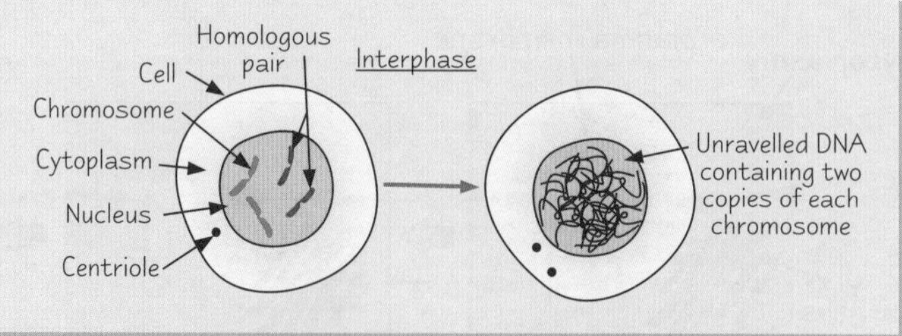

1) **Prophase** — The **chromosomes condense**, getting shorter and fatter. Tiny bundles of protein called **centrioles** start moving to opposite ends of the cell, forming a network of protein fibres across it called the **spindle**. The **nuclear envelope** (the membrane around the nucleus) **breaks down** and chromosomes lie free in the cytoplasm.

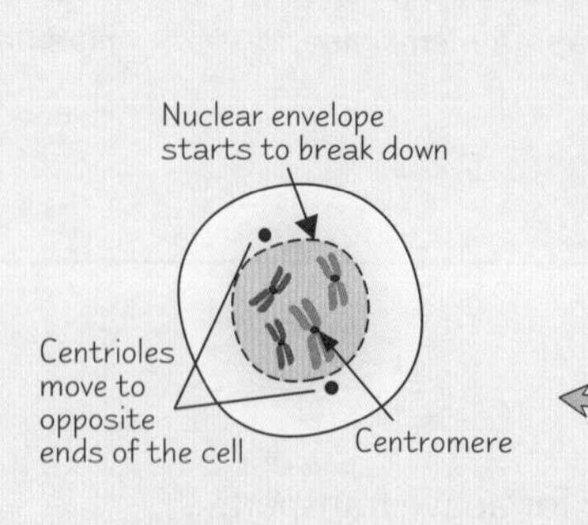

As mitosis begins, the chromosomes are made of two strands joined in the middle by a centromere.
The separate strands are called chromatids.

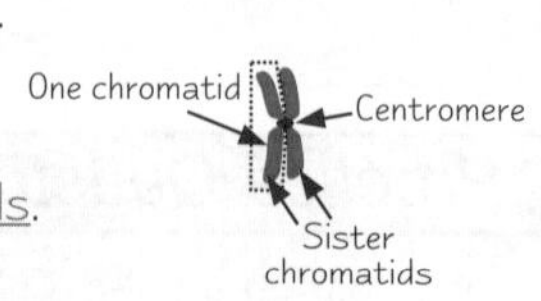

There are two strands because each chromosome has already made an identical copy of itself during interphase. When mitosis is over, the chromatids end up as one-strand chromosomes in the new daughter cells.

2) **Metaphase** — The chromosomes (each with two chromatids) **line up** along the middle of the cell and become **attached** to the **spindle** by their **centromere**.

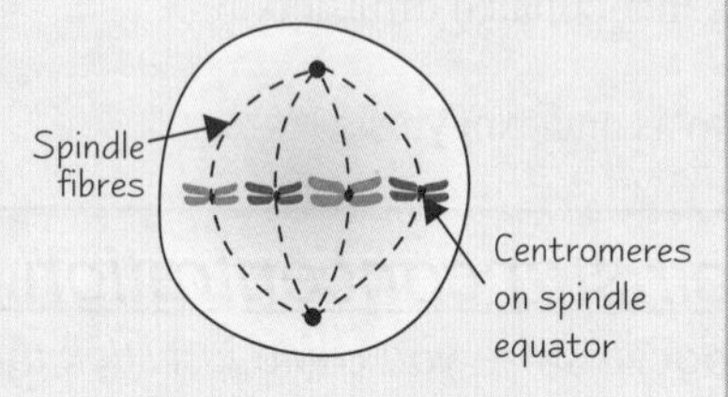

Cell Division — Mitosis

3) **Anaphase** — The centromeres divide, **separating** each pair of sister **chromatids**. The spindles contract, pulling chromatids to opposite ends of the cell, centromere first.

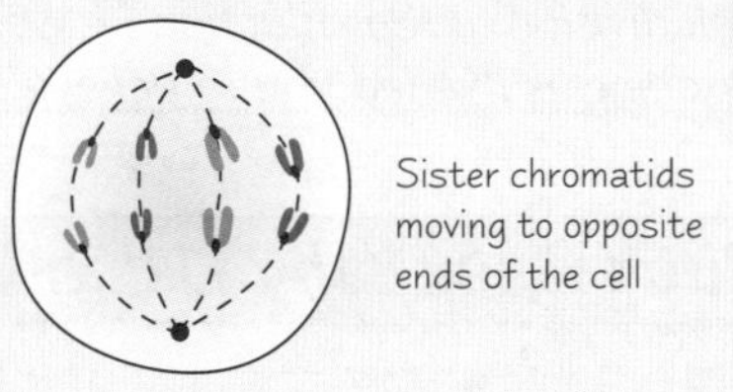

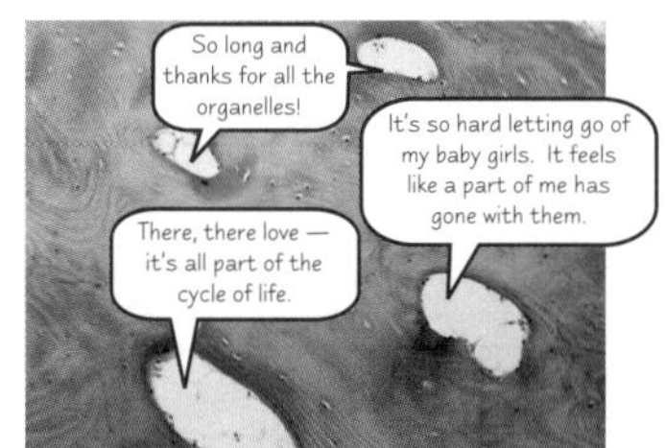

Mitosis can be a moving time.

4) **Telophase** — The chromatids reach the **opposite poles** on the spindle. They uncoil and become long and thin again. They're now called **chromosomes** again. A **nuclear envelope** forms around each group of chromosomes, so there are now **two nuclei**. The **cytoplasm divides** and there are now **two daughter cells** that are **genetically identical** to the original cell and to each other. Mitosis is finished and each daughter cell starts the **interphase** part of the cell cycle to get ready for the next round of mitosis.

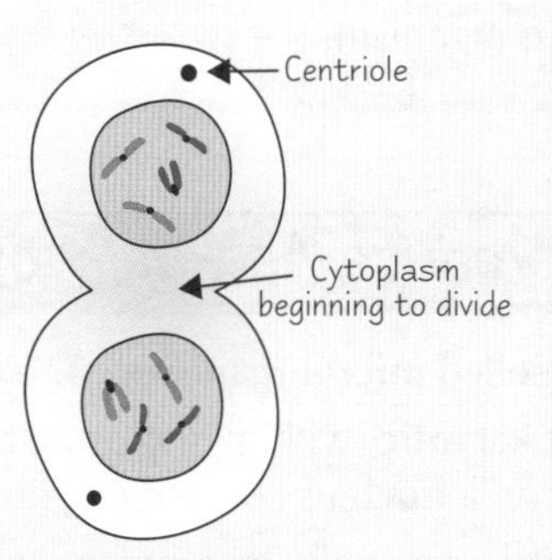

You can *Observe Mitosis* by *Staining Chromosomes*

You can **stain chromosomes** so you can see them under a **microscope**. This means you can watch what happens to them **during mitosis** — and it makes high-adrenaline viewing, I can tell you. You need to be able to **recognise** each stage in mitosis from diagrams and **photographs** — lucky you. You've seen the diagrams, now enjoy the photos:

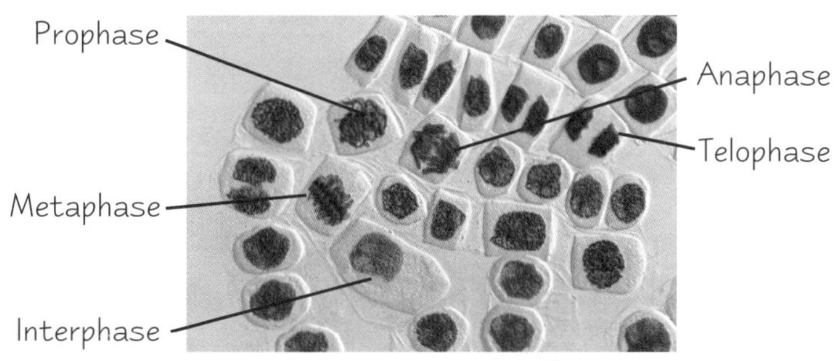

HERVE CONGE, ISM/SCIENCE PHOTO LIBRARY

Practice Questions

Q1 What happens during interphase?

Q2 List in order the four stages of mitosis.

Q3 At what stage in mitosis does the nuclear envelope break down?

Exam Question

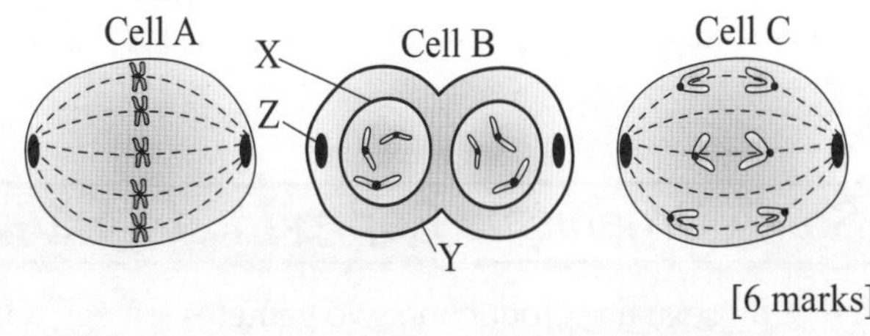

Q1 The diagrams show cells at different stages of mitosis.

a) For each of the cells A, B and C state the stage of mitosis, giving a reason for your answer. [6 marks]

b) Name the structures labelled X, Y and Z in cell B. [3 marks]

Doctor, Doctor, I'm getting short and fat — don't worry, it's just a phase...

Quite a lot to learn in this topic — but it's all dead important stuff, so no slacking. Most body cells undergo mitosis — it's how they multiply and how organisms like us grow and develop. Remember that chromosomes during mitosis are made up of two sister chromatids joined by a centromere. Nice to know family values are important to genetic material too.

Cell Division and Reproduction

And now on to the exciting topic of cell division in reproduction — well, on to a topic slightly more exciting than the workings of mitosis, but not quite as exciting as I've led you to believe... sorry...

Some Organisms **Reproduce Asexually** Using **Mitosis**

Some organisms (e.g. some **plants** and **fungi**) **reproduce asexually** (without sex) using mitosis. This means any new organisms produced are **genetically identical** to the original, parent organism.

Yeast Cells Reproduce Asexually by **Budding**

1) Yeast are single-celled **microorganisms**. They're a type of fungi.
2) Yeast cells are **eukaryotic**, with all the usual **organelles** in the cytoplasm (see pages 5-7) and a **nucleus** containing chromosomes (DNA).
3) Yeast can reproduce **asexually** by a process called **budding**.
4) Budding involves **mitosis**.
5) This means the offspring produced are **genetically identical** to the parent cell.

Vacuole
Nucleus containing DNA
Cell membrane
Cytoplasm
Cell wall

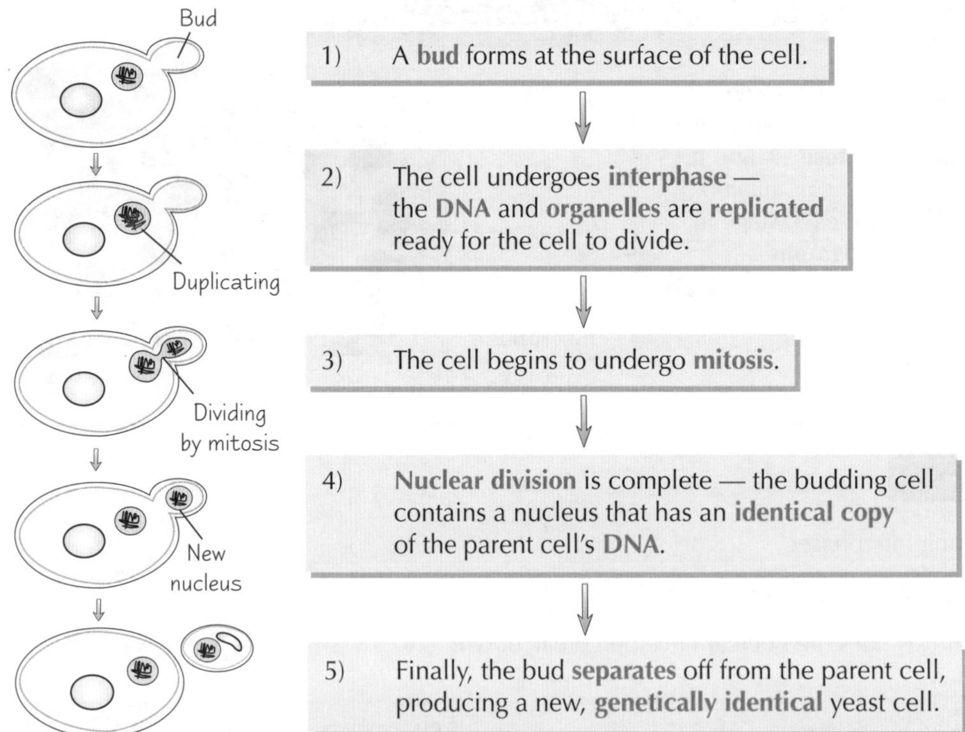

Some Organisms **Reproduce Sexually** Using **Meiosis**

1) In sexual reproduction two **gametes** (an egg and a sperm) join together at **fertilisation** to form a **zygote**. The zygote then divides and develops into a **new organism**.
2) **Meiosis** is a type of **cell division** that happens in the reproductive organs to **produce gametes**.
3) Cells that divide by meiosis have the **full number** of chromosomes to start with, but the cells that are formed from meiosis have **half the number**.
4) Cells formed by meiosis are all **genetically different** because each new cell ends up with a **different combination** of chromosomes.

Cell Division and Reproduction

Cell Division by **Meiosis** Creates **Genetically Different Cells**

You don't need to learn the details of meiosis, just understand that it produces genetically different cells. Here's how it happens:

1) The DNA **replicates** and coils up to form **chromosomes**.
2) The chromosomes **arrange** themselves into **homologous pairs**.
3) The chromosome pairs then **swap bits** with each other.

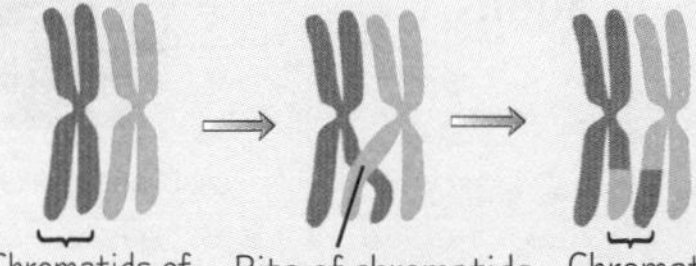

4) In the first division, these homologous pairs **split up**. Any one chromosome from **each pair** can go into **either cell**, as long as each cell gets one number 1, one number 2, etc.
5) In the second division, each chromosome **splits in half**. Any half can go into **any cell**.
6) **Four** new **genetically different** cells are produced.
7) They're genetically different from each other because the chromosomes **swap bits** during meiosis and each gamete gets a **combination of half** of them, at **random**.

Humans have **46 chromosomes** in total — **23 pairs**. **One chromosome** in each pair came from mum and one from dad, e.g. there are two number 1s (1 from mum and 1 from dad), two number 2s, etc. The chromosomes that make up each pair are the same size and have the **same genes**, although they could have **different versions** of those genes (called **alleles**). These pairs of chromosomes are called **homologous pairs**.

You do need to learn what a homologous chromosome is.

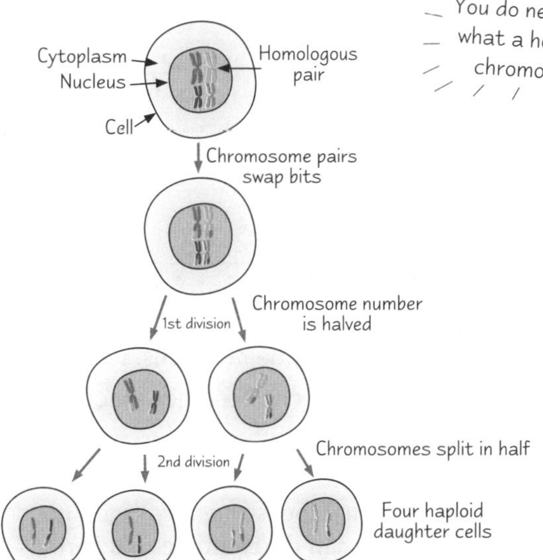

Practice Questions

Q1 Does asexual reproduction in yeast produce genetically identical cells or genetically different ones?

Q2 Which form of cell division, meiosis or mitosis, leads to the production of genetically different cells?

Exam Questions

Q1 The diagram opposite shows three stages of budding in a yeast cell.

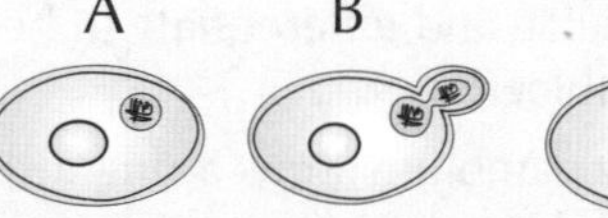

a) Describe what has happened between stages A and B. [3 marks]

b) Describe what has happened between stages B and C. [2 marks]

Q2 Explain the meaning of the term 'homologous pair of chromosomes'. [2 marks]

Reproduction isn't as exciting as some people would have you believe...

This stuff can take a while to sink in — but that's no excuse to sit there staring at the page muttering things like "I don't get it" and "guinea pigs don't have to learn this stuff — I wish I was a guinea pig". Use the diagrams to help you understand — they look evil, but they really help. And remember, mitosis produces genetically identical cells and meiosis genetically different cells.

Stem Cells and Differentiation

Life's pretty easy for single-celled organisms like yeast. One minute they're a little bud on the side of their parent cell and the next they're a fully grown organism, ready to face the exciting world of brewing or baking (or anything else a young yeast likes to do). But things aren't quite so easy for multicellular organisms like us — we have to grow and develop.

Stem Cells are Unspecialised Cells

1) **Multicellular organisms** are made up from many **different** cell types that are **specialised** for their function, e.g. liver cells, muscle cells, white blood cells.
2) **All** these specialised cell types originally came from **stem cells**.
3) Stem cells are **unspecialised** cells — they can develop into **any** type of cell.
4) **All** multicellular organisms have some form of **stem cell**.
5) In **humans**, stem cells are found in **early embryos** and in a few places in **adults**.

- In the first few days of an embryo's life, **any** of its cells can **develop** into **any** type of human cell — they're **all** stem cells.
- In adults, stem cells are found in a few places (e.g. **bone marrow**), but they're **not as flexible** — they can only develop into a **limited range** of cells (see below).

Joe knew his cells were specialised — specialised to look good.

Stem Cells Differentiate into Specialised Cells

1) Stem cells **divide** to become **new cells**, which then become **specialised**.
2) The process by which a cell becomes specialised for its job is called **differentiation**.
3) In animals, adult stem cells are used to replace **damaged cells**, e.g. to make **new skin** or **blood cells** (see below).
4) **Plants** are always growing, so stem cells are needed to make **new shoots** and **roots** throughout their lives. Stem cells in plants can **differentiate** into various plant tissues including **xylem and phloem** (see below).

There's more about the function of xylem and phloem on page 26.

Cells in the Bone Marrow Differentiate into Blood Cells

1) **Bones** are living organs, containing nerves and **blood vessels**.
2) The main bones of the body have **marrow** in the **centres**.
3) Here, **adult stem cells** divide and **differentiate** to replace worn out blood cells — **erythrocytes** (red blood cells) and **neutrophils** (white blood cells that help to fight infection).

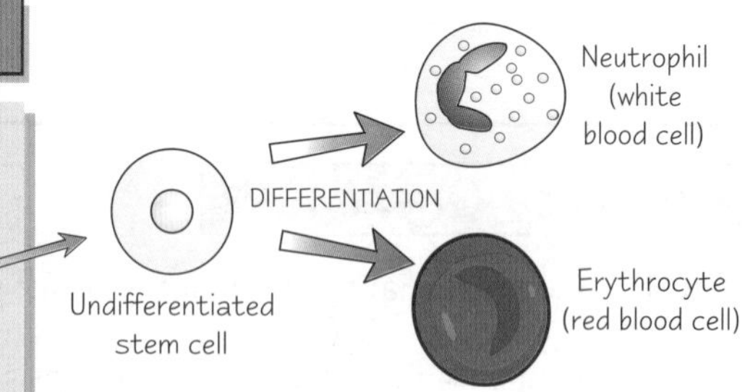

Cells in the Cambium Differentiate into Xylem and Phloem

1) In plants, **stem cells** are found in the **cambium**.
2) In the root and stem, stem cells of the **vascular cambium** divide and **differentiate** to become **xylem** and **phloem**.
3) The vascular cambium forms a **ring** inside the root and shoots.
4) The cells **divide** and grow out from the ring, **differentiating** as they **move away** from the cambium.

Root or shoot
Phloem tissue
Cambium
Xylem tissue
Xylem vessel
Phloem sieve tube
Cambium cell

Cambium cells divide and begin to differentiate

Xylem and phloem differentiate on either side of the cambium

Stem Cells and Differentiation

Cells are **Specialised** for their Particular Function

Once cells **differentiate**, they have a **specific function**. Their **structure** is **adapted** to perform that function. You need to **know** how the following cell types are specialised for their functions:

Animal cells

1) **Neutrophils** (white blood cells, e.g. phagocytes) defend the body against disease. Their **flexible shape** allows them to **engulf** foreign particles or pathogens (see p. 80). The many **lysosomes** in their cytoplasm contain **digestive enzymes** to **break down** the engulfed particles.

2) **Erythrocytes** (red blood cells) carry oxygen in the blood. The **biconcave** disc shape provides a **large surface area** for gas exchange. They have **no nucleus** so there's more room for **haemoglobin** (see p. 42), the protein that carries oxygen.

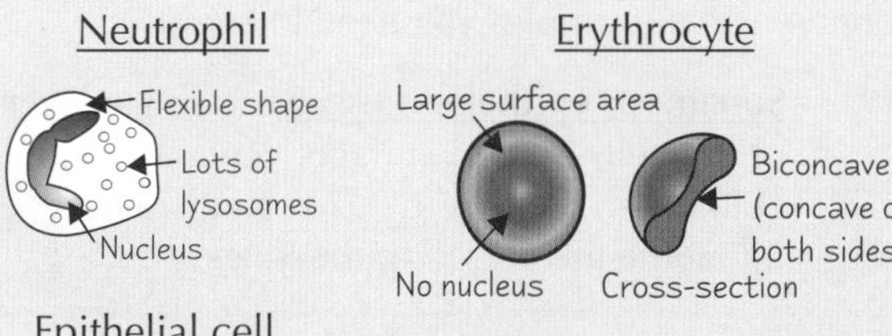

3) **Epithelial cells** cover the surfaces of organs. The cells are **joined** by **interlinking** cell membranes and a membrane at their base. Some epithelia (e.g. in the **lungs**) have **cilia** that beat to move particles away. Other epithelia (e.g. in the **small intestine**) have **microvilli** — folds in the cell membrane that increase the cell's **surface area**.

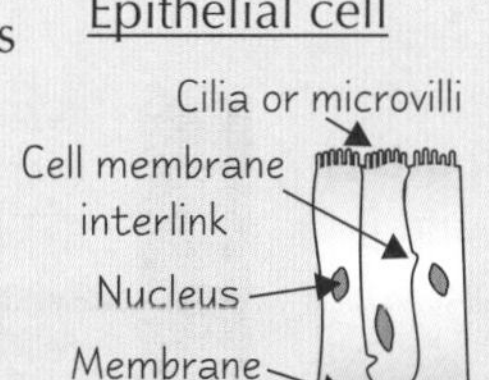

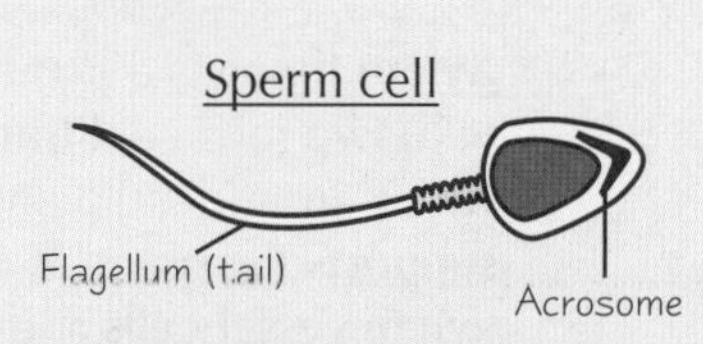

4) **Sperm cells** (male sex cells) have a **flagellum** (tail) so they can **swim** to the egg (female sex cell). They also have lots of **mitochondria** to provide the **energy** to swim. The **acrosome** contains **digestive enzymes** to enable the sperm to **penetrate** the surface of the egg.

Plant cells

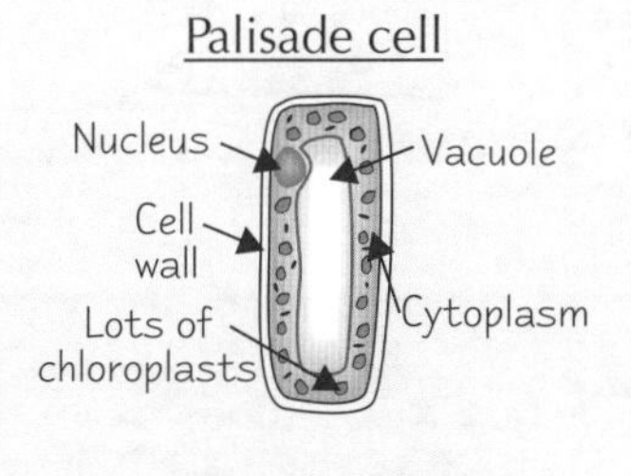

Guard cells

Cells turgid, stoma opens

Cells flaccid, stoma closes

1) **Palisade mesophyll cells** in leaves do most of the **photosynthesis**. They contain **many chloroplasts**, so they can absorb a lot of sunlight. The walls are **thin**, so carbon dioxide can **easily diffuse** into the cell.

2) **Root hair cells** absorb water and mineral ions from the soil. They have a **large surface area** for absorption and a **thin**, permeable cell wall, for entry of water and ions. The cytoplasm contains **extra mitochondria** to provide the **energy** needed for **active transport** (see p. 18).

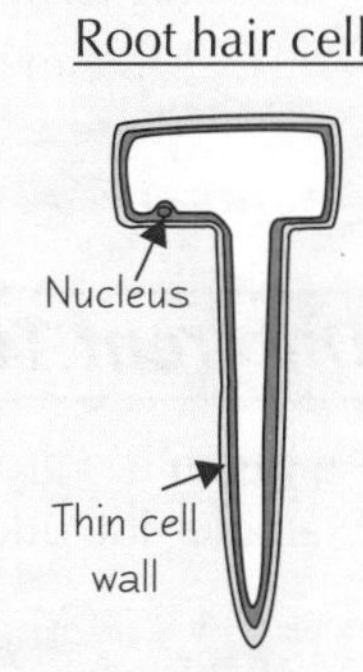

3) **Guard cells** line the **stomata** — the tiny pores in the surface of the leaf used for **gas exchange**. In the **light**, guard cells **take up water** and become **turgid**. Their **thin outer walls** and **thickened inner walls** force them to bend outwards, **opening** the stomata. This allows the leaf to exchange gases for photosynthesis.

Practice Questions

Q1 What are stem cells?

Q2 Stem cells in bone marrow can differentiate into other cell types. Name two of these cell types.

Exam Questions

Q1 Describe how a palisade cell is adapted for its role in photosynthesis. [4 marks]

Q2 Describe, with examples, the role of stem cells in adult animals and plants. [5 marks]

And you thought differentiation was just boring maths stuff...

Stem cells are pretty amazing when you think about it — they can differentiate to become any cell in the whole body. Scientists are excited about them because they could be used to repair damaged cells, like muscle cells after a heart attack.

Tissues, Organs and Systems

Multicellular organisms are made up of lots of different cell types, which are organised to work together — cells that carry out the same job are organised into tissues (e.g. epithelium), different tissues are organised into organs (e.g. the lungs) and organs work together as organ systems (e.g. the respiratory system).

Similar Cells** are Organised into **Tissues

A **tissue** is a group of cells (plus any **extracellular material** secreted by them) that are specialised to **work together** to carry out a **particular function**. A tissue can contain **more than one** cell type. Here are some examples you need to know:

1) Squamous epithelium tissue is a **single layer** of **flat cells** lining a surface. Squamous epithelium tissue is found in many places including the alveoli in the lungs.

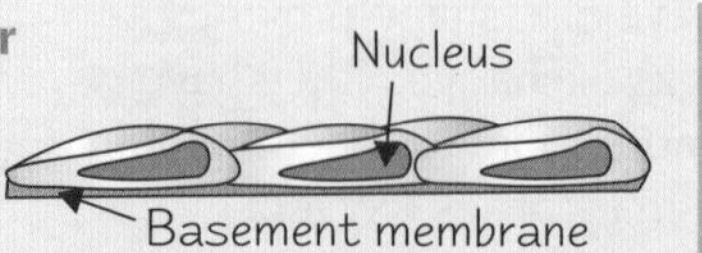

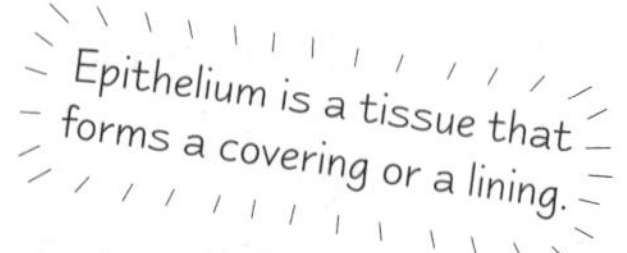

2) Xylem tissue is a plant tissue with two jobs — it **transports water** around the plant, and it **supports** the plant. It contains **xylem vessel cells** and **parenchyma cells**.

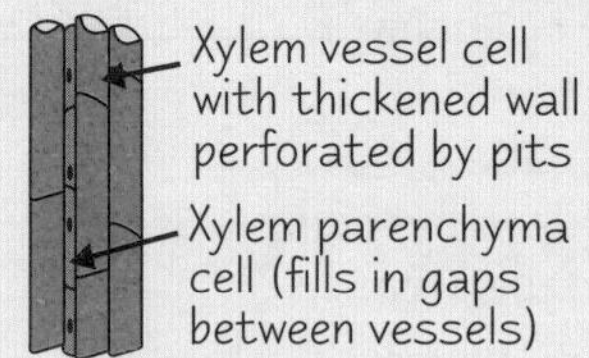

3) Ciliated epithelium is a layer of cells covered in **cilia** (see p. 7). It's found on surfaces where things need to be **moved** — in the trachea for instance, where the cilia waft mucus along.

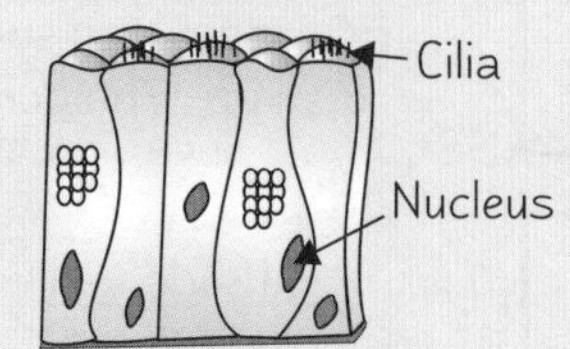

4) Phloem tissue **transports sugars** around the plant. It's arranged in **tubes** and is made up of **sieve cells**, **companion cells**, and some **ordinary** plant cells. Each sieve cell has end walls with **holes** in them, so that sap can move easily through them. These end walls are called **sieve plates**.

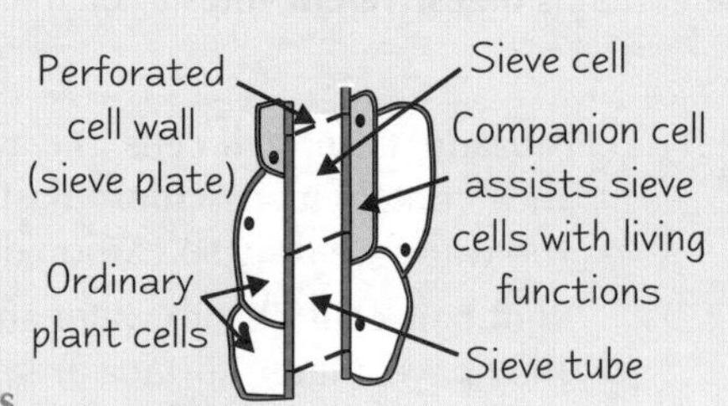

Different Tissues** Make up an **Organ

An **organ** is a group of different tissues that **work together** to perform a particular function. Examples include:

- The **lungs** — they contain **squamous epithelium** tissue (in the alveoli) and **ciliated epithelium** tissue (in the bronchi etc.). They also have **elastic connective tissue** and **vascular tissue** (in the blood vessels).
- **Leaves** — they contain **palisade tissue** for photosynthesis, as well as **epidermal** tissue, and **xylem** and **phloem** tissues in the veins.

Different Organs** Make up an **Organ System

Organs work together to form **organ systems** — each system has a **particular function**. Yup, you've guessed it, more examples:

1) The **respiratory system** is made up of all the organs, tissues and cells involved in **breathing**. The lungs, trachea, larynx, nose, mouth and diaphragm are all part of the respiratory system.
2) The **circulatory system** is made up of the organs involved in **blood supply**. The heart, arteries, veins and capillaries are all parts of this system.

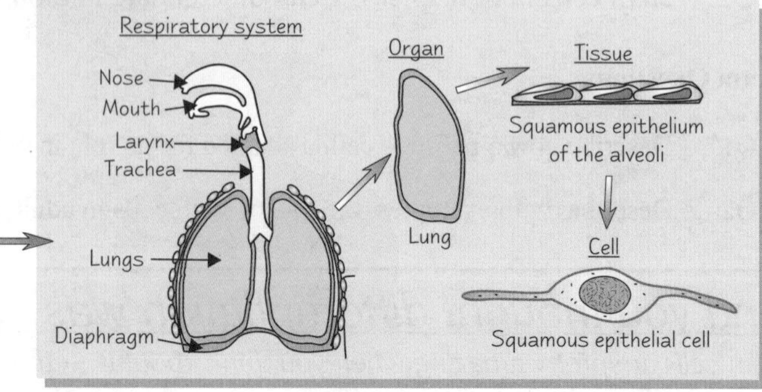

Tissues, Organs and Systems

Different Tissues, Organs and Systems **Cooperate Together**

1) Multicellular organisms work **efficiently** because they have **different cells** specialised for **different functions**.
2) It's **advantageous** because **each** different cell type can carry out its specialised function **more effectively** than an **unspecialised** cell could.
3) Specialised cells can't do everything on their own though.
4) Each cell type **depends** on other cells for the functions it **can't** carry out.
5) This means the **cells**, **tissues and organs** within multicellular organisms must **cooperate** with each other to keep the organism **alive** and **running**.
6) For example:

Cooperation, that's what got Hugo and Cuthbert to where they are today — National Wheel-of-Cheese-Carrying Champions.

- A **palisade cell** (see p. 25) is good at **photosynthesising**, but it's **no good** at absorbing water and minerals from the soil. It **depends** on **root hair cells** (see p. 25) for this. And vice versa.
- **Muscles cells** are great for getting you where you want to go, but to do this they need **oxygen**. They **depend** on **erythrocytes** (red blood cells) to carry oxygen to them from the **lungs**.

7) Multicellular organisms have developed different **systems of cooperation** between different cells:

1) Transport systems

These are used to **carry substances** between the different cells. For example, **xylem cells** carry water and minerals from the root hair cells to the palisade cells, and **phloem cells** carry sugars around the plant. In humans, the **circulatory system** helps to move substances around the body in the **blood**.

2) Communication systems

These allow communication **between** cells in different **parts** of the organism. Both plants and animals have **chemical** communication systems that use **messenger molecules** such as **hormones** (see p. 14). Animals also have a **nervous system** for communication, sending **electrical signals** to different tissues and organs.

Practice Questions

Q1 Define what is meant by a tissue.

Q2 Briefly describe squamous epithelium tissue.

Q3 What is the difference between the functions of xylem and phloem tissues?

Q4 Name one organ found in plants and one organ found in animals.

Exam Questions

Q1 The liver is made of hepatocyte cells that form the main tissue, blood vessels to provide nutrients and oxygen, and connective tissue that holds the organ together. Discuss whether the liver is best described as a tissue or an organ. [2 marks]

Q2 Name one organ system and list the organs it contains. [3 marks]

Soft and quilted — the best kind of tissues...

There's a bit to get through on these pages, but it's all important stuff. If the cells of multicellular animals like you and me didn't cooperate we'd never get anything done. Still, it's better than being a lazy-boned yeast cell — well, to be fair, not lazy-boned as they don't have bones. Obviously I've not been paying attention properly to this section. Oh, dear...

Gas Exchange

Exchanging things with the environment is pretty easy if you're a single-celled organism, but if you're multicellular it all gets a bit more complicated... and it's all down to this 'surface area to volume ratio' malarkey.

Organisms Need to Exchange Substances with their Environment

Every organism, whatever its size, needs to exchange things with its environment.

1) Cells need to take in **oxygen** (for aerobic respiration) and **nutrients**.
2) They also need to excrete **waste products** like **carbon dioxide** and **urea**.

How easy the exchange of substances is depends on the organism's **surface area to volume ratio**.

Raj was glad he'd exchanged his canoe for a bigger boat.

Smaller Animals have Higher Surface Area : Volume Ratios

A mouse has a bigger surface area **relative to its volume** than a hippo. This can be hard to imagine, but you can prove it mathematically. Imagine these animals as cubes:

The hippo could be represented by a block measuring 2 cm × 4 cm × 4 cm.

Its **volume** is 2 × 4 × 4 = **32 cm³**

Its **surface area** is 2 × 4 × 4 = 32 cm² (top and bottom surfaces of cube)

+ 4 × 2 × 4 = 32 cm² (four sides of the cube)

Total surface area = **64 cm²**

So the hippo has a **surface area : volume ratio** of 64 : 32 or **2 : 1**.

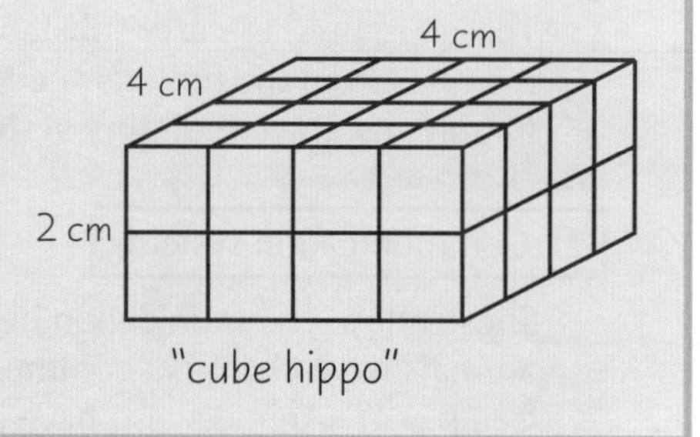

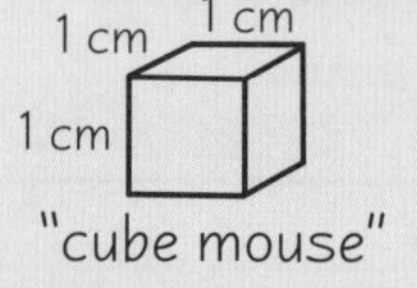

Compare this to a mouse cube measuring 1 cm × 1 cm × 1 cm

Its **volume** is 1 x 1 x 1 = **1 cm³**

Its **surface area** is 6 x 1 x 1 = **6 cm²**

So the mouse has a **surface area : volume ratio** of **6 : 1**.

The cube mouse's surface area is six times its volume, but the cube hippo's surface area is only twice its volume. Smaller animals have a bigger surface area compared to their volume.

To calculate the surface area to volume ratio you just **divide** the **surface area** by the **volume**. Easy.

Multicellular Organisms need Exchange Organs

An organism needs to supply **every one of its cells** with substances like **glucose** and **oxygen** (for respiration). It also needs to **remove waste products** from every cell to avoid damaging itself.

1) In **single-celled** organisms, these substances can **diffuse directly** into (or out of) the cell across the cell surface membrane. The diffusion rate is quick because of the small distances the substances have to travel (see p. 16).
2) In **multicellular** animals, diffusion across the outer membrane is **too slow**, for two reasons:
   - Some cells are deep **within the body** — there's a big distance between them and the **outside environment**.
   - Larger animals have a **low surface area to volume ratio** — it's difficult to exchange **enough** substances to supply a **large volume of animal** through a relatively **small outer surface**.

So rather than using straightforward diffusion to absorb and excrete substances, multicellular animals need specialised **exchange organs** like **lungs**...

Gas Exchange

In Mammals the Lungs are Exchange Organs

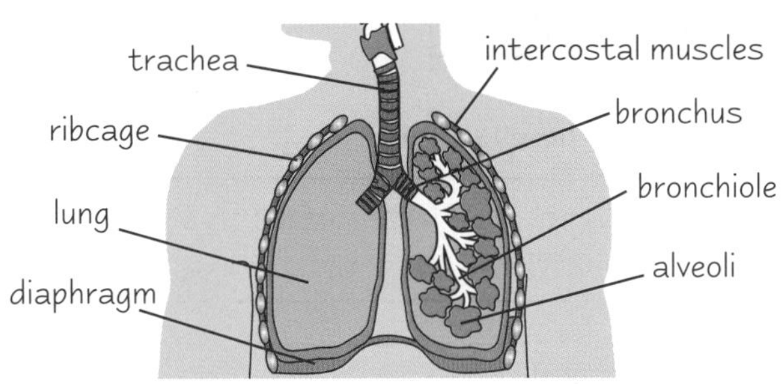

1) As you breathe in, air enters the **trachea** (windpipe).
2) The trachea splits into two **bronchi** — one **bronchus** leading to each lung.
3) Each bronchus then branches off into smaller tubes called **bronchioles**.
4) The bronchioles end in small 'air sacs' called **alveoli** — this is where gases are exchanged.
5) The **ribcage**, **intercostal muscles** and **diaphragm** all work together to move air in and out (see page 32).

Gas Exchange Happens in the Alveoli

Lungs contain millions of **alveoli** — the gas **exchange surface**.
Each alveolus is made from a single layer of thin, flat cells called the **alveolar epithelium**.

1) Alveoli are arranged in **bunches** at the end of bronchioles.
2) They're surrounded by a network of **capillaries**, giving each alveolus its **own blood supply**.

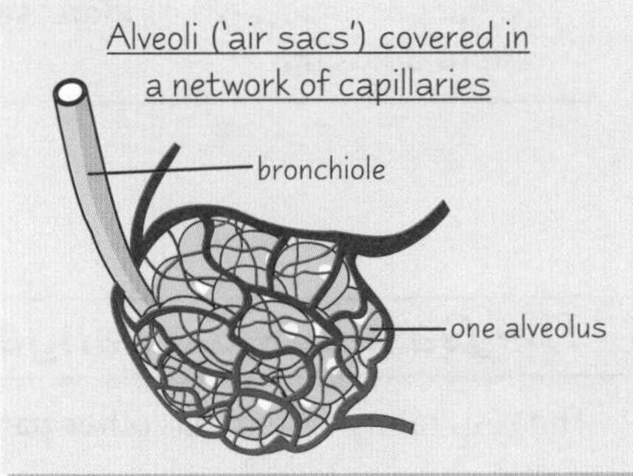

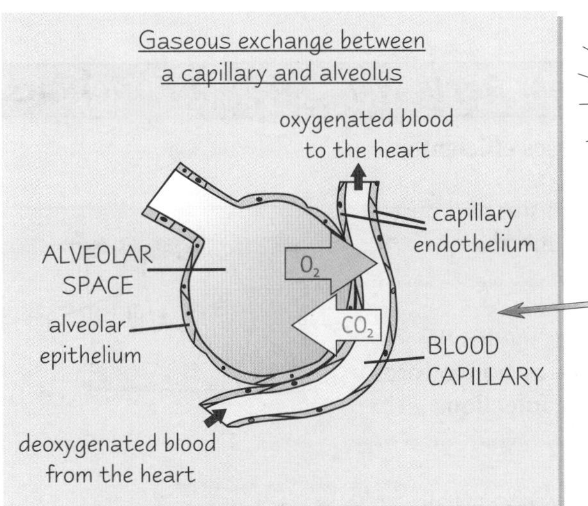

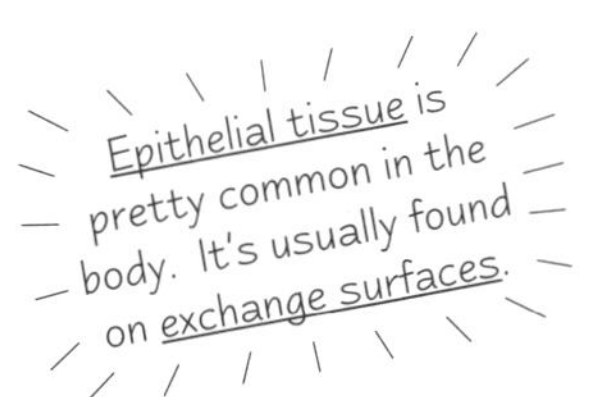

3) O_2 **diffuses out of** the alveoli, across the **alveolar epithelium** and the **capillary endothelium** (a type of epithelium that forms the capillary wall), and into **haemoglobin** in the **blood**.
4) CO_2 **diffuses into** the alveoli from the blood, crossing the capillary endothelium then the alveolar epithelium. After entering the alveolar space, it's **breathed out**.

Practice Questions

Q1 Name four substances an organism needs to exchange with its environment.

Q2 How do the surface area to volume ratios of large and small organisms differ?

Q3 Describe the passage of air from the mouth to the alveoli.

Exam Questions

Q1 Explain why humans have a specialised gas exchange system. [5 marks]

Q2 Describe gaseous exchange in the alveoli. [4 marks]

Cube hippos... very Picasso...

I know you've just got to the end of a page, but it would be a pretty smart idea to have another look at diffusion on page 16. Not the most thrilling prospect I realise, but it'll help these pages make more sense — all I can think about at the moment is cube hippos. You need to understand why large multicellular organisms need exchange organs, so get learnin'.

The Gaseous Exchange System

Lungs aren't just a couple of bags full of gas... probably a good thing too, since breathing's kind of important...

*The **Lungs** are **Adapted** for **Efficient Gaseous Exchange***

See page 16 for more on diffusion.

Most **gas exchange surfaces** have two things in common:

1) They have a **large surface area**, which **increases** the **rate of diffusion**.

2) They're **thin** (often just one layer of epithelial cells) — this provides a **short diffusion pathway** across the gas exchange surface, which **increases** the **rate of diffusion**.

The organism also maintains a **steep concentration gradient** of gases across the exchange surface, which **increases** the **rate of diffusion**.

The lungs have these features:

- **Many alveoli** provide a **large surface area** for diffusion to occur across.
- The **alveolar epithelium** and **capillary endothelium** are each only **one cell thick**, giving a **short diffusion pathway**.
- All the alveoli have a **good blood supply** from capillaries — they constantly **take away oxygen** and **bring more carbon dioxide**, maintaining the **concentration gradient**.
- **Breathing in and out** refreshes the air in the alveoli, keeping the **concentration gradients** high.

*The **Gaseous Exchange System** has Different **Parts** with Different **Functions***

The respiratory system has **other parts** that help it to exchange gases **efficiently**.

1) **Goblet cells** secrete **mucus**. The mucus **traps** microorganisms and dust particles in the inhaled air, stopping them from reaching the alveoli.

2) **Cilia** on the surface of cells **beat** the mucus, which **moves** it (plus the trapped microorganisms and dust) upward away from the alveoli towards the throat, where it's swallowed. This helps **prevent lung infections**.

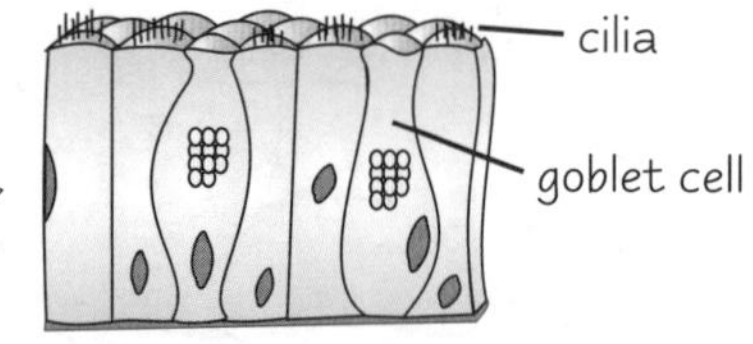

3) **Elastic fibres** in the walls of the trachea, bronchi, bronchioles and alveoli help the process of **breathing out** (see p. 32). On breathing in, the lungs inflate and the elastic fibres are **stretched**. Then, the fibres **recoil** to help push the air out when exhaling.

4) **Smooth muscle** in the walls of the trachea, bronchi and bronchioles allows their **diameter to be controlled**. During exercise the smooth muscle **relaxes**, making the tubes **wider**. This means there's **less resistance** to airflow and air can move in and out of the lungs more easily.

Derek was quickly mastering efficient gaseous exchange.

5) **Rings of cartilage** in the walls of the trachea and bronchi **provide support**. It's strong but flexible — it stops the trachea and bronchi **collapsing** when you breathe in and the pressure drops (see p. 32).

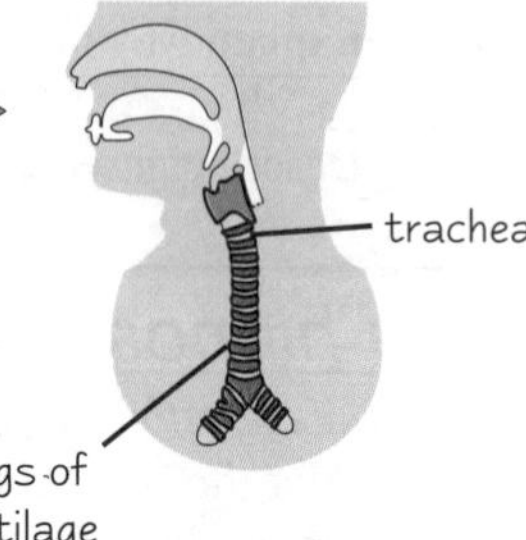

The Gaseous Exchange System

The Different **Parts** are Found in **Different Places** in the System

Part of the lung	Cross section	Cartilage	Smooth muscle	Elastic fibres	Goblet cells	Epithelium
trachea	smooth muscle, elastic fibres, c-shaped cartilage, ciliated epithelium	large C-shaped pieces	✓	✓	✓	ciliated
bronchi	smooth muscle, small cartilage pieces, elastic fibres, ciliated epithelium	smaller pieces	✓	✓	✓	ciliated
larger bronchiole	smooth muscle and elastic fibres, ciliated epithelium	none	✓	✓	✓	ciliated
smaller bronchiole		none	✓	✓	✗	ciliated
smallest bronchiole		none	✗	✓	✗	no cilia
alveoli	blood capillary, elastic fibres, alveolar epithelium	none	✗	✓	✗	no cilia

Practice Questions

Q1 Describe the distribution of cartilage in the mammalian gas exchange system.

Q2 Describe the distribution of elastic fibres in the mammalian gas exchange system.

Q3 How does the structure of the trachea differ from the structure of the bronchi?

Exam Questions

Q1 Efficient gas exchange surfaces have the following characteristics:

- large surface area
- short diffusion pathway
- high concentration gradient

Explain how these characteristics apply to human lungs. [5 marks]

Q2 Name five tissues, cells or cell structures found in the mammalian gas exchange system and explain the function of each. [10 marks]

Rings of cartilage — I prefer mine in gold... with diamonds...

There's a lot to learn on these two pages. Copying out my beautiful blue table will help — and then you can write out what the function of each part is. Make sure you understand what makes a good exchange surface and how the lungs are adapted to efficient gas exchange too. You won't be coughing and spluttering in the exam once you know this lot.

Breathing

If you're in need of inspiration then there's plenty on this page... sadly I'm only talking about the kind of inspiration that gets air into your lungs — if you want the other sort head over to the Grand Canyon.

Ventilation is Breathing In and Out

Ventilation consists of **inspiration** (breathing in) and **expiration** (breathing out).
It's controlled by the movements of the **diaphragm**, **intercostal muscles** and **ribcage**.

Inspiration

1) The **intercostal** and **diaphragm muscles contract**.
2) This causes the **ribcage** to move **upwards and outwards** and the **diaphragm** to **flatten**, **increasing the volume** of the thorax (the space where the lungs are).
3) As the volume of the thorax increases the lung pressure **decreases** (to below atmospheric pressure).
4) This causes air to flow **into the lungs**.
5) Inspiration is an **active process** — it requires **energy**.

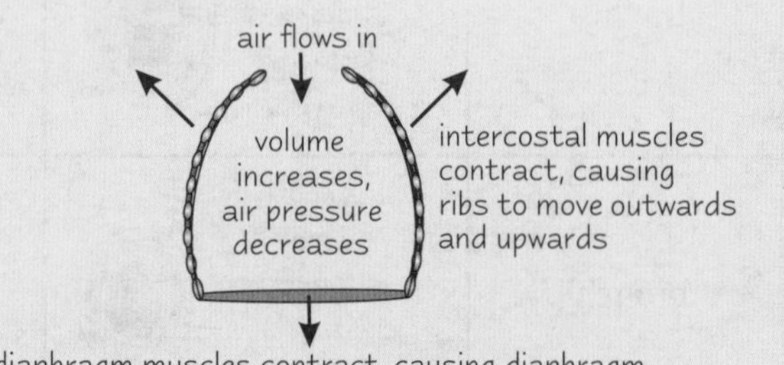

Expiration

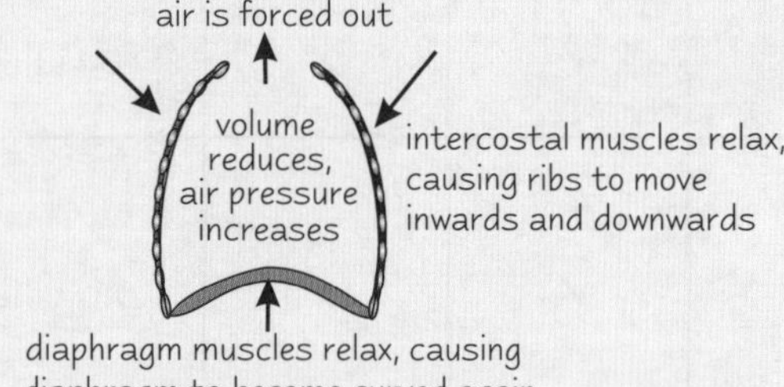

1) The **intercostal** and **diaphragm muscles relax**.
2) The **ribcage** moves **downwards and inwards** and the **diaphragm** becomes **curved** again.
3) The thorax volume **decreases**, causing the air pressure to **increase** (to above atmospheric pressure).
4) Air is forced **out of the lungs**.
5) Expiration is a **passive process** — it **doesn't** require energy.

Tidal Volume is the Volume of Air in a Normal Breath

Here are some terms that you need to know about breathing:

1) **Tidal volume (TV)** — the volume of air in **each breath** — usually about **0.4 dm³**.
2) **Vital capacity** — the **maximum** volume of air that can be breathed **in** or **out**.
3) **Breathing rate** — **how many** breaths are taken — usually in a minute.
4) **Oxygen uptake** — the rate at which a person **uses up** oxygen (e.g. the number of dm³ used per minute).

dm³ is short for decimetres cubed — it's the same as litres.

Jane couldn't maintain her breathing rate when she saw all those TVs.

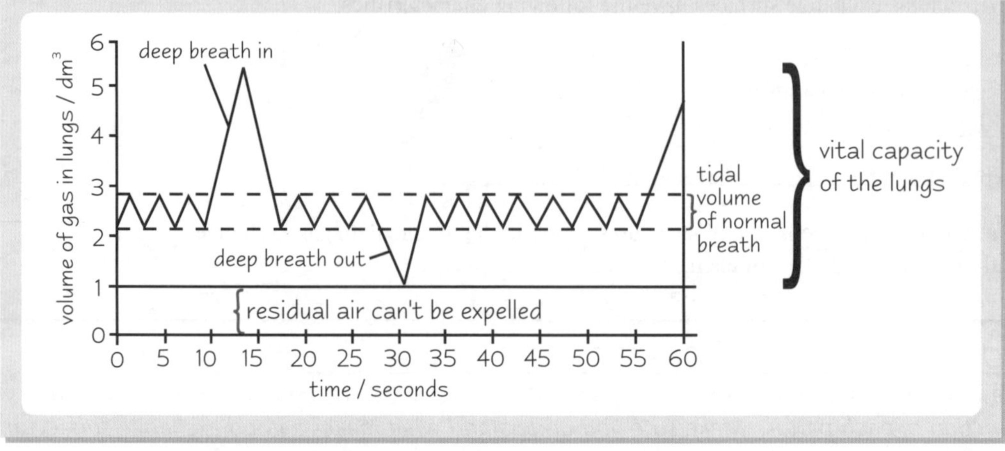

Breathing

Spirometers Can be Used to Investigate Breathing

A spirometer is a machine that can give readings of **tidal volume**, **vital capacity**, **breathing rate** and **oxygen uptake**.

1) A spirometer has an **oxygen-filled** chamber with a **movable lid.**
2) The person breathes through a **tube** connected to the oxygen chamber.
3) As the person breathes in and out, the lid of the chamber moves **up and down**.
4) These movements are recorded by a **pen** attached to the lid of the chamber — this writes on a **rotating drum**, creating a **spirometer trace.**
5) The **soda lime** in the tube the subject breathes into absorbs **carbon dioxide**.

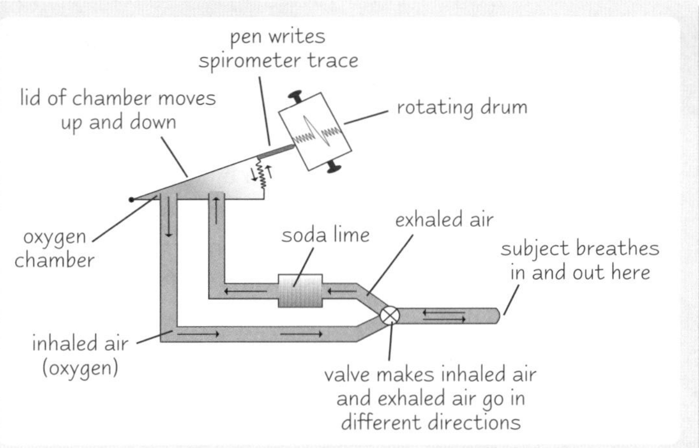

The **total volume of gas** in the chamber **decreases** over time. This is because the air that's breathed out is a **mixture** of oxygen and carbon dioxide. The carbon dioxide is absorbed by the **soda lime** — so there's **only oxygen** in the chamber which the subject inhales from. As this oxygen gets used up by respiration, the total volume decreases.

You Need to be Able to Analyse Data from a Spirometer

In the exam, you might have to work out **breathing rate**, **tidal volume**, **vital capacity** and **oxygen consumption** from a spirometer trace. For example:

This graph looks different to the one on the previous page because it shows the volume of air in the spirometer, not in the lungs.

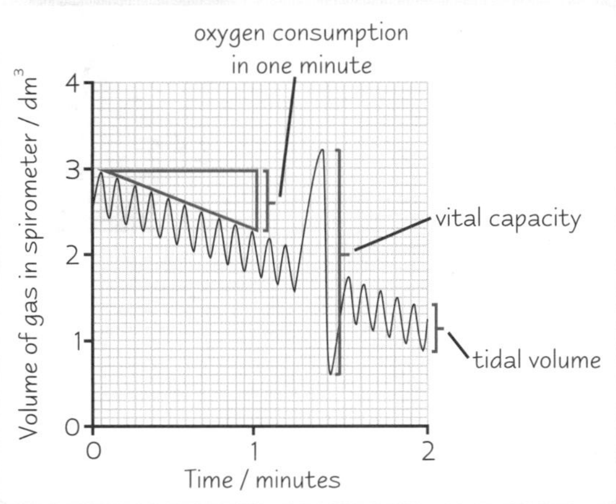

1) In this trace, the **breathing rate** in the first minute is **10 breaths per minute** (there are 10 'peaks' in the first minute).
2) The **tidal volume** may change from time to time, but in this trace it's about **0.5 dm³**.
3) The graph shows a **vital capacity** of **2.65 dm³**.
4) **Oxygen consumption** is the **decrease** in the **volume of gas** in the **spirometer chamber**. It can be read from the graph by taking the **average slope** of the trace. In this case, it drops by 0.7 dm³ in the first minute — so, oxygen consumption is **0.7 dm³/min.**

Practice Questions

Q1 What is meant by tidal volume and vital capacity?

Q2 Describe how a spirometer can be used to measure oxygen uptake.

Exam Question

Q1 Describe the changes that take place in the human thorax during inspiration. [5 marks]

Investigate someone's breathing — make sure they've had a mint first...

I thought spirometers were those circular plastic things you draw crazy patterns with... apparently not. I know the graphs don't look that approachable, but it's important you understand what the squiggly lines show, and the four terms used when investigating breathing — I'd bet my right lung there'll be a question on spirometer graphs in the exam.

The Circulatory System

Right then, this section's all about blood and hearts and veins and things, so if you're a bit squeamish then it's not gonna float your boat. Unfortunately for you, it's all really important for the exams. And besides, without a circulatory system you'd probably have some issues when it comes to things like... ooh I dunno... living.

Multicellular Organisms need Transport Systems

1) As you saw on page 28, **single-celled** organisms can get all the substances they need by **diffusion** across their outer membrane.
2) If you're **multicellular** though, it's a bit **harder** to supply all your cells with everything they need — multicellular organisms are relatively **big** and they have a **low surface area to volume ratio**.
3) A lot of multicellular organisms (e.g. mammals) are also **very active**. This means that a **large number of cells** are all **respiring very quickly**, so they need a constant, rapid supply of glucose and oxygen.
4) To make sure that every cell has a good enough supply, multicellular organisms need a **transport system**.
5) In mammals, this is the **circulatory system**, which uses **blood** to carry glucose and oxygen around the body. It also carries hormones, antibodies (to fight disease) and waste (like CO_2).

Fish and Mammals have Different Circulatory Systems

Not all organisms have the same type of circulatory system — **fish** have a **single circulatory system** and **mammals** have a **double circulatory system**.

1) In a **single** circulatory system, blood only passes through the heart **once** for each complete circuit of the body.
2) In a **double** circulatory system, the blood passes through the heart **twice** for each complete circuit of the body.

FISH

In **fish**, the **heart** pumps blood to the **gills** (to pick up oxygen) and then on through the **rest of the body** (to deliver the oxygen) in a single circuit.

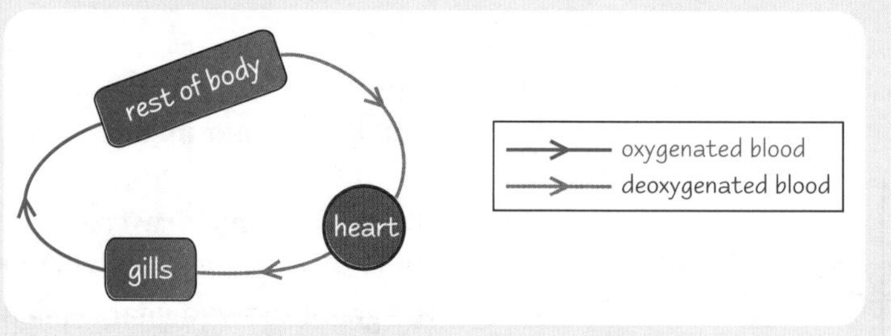

Single what now? Just pass me the tartar sauce.

MAMMALS

In **mammals**, the heart is **divided** down the middle, so it's really like **two** hearts joined together.

1) The **right side** of the heart pumps blood to the **lungs** (to pick up oxygen).
2) From the lungs it travels to the **left side** of the heart, which pumps it to the rest of the **body**.
3) When blood **returns** to the heart, it enters the right side again.

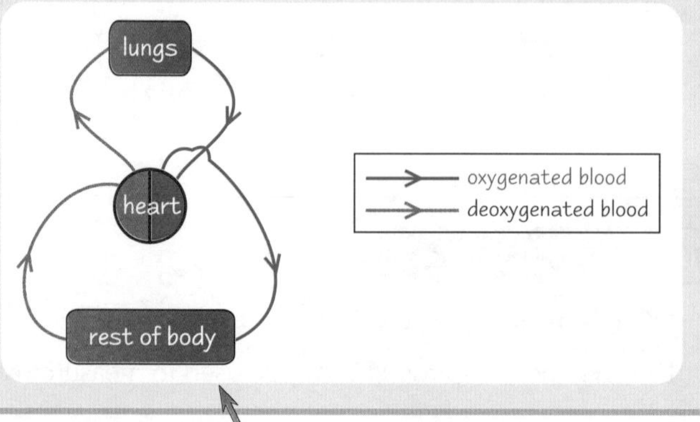

The right and left sides of the heart are reversed in the diagram because it's the right and left of the person the heart belongs to.

So, our circulatory system is really two linked loops. One sends blood to the lungs — this is called the **pulmonary** system, and the other sends blood to the rest of the body — this is called the **systemic** system.

The **advantage** of the mammalian double circulatory system is that the heart can give the blood an **extra push** between the lungs and the rest of the body. This makes the blood travel **faster**, so oxygen is delivered to the tissues **more quickly**.

The Circulatory System

Circulatory Systems can be **Open or Closed**

All vertebrates (e.g. fish and mammals) have **closed circulatory systems** — the blood is **enclosed** inside **blood vessels**.

1) The heart pumps blood into **arteries**. These **branch out** into millions of **capillaries** (see p. 40).
2) Substances like oxygen and glucose **diffuse** from the blood in the capillaries into the body cells, but the blood **stays inside** the blood vessels as it circulates.
3) **Veins** take the blood back to the heart.

Some invertebrates (e.g. insects) have an **open circulatory system** — blood **isn't enclosed** in blood vessels all the time. Instead, it flows freely through the **body cavity**.

1) The heart is **segmented**. It **contracts** in a **wave**, starting from the back, pumping the blood into a **single main artery**.
2) That artery **opens up** into the body cavity.
3) The blood flows around the insect's **organs**, gradually making its way back into the heart segments through a series of **valves**.

The circulatory system supplies the insect's cell with nutrients, and transports things like hormones around the body. It **doesn't supply** the insect's cells with **oxygen** though — this is done by a system of tubes called the **tracheal system** (see p. 102 for more).

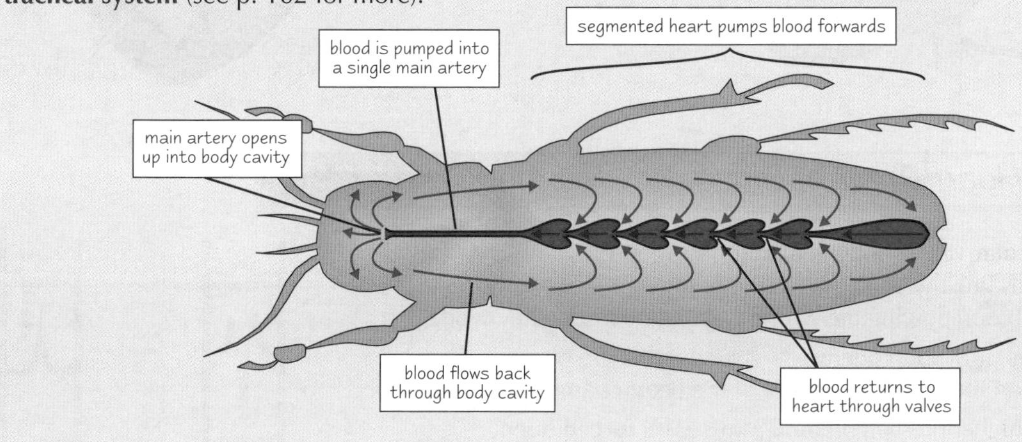

Practice Questions

Q1 Give three reasons why multicellular organisms usually need a transport system, but unicellular organisms don't.

Q2 Explain why the mammalian circulatory system is described as a double circulatory system.

Q3 What is an open circulatory system?

Exam Questions

Q1 Explain why the circulatory system of a fish is described as being closed. [1 mark]

Q2 Briefly describe the circulatory system of an insect. [2 marks]

Q3 Describe one way in which the circulatory system of a fish is:

a) similar to that of a mammal. [1 mark]

b) different from that of a mammal. [1 mark]

OK, open circulatory systems are officially grim. Body cavities?! Bleurgh...

After reading this page, we can all finally put to rest the idea that the Earth will eventually be overrun by giant insects. Their circulatory system just isn't up to it you see... All the nutrients and stuff in their blood have to diffuse through the whole body cavity, so if they were giant they wouldn't be able to supply all their organs and bits and pieces properly. Phew.

The Heart

You saw on page 34 that mammals have a double circulatory system — well that means that our hearts have to be a bit more complicated than just a big old pump.

The **Heart** Consists of **Two Muscular Pumps**

The diagrams below show the **internal** and **external structure** of the heart. The **right side** of the heart pumps **deoxygenated blood** to the **lungs** and the **left side** pumps **oxygenated blood** to the **rest of the body**.

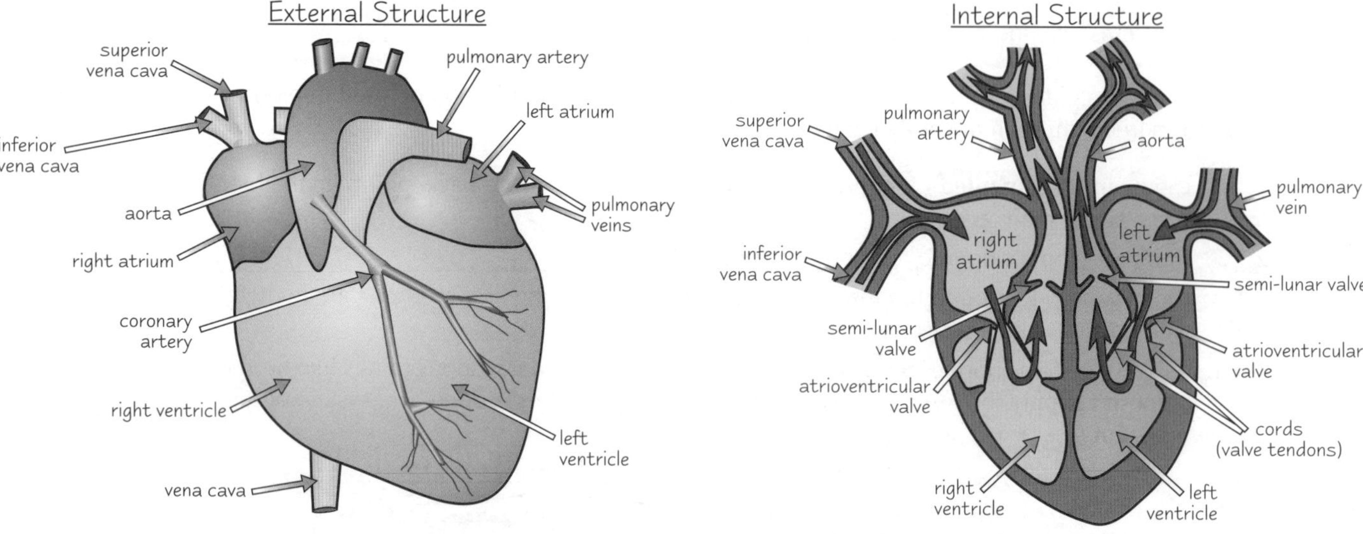

Valves in the Heart **Prevent** Blood Flowing the **Wrong Way**

The **atrioventricular valves** link the atria to the ventricles, and the **semi-lunar** valves link the ventricles to the pulmonary artery and aorta — they all stop blood flowing the **wrong way**. Here's how they work:

1) The **valves** only open one way — whether they're open or closed depends on the **relative pressure** of the heart chambers.
2) If there's higher pressure **behind** a valve, it's **forced open**.
3) If pressure is higher **in front** of the valve, it's **forced shut**.

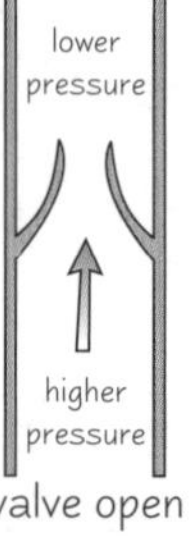

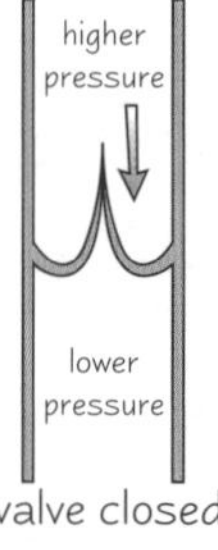

The **Thickness** of the **Chamber Walls** Depends on Their **Function**

The heart is mainly **muscle**. When it contracts it creates **high pressure** — enough to force blood all the way around the body.

Each of the four **chambers** of the heart has a **different function**. The more **work** that a heart chamber has to do, the more **muscle** it needs — so, the **thicker** its wall is.

1) The **left ventricle** of the heart has **thicker**, more muscular walls than the **right ventricle**, because it needs to contract powerfully to pump blood all the way round the body. The right side only needs to get blood to the lungs, which are nearby.
2) The **ventricles** have **thicker walls** than the **atria**, because they have to push blood out of the heart whereas the atria just need to push blood a short distance into the ventricles.

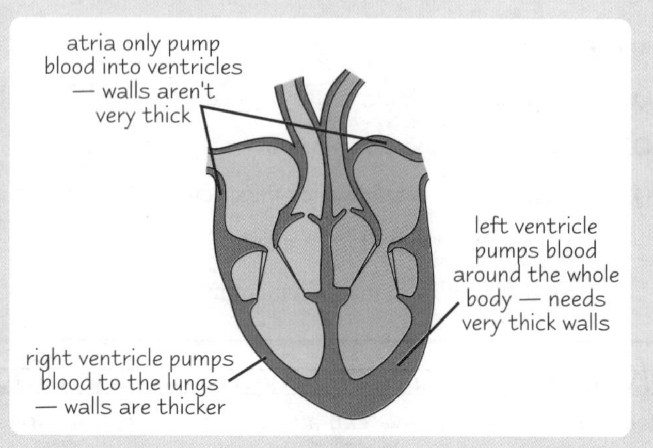

The Heart

The Cardiac Cycle Pumps Blood Round the Body

The cardiac cycle is an ongoing sequence of **contraction** and **relaxation** of the atria and ventricles that keeps blood **continuously circulating** round the body. The **volume** of the atria and ventricles **changes** as they contract and relax, altering the **pressure** in each chamber. This causes **valves** to open and close, which directs the **blood flow** through the heart. The cardiac cycle can be simplified into three stages:

1. Ventricles relax, atria contract

The **ventricles are relaxed**. The atria fill with blood, which **decreases** their **volume** and **increases** the **pressure**. The **higher pressure** in the atria causes the **atrioventricular valves** to **open**, allowing the blood to flow into the **ventricles**. The atria then **contract**, **decreasing** their **volume** and **increasing** the **pressure** even further — forcing the remaining blood out.

2. Ventricles contract, atria relax

The **ventricles contract** and the **atria relax**. The pressure is **higher** in the ventricles than the atria, so the atrioventricular valves **close** to prevent **backflow**. The high pressure in the ventricles **opens** the semilunar valves — blood is forced out into the **pulmonary artery** and **aorta**.

3. Ventricles relax, atria relax

The **ventricles and atria both relax**, increasing their volume and lowering the pressure in the heart chambers. The higher pressure in the pulmonary artery and aorta causes the semilunar valves to **close**, preventing backflow. Then the atria **fill with blood** again due to the higher pressure in the vena cava and pulmonary vein, and the cycle **starts over again**.

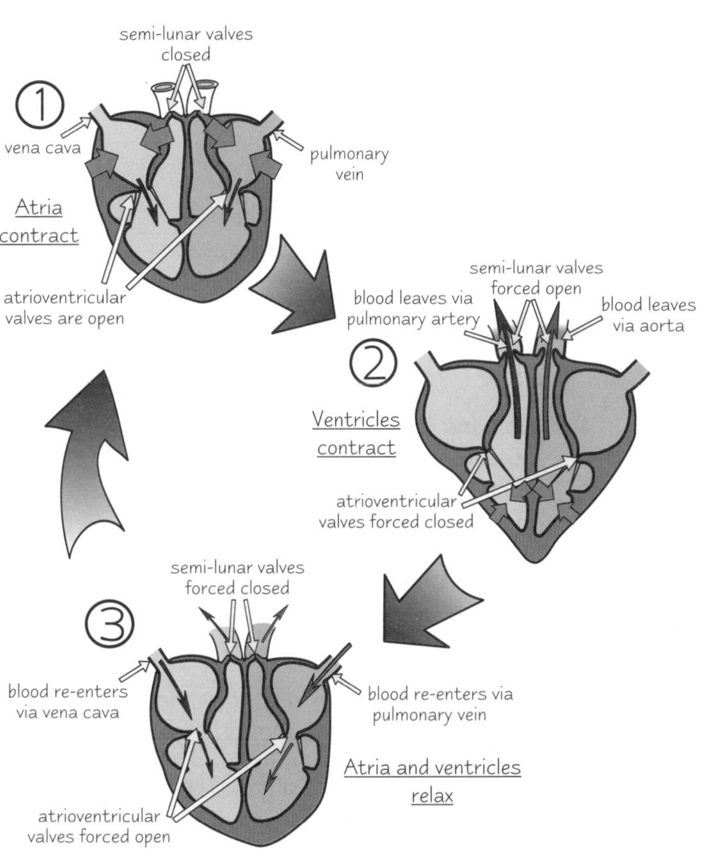

Practice Questions

Q1 Which chamber of the heart receives blood from the lungs?

Q2 Why does the left ventricle of the heart have such a thick wall?

Exam Questions

Q1 The graph shows the pressure changes in the left side of the heart during one heartbeat.

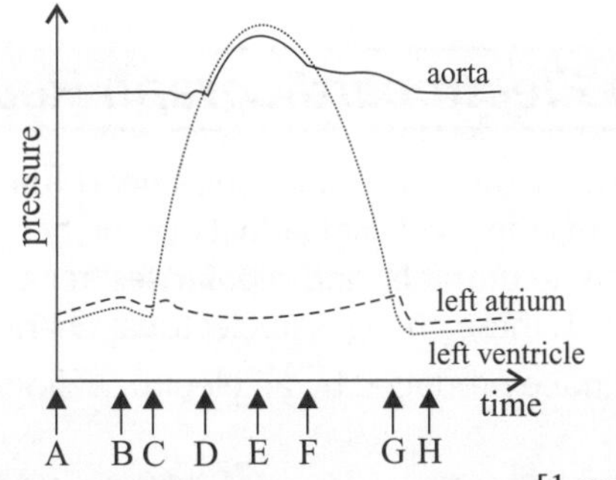

a) At which labelled point (A-H) on the graph does:

i) the semi-lunar valve open? [1 mark]

ii) the atrioventricular valve close? [1 mark]

b) On the diagram, sketch the graph that you would expect for the right ventricle. [2 marks]

Q2 Describe the events that take place in one complete cardiac cycle, beginning with when the heart muscle is completely relaxed. [8 marks]

Apparently an adult heart is the size of two fists. Two whole fists! That's huge!

It's not really surprising that your left ventricle wall is so much thicker than the other bits of your heart — just think about how far it has to pump all that blood. It's a good job we've got those valves to stop everything shooting backwards though...

The Heart

You don't have to think about making your heart beat — your body does it for you. So you couldn't stop it beating even if for some strange reason you wanted to. Which is nice to know.

Cardiac Muscle Controls the Regular Beating of the Heart

Cardiac (heart) muscle is '**myogenic**' — it can contract and relax without receiving signals from nerves. This pattern of contractions controls the **regular heartbeat**.

1) The process starts in the **sino-atrial node (SAN)**, which is in the wall of the **right atrium**.
2) The SAN is like a pacemaker — it sets the **rhythm** of the heartbeat by sending out regular **waves of electrical activity** to the atrial walls.
3) This causes the right and left **atria** to **contract at the same time**.
4) A band of non-conducting **collagen tissue** prevents the waves of electrical activity from being passed directly from the atria to the ventricles.
5) Instead, these waves of electrical activity are transferred from the SAN to the **atrioventricular node (AVN)**.

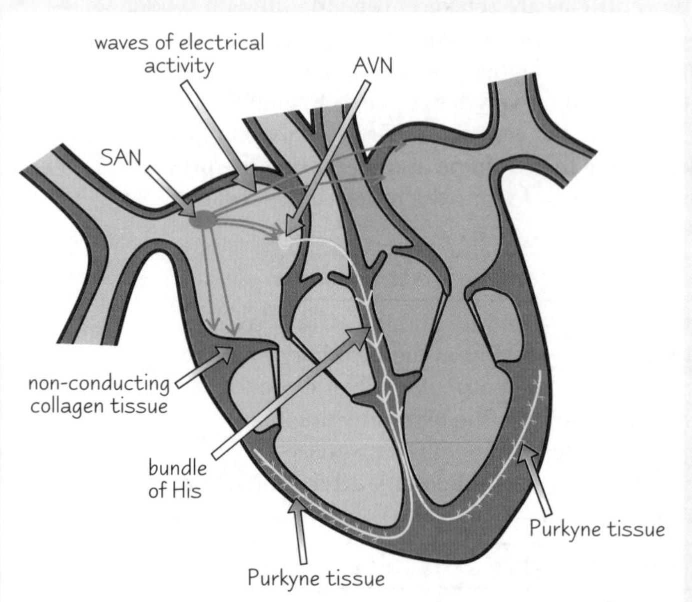

6) The AVN is responsible for passing the waves of electrical activity onto the bundle of His. But, there's a **slight delay** before the AVN reacts, to make sure the ventricles contract **after** the atria have emptied.
7) The **bundle of His** is a group of muscle fibres responsible for conducting the waves of electrical activity to the finer muscle fibres in the right and left ventricle walls, called the **Purkyne tissue**.
8) The Purkyne tissue carries the waves of electrical activity into the muscular walls of the right and left ventricles, causing them to **contract simultaneously**, from the bottom up.

An Electrocardiograph Records the Electrical Activity of the Heart

A doctor can check someone's **heart function** using an **electrocardiograph** — a machine that **records** the **electrical activity** of the heart. The heart muscle **depolarises** (loses electrical charge) when it **contracts**, and **repolarises** (regains charge) when it **relaxes**. An electrocardiograph records these changes in electrical charge using **electrodes** placed on the chest.

The trace produced by an electrocardiograph is called an **electrocardiogram**, or **ECG**. A **normal** ECG looks like this:

1) The **P wave** is caused by **contraction** (depolarisation) of the **atria**.
2) The main peak of the heartbeat, together with the dips at either side, is called the **QRS complex** — it's caused by **contraction** (depolarisation) of the **ventricles**.
3) The **T wave** is due to **relaxation** (repolarisation) of the **ventricles**.

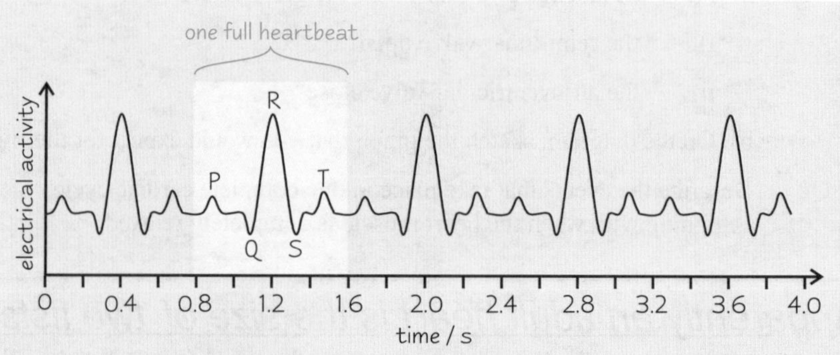

The Heart

Doctors use ECGs to **Diagnose Heart Problems**

Doctors **compare** their patients' ECGs with a **normal trace**. This helps them to diagnose any heart problems.

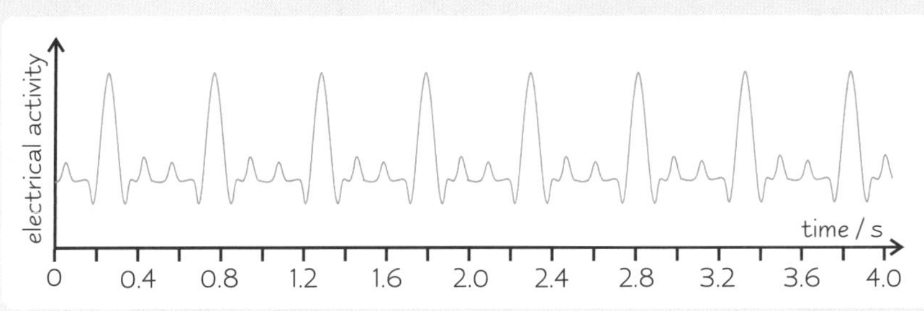

This heartbeat is **too fast** — around 120 beats per minute. That might be OK during **exercise**, but at **rest** it shows that the heart **isn't pumping blood efficiently**.

Here, the **atria** are contracting but sometimes the **ventricles** are **not** (some **P waves** aren't followed by a **QRS complex**). This might mean there's a problem with the **AVN** — impulses aren't travelling from the atria through to the ventricles.

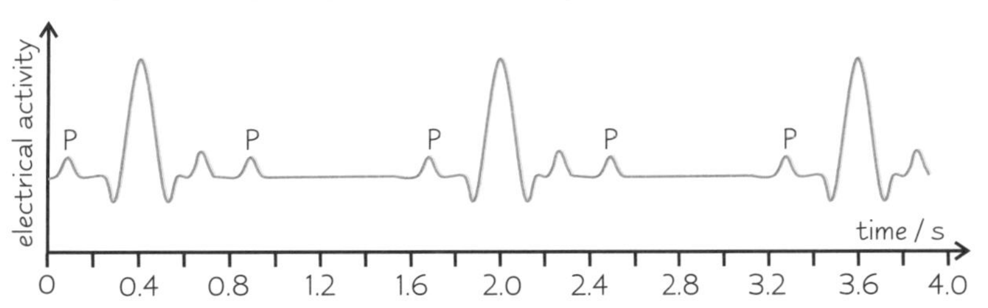

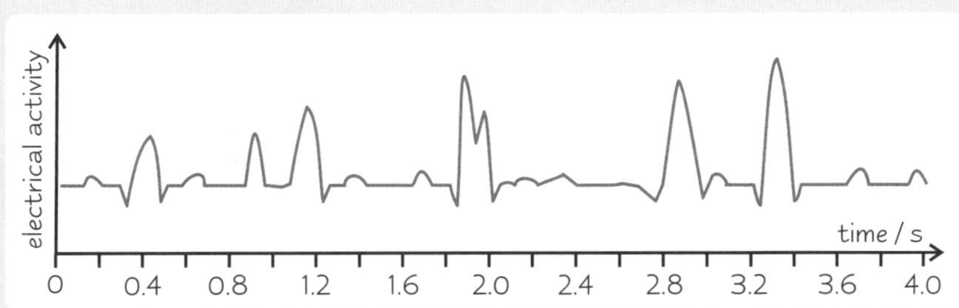

This is **fibrillation** — a really **irregular heartbeat**. The atria or ventricles completely **lose their rhythm** and **stop contracting properly**. It can result in anything from chest pain and fainting to lack of pulse and death.

Practice Questions

Q1 What prevents impulses from the atria travelling straight into the ventricles?

Q2 What is the name of the structure that picks up impulses from the atria and passes them on to the ventricles?

Q3 What causes the QRS part of an ECG trace?

Exam Questions

Q1 Describe the function of:

a) the sino-atrial node? [1 mark]

b) the Purkyne tissue? [1 mark]

Q2 Suggest the cause of an ECG which has a QRS complex that is smaller than normal. [2 marks]

Perhaps if I plug myself into the mains, my heart'll be supercharged...

It's pretty incredible that your heart manages to go through all those stages in the right order, at exactly the right time, without getting it even slightly wrong. It does it perfectly, about 70 times every minute. That's about 100 800 times a day. If only my brain was that efficient. I'd have all this revision done in five minutes, then I could go and watch TV...

Blood Vessels

So, provided all the electrical bits and pieces in your heart are working properly, it'll be pumping out about a litre of blood every 15 seconds. You'll be needing some vessels or something to put that in, otherwise it'll be all over the place...

Blood Vessels Transport Substances Round the Body

The three types of blood vessel that you need to know about are **arteries**, **capillaries** and **veins**:

1) **Arteries** carry blood **from** the heart **to** the rest of the body. Their walls are thick and **muscular** and have elastic tissue to cope with the **high pressure** produced by the heartbeat. The inner lining (**endothelium**) is **folded**, allowing the artery to **expand** — this also helps it to cope with high pressure. All arteries carry **oxygenated** blood except for the **pulmonary arteries**, which take deoxygenated blood to the lungs.

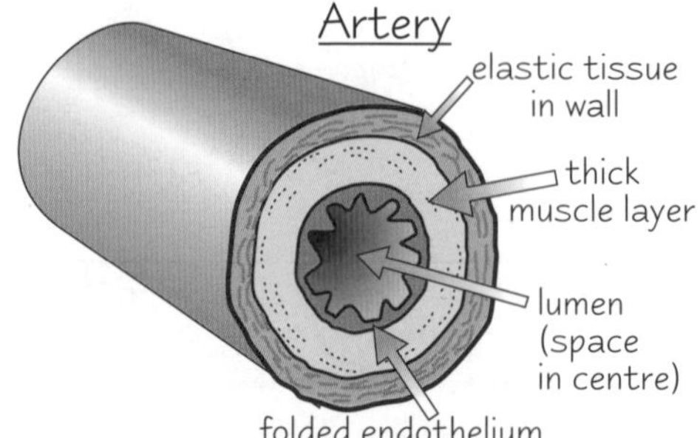

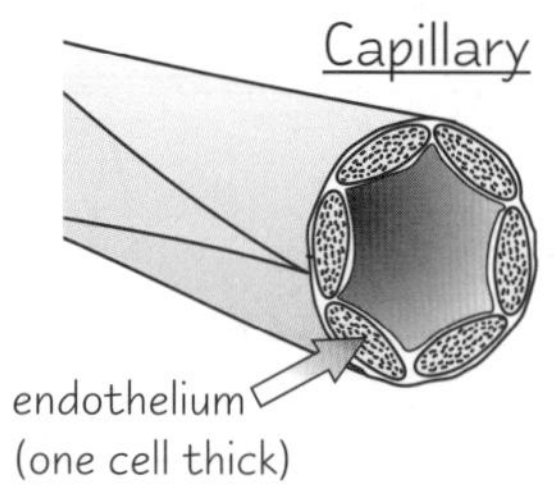

2) Arteries branch into **capillaries**, which are the **smallest** of the blood vessels. Substances like glucose and oxygen are exchanged between cells and capillaries, so they're adapted for **efficient diffusion**, e.g. their walls are only **one cell thick**. Capillaries connect to veins.

3) **Veins** take blood **back to the heart** under low pressure. They're **wider** than equivalent arteries, with very little elastic or muscle tissue. Veins contain **valves** to stop the blood flowing backwards (see p. 36). Blood flow through the veins is helped by contraction of the **body muscles** surrounding them. All veins carry **deoxygenated** blood (because oxygen has been used up by body cells), except for the **pulmonary veins**, which carry oxygenated blood to the heart from the lungs.

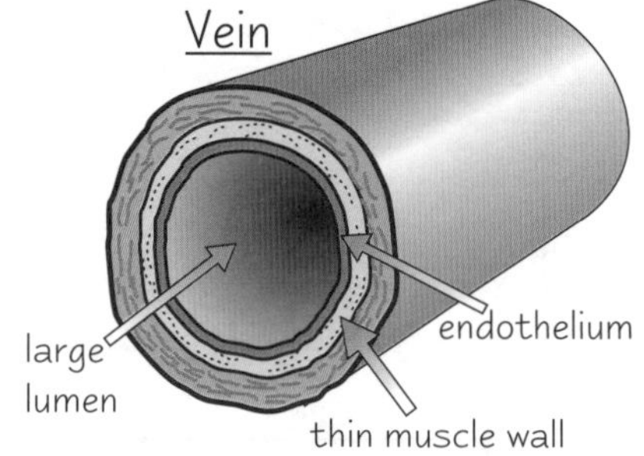

Tissue Fluid is Formed from Blood

Tissue fluid is the fluid that **surrounds cells** in tissues. It's made from substances that leave the blood, e.g. oxygen, water and nutrients. Cells take in oxygen and nutrients from the tissue fluid, and release metabolic waste into it. In a **capillary bed** (the network of capillaries in an area of tissue), substances move out of the capillaries, into the tissue fluid, by **pressure filtration**:

1) At the **start** of the capillary bed, nearest the arteries, the pressure inside the capillaries is **greater** than the pressure in the tissue fluid. This difference in pressure **forces fluid out** of the **capillaries** and into the **spaces** around the cells, forming tissue fluid.
2) As fluid leaves, the pressure reduces in the capillaries — so the pressure is much **lower** at the **end** of the capillary bed that's nearest to the veins.
3) Due to the fluid loss, the **water potential** at the end of the capillaries nearest the veins is **lower** than the water potential in the **tissue fluid** — so some **water re-enters** the capillaries from the tissue fluid at the vein end by **osmosis** (see p. 16 for more on osmosis).

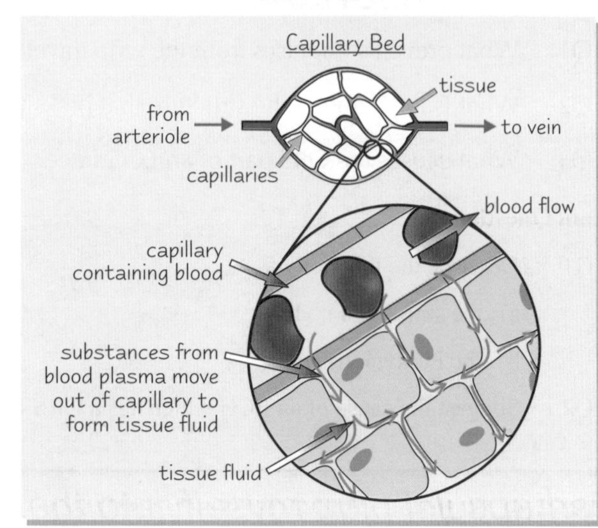

Unlike blood, tissue fluid **doesn't** contain **red blood cells** or **big proteins**, because they're **too large** to be pushed out through the capillary walls.

Blood Vessels

Excess Tissue Fluid Drains into the Lymph Vessels

Not all of the tissue fluid **re-enters** the capillaries at the vein end of the capillary bed — some **excess tissue fluid** is left over. This extra fluid eventually gets returned to the blood through the **lymphatic system** — a kind of **drainage** system, made up of **lymph vessels**.

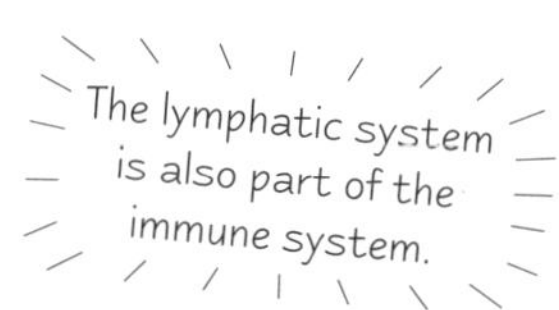

1) The smallest lymph vessels are the **lymph capillaries**.
2) Excess tissue fluid passes into lymph vessels. Once inside, it's called **lymph**.
3) **Valves** in the lymph vessels stop the lymph going **backwards**.
4) Lymph gradually moves towards the main lymph vessels in the **thorax**. Here, it's returned to the **blood**, near the **heart**.

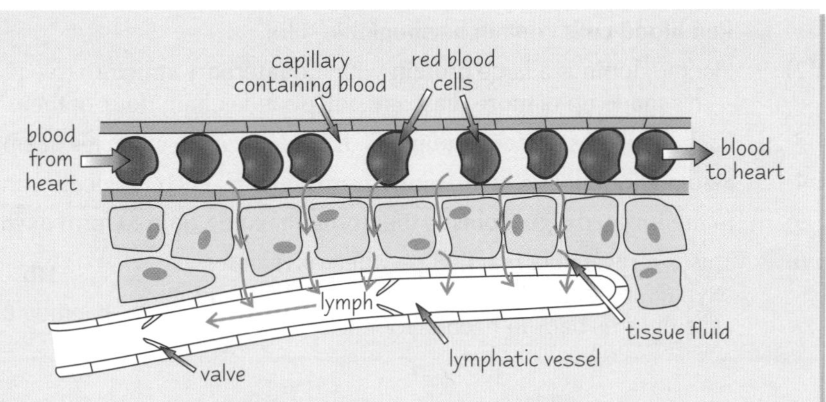

You Need to Know the Differences Between Blood, Tissue Fluid and Lymph

Blood, tissue fluid and lymph are all quite **similar** — **tissue fluid** is formed from **blood**, and **lymph** is formed from **tissue fluid**. The main differences are shown in the table.

	blood	tissue fluid	lymph	comment
red blood cells	✓	✗	✗	Red blood cells are too big to get through capillary walls into tissue fluid.
white blood cells	✓	very few	✓	Most white blood cells are in the lymph system. They only enter tissue fluid when there's an infection.
platelets	✓	✗	✗	Only present in tissue fluid if the capillaries are damaged.
proteins	✓	very few	only antibodies	Most plasma proteins are too big to get through capillary walls.
water	✓	✓	✓	Tissue fluid and lymph have a higher water potential than blood.
dissolved solutes	✓	✓	✓	Solutes (e.g. salt) can move freely between blood, tissue fluid and lymph.

Practice Questions

Q1 Is the blood pressure highest in veins or arteries?

Q2 Explain the differences between blood, tissue fluid and lymph.

Exam Questions

Q1 Explain how the structure of each of the following blood vessels is adapted to its function:

a) arteries [2 marks]

b) capillaries [1 mark]

c) veins [1 mark]

Q2 Explain how tissue fluid is formed and how it is returned to the circulation. [4 marks]

Tissue fluid... Imagine draining the fluid out of a used tissue. Urrrgh.

That table looks a bit terrifying, but a lot of it's pretty obvious when you think about it — there can't be any red blood cells floating around loose in your tissues, otherwise you'd be bright red. And platelets are the bits that cause blood clots, so they're going to be in your blood... In fact, proteins and white blood cells are the only tricky bits.

Haemoglobin

Aaagh, complicated topic alert. Don't worry though, because your poor, over-worked brain cells will recover from the brain-strain of these pages thanks to haemoglobin. So the least you can do is learn how it works.

Oxygen is Carried Round the Body as **Oxyhaemoglobin**

'Affinity' for oxygen means tendency to combine with oxygen.

1) **Red blood cells** contain **haemoglobin** (Hb).
2) Haemoglobin is a large **protein** with a **quaternary** structure (see p. 54 for more) — it's made up of **more than one** polypeptide chain (**four** of them in fact).
3) Each chain has a **haem group** which contains **iron** and gives haemoglobin its **red** colour.
4) Haemoglobin has a **high affinity for oxygen** — each molecule can carry **four oxygen molecules.**
5) In the lungs, oxygen **joins** to the **iron** in haemoglobin to form **oxyhaemoglobin.**
6) This is a **reversible reaction** — when oxygen leaves oxyhaemoglobin (**dissociates** from it) near the body cells, it turns back to haemoglobin.

$$\mathbf{Hb} + \mathbf{4O_2} \rightleftharpoons \mathbf{HbO_8}$$

haemoglobin + oxygen ⇌ oxyhaemoglobin

Haemoglobin Saturation Depends on the **Partial Pressure** of **Oxygen**

1) The **partial pressure** of **oxygen** (**pO_2**) is a measure of **oxygen concentration.** The **greater** the concentration of dissolved oxygen in cells, the **higher** the partial pressure.
2) Similarly, the **partial pressure** of **carbon dioxide** (**pCO_2**) is a measure of the concentration of CO_2 in a cell.
3) Haemoglobin's **affinity** for oxygen **varies** depending on the **partial pressure** of **oxygen**:

> Oxygen **loads onto** haemoglobin to form oxyhaemoglobin where there's a **high pO_2**.
> Oxyhaemoglobin **unloads** its oxygen where there's a **lower pO_2**.

4) Oxygen enters blood capillaries at the **alveoli** in the **lungs**. Alveoli have a **high pO_2** so oxygen **loads onto** haemoglobin to form oxyhaemoglobin.
5) When **cells respire**, they use up oxygen — this **lowers** the **pO_2**. Red blood cells deliver oxyhaemoglobin to respiring tissues, where it unloads its oxygen.
6) The haemoglobin then returns to the lungs to pick up more oxygen.

There was no use pretending — the pCH_4 had just increased, and Keith knew who was to blame.

Dissociation Curves Show How **Affinity for Oxygen** Varies

A **dissociation curve** shows how **saturated** the haemoglobin is with oxygen at any given partial pressure.

100% saturation means every haemoglobin molecule is carrying the maximum of 4 molecules of oxygen.

0% saturation means none of the haemoglobin molecules are carrying any oxygen.

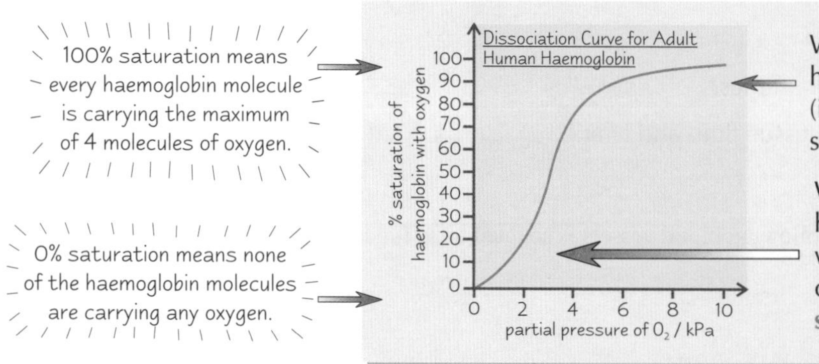

Where **pO_2 is high** (e.g. in the lungs), haemoglobin has a **high affinity** for oxygen (i.e. it will **readily combine** with oxygen), so it has a **high saturation** of oxygen.

Where **pO_2 is low** (e.g. in respiring tissues), haemoglobin has a **low affinity** for oxygen, which means it **releases oxygen** rather than combines with it. That's why it has a **low saturation** of oxygen.

1) The graph is **'S-shaped'** because when haemoglobin (Hb) combines with the **first O_2 molecule**, its **shape alters** in a way that makes it **easier** for other molecules to join too.
2) But as the Hb starts to become saturated, it gets **harder** for more oxygen molecules to join.
3) As a result, the curve has a **steep** bit in the middle where it's really easy for oxygen molecules to join, and **shallow** bits at each end where it's harder. When the curve is steep, a **small change in pO_2** causes a **big change** in the **amount of oxygen** carried by the Hb.

Haemoglobin

Fetal Haemoglobin has a Higher Affinity for Oxygen than Adult Haemoglobin

Adult haemoglobin and **fetal** haemoglobin have different affinities for oxygen. Fetal haemoglobin has a **higher affinity** for oxygen (the fetus's blood is **better at absorbing** oxygen than its mother's blood). This is really important:

1) The fetus gets oxygen from its **mother's blood** across the placenta.
2) By the time the mother's blood reaches the placenta, its oxygen saturation has **decreased** (because some has been used up by the mother's body).
3) For the fetus to get **enough oxygen** to survive its haemoglobin has to have a **higher affinity** for oxygen (so it takes up enough).
4) If its haemoglobin had the **same** affinity for oxygen as adult haemoglobin its blood **wouldn't** be **saturated enough**.

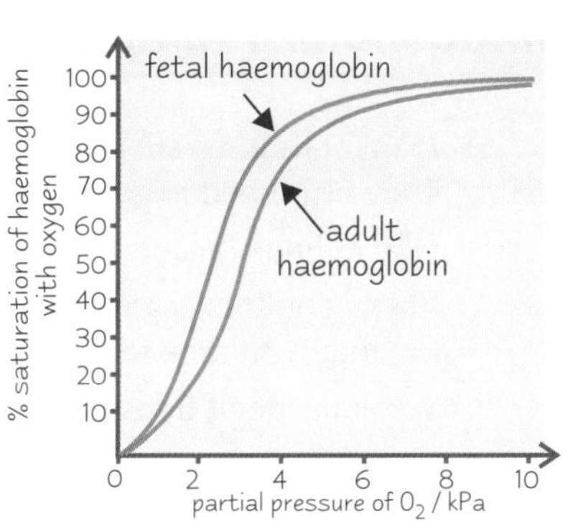

Carbon Dioxide Concentration Affects Oxygen Unloading

To complicate matters, haemoglobin gives up its oxygen **more readily** at **higher partial pressures of carbon dioxide** (pCO_2). It's a cunning way of getting more oxygen to cells during activity. When cells respire they produce carbon dioxide, which raises the pCO_2, increasing the rate of oxygen unloading. The reason for this is linked to how CO_2 affects blood pH.

1) Most of the CO_2 from respiring tissues diffuses into red blood cells and is converted to **carbonic acid** by the enzyme **carbonic anhydrase**. (The rest of the CO_2, around 10%, binds directly to haemoglobin and is carried to the lungs.)
2) The carbonic acid **splits up** to give **hydrogen ions** and **hydrogencarbonate ions**.
3) This increase in hydrogen ions causes oxyhaemoglobin to **unload** its oxygen so that haemoglobin can take up the hydrogen ions. This forms a compound called **haemoglobinic acid**. (This process also stops the hydrogen ions from increasing the cell's acidity).
4) The **hydrogencarbonate ions** diffuse out of the red blood cells and are **transported in the blood plasma**.
5) When the blood reaches the **lungs** the low pCO_2 causes the hydrogencarbonate and hydrogen ions to **recombine into CO_2**.
6) The CO_2 then diffuses into the **alveoli** and is breathed out.

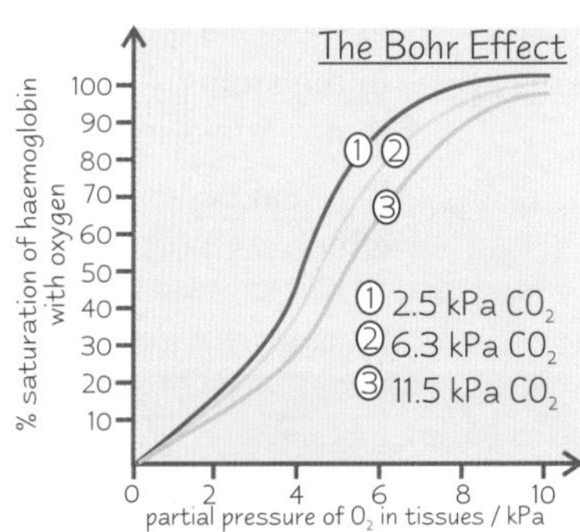

When carbon dioxide levels increase, the dissociation curve 'shifts' down, showing that more oxygen is released from the blood (because the lower the saturation of haemoglobin with O_2, the more O_2 is released). This is called the Bohr effect.

Practice Questions

Q1 How many oxygen molecules can each haemoglobin molecule carry?

Q2 What effect does respiration have on a cell's pO_2?

Q3 What is carbon dioxide converted to in red blood cells?

Exam Questions

Q1 Explain why fetal haemoglobin is different from adult haemoglobin. [3 marks]

Q2 Describe how carbon dioxide from respiring tissues is transported to the lungs. [6 marks]

The Bore effect — it's happening right now...

Dissociation graphs can be a bit confusing — but basically, when tissues contain lots of oxygen (i.e. pO_2 is high), haemoglobin readily combines with the oxygen, so the blood has a high saturation of oxygen (and vice versa when pO_2 is low). Simple. Also, make sure you get the lingo right, like 'partial pressure' and 'affinity' — hey, I'm hip, I'm groovy. Honest.

Xylem and Phloem

A whole section on transport in plants... just what I always dreamed of... you too? Oh good, because you need to learn it all for your exam.

Multicellular Plants Need Transport Systems

Plants also need carbon dioxide, but this enters at the leaves (where it's needed).

1) Plant cells need substances like **water**, **minerals** and **sugars** to live. They also need to **get rid of waste substances**.
2) Like animals, plants are **multicellular** so have a **small surface area : volume ratio** (see page 28).
3) Plants could exchange substances by **direct diffusion** (from the outer surface to the cells), but that would be **too slow**.
4) So plants **need transport systems** to move substances to and from individual cells **quickly**.

Two Types of Tissue are Involved in Transport in Plants

Xylem tissue transports **water** and **mineral ions**. **Phloem tissue** transports **dissolved substances**, like **sugars**. Xylem and phloem are found **throughout** a plant — they **transport materials** to all parts. **Where** they're found in each part is connected to the **xylem's** other function — **support**:

Emma had been through 12 rolls but she still couldn't find any phloem.

1) In a **root**, the xylem and phloem are in the **centre** to provide support for the root as it **pushes** through the soil.
2) In the **stems**, the xylem and phloem are **near the outside** to provide a sort of 'scaffolding' that reduces bending.
3) In a **leaf**, xylem and phloem make up a **network of veins** which support the thin leaves.

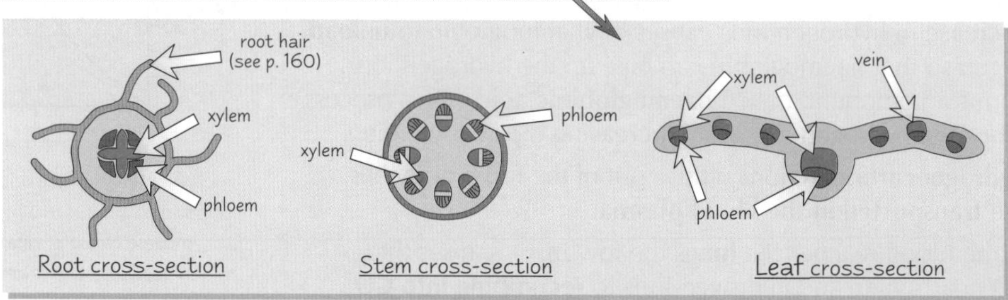

Xylem Vessels are Adapted for Transporting Water and Mineral Ions

Xylem is a **tissue** made from several **different cell types** (see page 26). You need to learn about **xylem vessels** — the part of xylem tissue that actually transports the water and ions. Xylem vessels are adapted for their **function**:

1) Xylem vessels are very **long**, **tube-like** structures formed from cells (**vessel elements**) joined end to end.
2) There are **no end walls** on these cells, making an **uninterrupted tube** that allows water to pass up through the middle easily.
3) The cells are **dead**, so they contain **no cytoplasm**.
4) Their walls are **thickened** with a **woody** substance called **lignin**, which helps to **support** the xylem vessels and stops them **collapsing inwards**.
5) The amount of lignin **increases** as the cell gets **older**.
6) **Water** and **ions** move **into** and **out of** the vessels through **small pits** in the walls where there's **no lignin**.

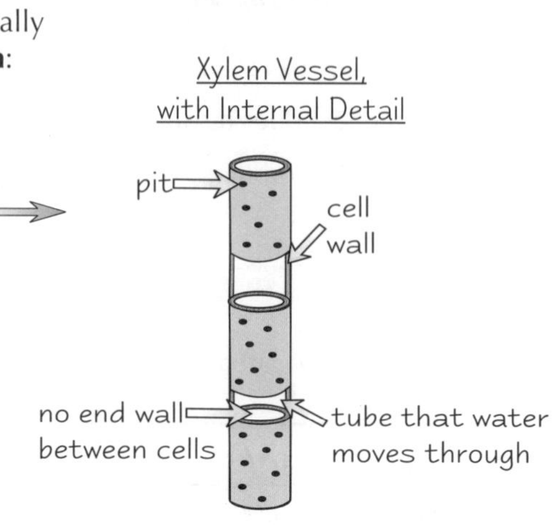

Xylem and Phloem

Phloem Tissue is Adapted for Transporting Solutes

1) Phloem tissue transports **solutes** (dissolved substances), mainly sugars like sucrose, round plants.
2) Like xylem, phloem is formed from cells arranged in **tubes**.
3) But, unlike xylem, it's purely a **transport tissue** — it **isn't** used for support as well.
4) Phloem tissue contains **phloem fibres**, **phloem parenchyma**, **sieve tube elements** and **companion cells**.
5) **Sieve tube elements** and **companion cells** are the most important cell types in phloem for **transport**:

1 Sieve Tube Elements

1) These are **living cells** that form the tube for **transporting solutes** through the plant.
2) They are joined **end to end** to form **sieve tubes.**
3) The '**sieve**' parts are the **end walls**, which have lots of **holes** in them to allow **solutes** to pass through.
4) Unusually for living cells, sieve tube elements have **no nucleus**, a **very thin** layer of **cytoplasm** and **few organelles**.
5) The cytoplasm of adjacent cells is **connected** through the holes in the sieve plates.

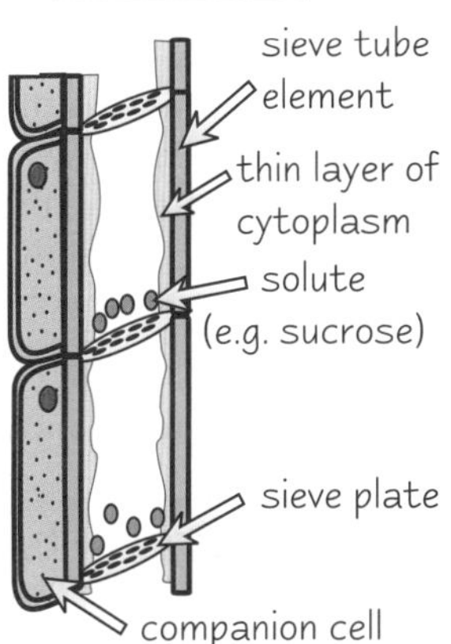

2 Companion Cells

1) The **lack** of a **nucleus** and **other organelles** in sieve tube elements means that they **can't survive** on their own.
2) So there's a **companion cell** for **every** sieve tube element.
3) Companion cells carry out the living functions for **both** themselves and their sieve cells. For example, they provide the **energy** for the **active transport** of solutes.

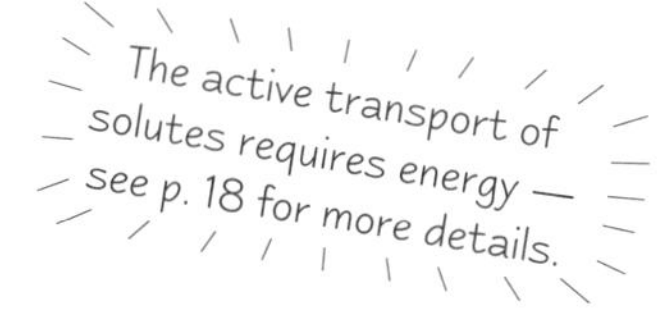

Practice Questions

Q1 Why do multicellular plants need transport systems?

Q2 State two functions of xylem vessels in plants.

Q3 What is the name of the substance that thickens the walls of xylem vessels?

Q4 What is the function of phloem tissue?

Q5 What is the function of companion cells?

Exam Questions

Q1 Describe the distribution of the xylem and phloem tissue in stems, roots and leaves. Explain how this distribution is linked to the support function of the xylem. [6 marks]

Q2 Describe how the structure of xylem vessels relates to their function. [8 marks]

Sieve tube — WLTM like-minded cell for companionship and maybe more...

Sieve tube elements sound a bit feeble to me — not being able to survive on their own, and all that. Anyway, it's vital your mind doesn't wander on this page, because the structures and functions of some of these cell types are quite similar. It can be easy to get mixed up if you haven't learnt it properly, so take the time now to sort out which cell type does what.

Water Transport

Water enters a plant through its roots and eventually, if it's not used, exits via the leaves. "Ah-ha", I hear you say, "but how does it flow upwards, against gravity?" Well that, my friends, is a mystery that's about to be explained...

Water** Enters a Plant through its **Root Hair Cells

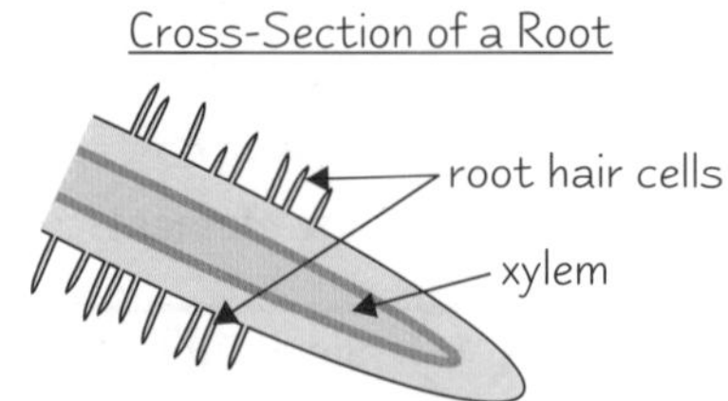

1) Water has to get from the **soil**, through the **root** and into the **xylem** to be transported around the plant.
2) Water enters through **root hair cells** and then passes through **the root cortex**, including the **endodermis**, to reach the xylem (see below).
3) Water is drawn into the roots down a **water potential gradient**:

> Water always moves from areas of **higher water potential** to areas of **lower water potential** — it goes down a **water potential gradient**. The **soil** around roots generally has a **high water potential** (i.e. there's lots of water there) and **leaves** have a **lower water potential** (because water constantly **evaporates** from them). This creates a water potential gradient that keeps water moving through the plant in the right direction, **from roots** (**high**) to **leaves** (**low**).

*Water **Moves** Through the **Root** into the **Xylem**...*

The prison had been strangely quiet ever since plasmodesmata were installed.

Water travels through the **roots** (via the **root cortex**) into the **xylem** by **two** different paths:

1) The **symplast pathway** — goes through the **living** parts of cells — the **cytoplasm**. The cytoplasm of neighbouring cells connect through **plasmodesmata** (small gaps in the cell walls).
2) The **apoplast pathway** — goes through the **non-living** parts of the cells — the **cell walls**. The walls are very absorbent and water can simply **diffuse** through them, as well as passing through the spaces between them.

> - When water in the **apoplast pathway** gets to the **endodermis** cells in the root, its path is blocked by a **waxy strip** in the cell walls, called the **Casparian strip**. Now the water has to take the **symplast pathway**.
> - This is useful, because it means the water has to go through a **cell membrane**. Cell membranes are able to control whether or not substances in the water get through (see p. 12).
> - Once past this barrier, the water moves into the **xylem**.

3) Both pathways are used, but the main one is the **apoplast pathway** because it provides the **least resistance**.

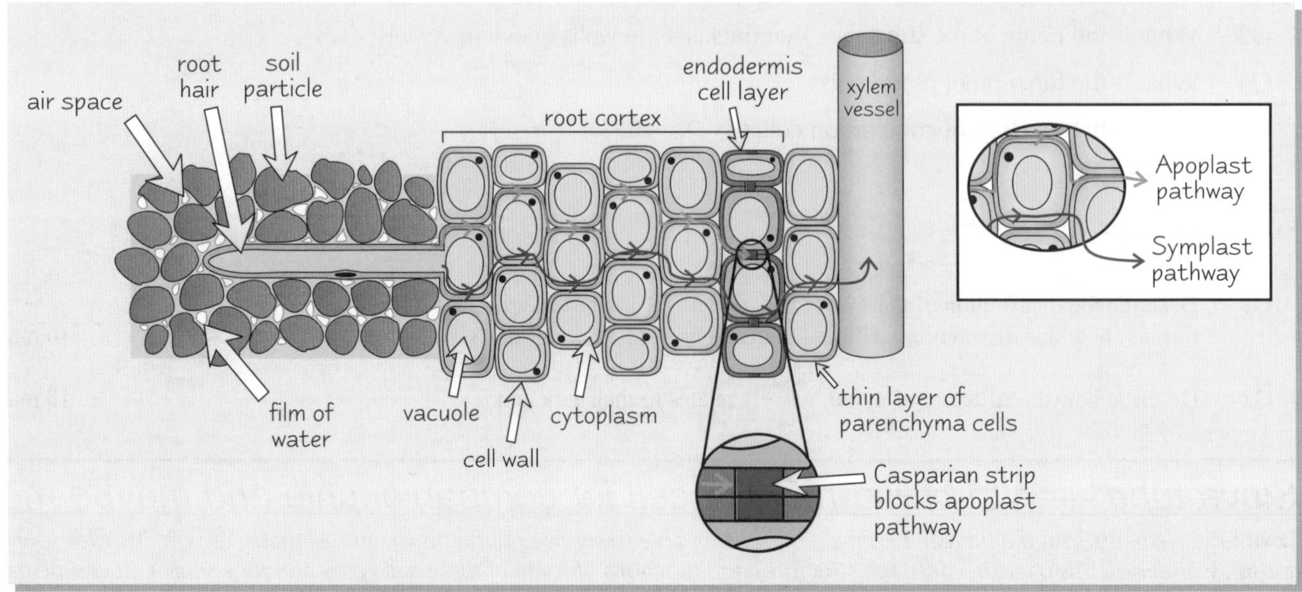

Water Transport

...then Up the Xylem and Out at the Leaves

1) **Xylem vessels** transport the water **all around** the plant.
2) At the **leaves**, water leaves the xylem and moves into the cells mainly by the **apoplast pathway**.
3) Water **evaporates** from the cell walls into the **spaces** between cells in the leaf.
4) When the **stomata** (tiny pores in the surface of the leaf) open, the water moves out of the leaf (down the **water potential gradient**) into the **surrounding air**.
5) The loss of water from a plant's surface is called **transpiration** (see next page).

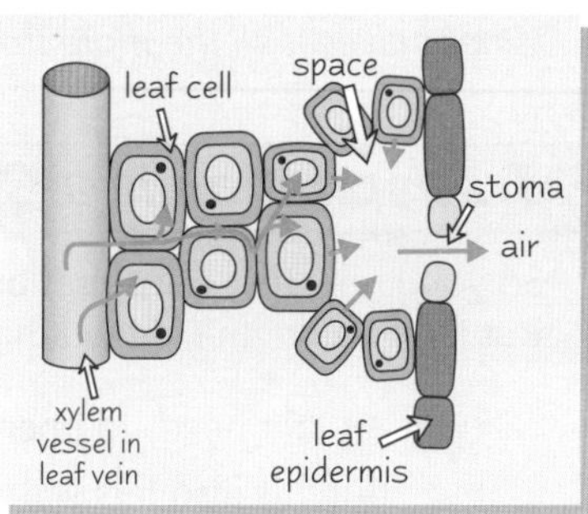

Water Moves Up a Plant Against the Force of Gravity

The movement of water from **roots to leaves** is called the **transpiration stream**. The **mechanisms** that **move** the water include **cohesion**, **tension** and **adhesion**.

Cohesion and **tension** help water move up plants, from roots to leaves, **against** the force of gravity.

1) Water **evaporates** from the **leaves** at the 'top' of the xylem (**transpiration**).
2) This creates a **tension** (**suction**), which pulls more water into the leaf.
3) Water molecules are **cohesive** (they **stick together**) so when some are pulled into the leaf others follow. This means the whole **column** of water in the **xylem**, from the leaves down to the roots, **moves upwards**.
4) **Water** enters the stem through the **root cortex cells**.

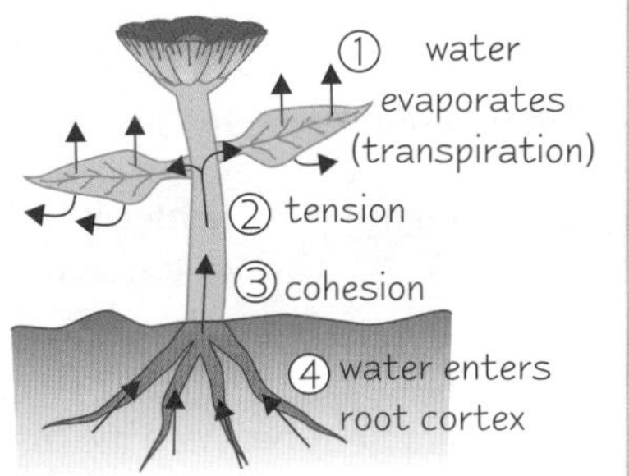

Adhesion is also partly responsible for the **movement of water**.

1) As well as being attracted to each other, water molecules are **attracted to** the **walls** of the xylem vessels.
2) This helps water to **rise up** through the xylem vessels.

Practice Questions

Q1 In terms of water potential, why does water move into the roots from the soil?

Q2 What is the Casparian strip?

Q3 What is cohesion?

Q4 How does adhesion help to move water through a plant?

Exam Questions

Q1 Explain why the movement of water in the xylem stops if the leaves of a plant are removed. [4 marks]

Q2 Water can take two different paths through the roots of a plant.

a) Describe the symplast pathway through the roots of a plant. [2 marks]

b) Describe the apoplast pathway through the roots of a plant. [4 marks]

So many routes through the roots...

As you've probably noticed, there are lots of impressive biological words on this page, to amaze your friends and confound your enemies. Go through the page again, and whenever you see a word like plasmodesmata, just stop and check you know exactly what it means. (Personally I think they should just call them cell wall gaps, but nobody ever listens to me.)

Transpiration

Plants can't sing, juggle or tap-dance (as you will hopefully be aware). But they can exchange gases — how exciting. What makes it all the more thrilling though is that they lose water vapour as they do it. Gripping stuff.

Transpiration is a Consequence of Gas Exchange

So you know that **transpiration** is the evaporation of **water** from a plant's surface, especially the **leaves**. But I bet you didn't know it happens as a result of **gas exchange**. Read on...

1) A plant needs to **open** its **stomata** to let in **carbon dioxide** so that it can produce **glucose** (by **photosynthesis**).
2) But this **also lets water out** — there's a **higher concentration** of water **inside** the leaf than in the air **outside**, so water moves **out** of the leaf down the **water potential gradient** when the stomata open.
3) So transpiration's really a **side effect** of the gas exchange needed for photosynthesis.

Water moves from areas of higher water potential to areas of lower water potential — it moves down the water potential gradient.

Four Main Factors Affect Transpiration Rate

Temperature, humidity and wind all alter the **water potential gradient**, but **light** is a bit different:

1) **Light** — the **lighter** it is the **faster** the **transpiration rate**. This is because the **stomata open** when it gets **light**. When it's **dark** the stomata are usually **closed**, so there's little transpiration.
2) **Temperature** — the **higher the temperature** the **faster** the **transpiration rate**. Warmer water molecules have more energy so they **evaporate** from the cells inside the leaf **faster**. This **increases** the **water potential gradient** between the inside and outside of the leaf, making water **diffuse** out of the leaf **faster**.
3) **Humidity** — the **lower** the **humidity**, the **faster** the **transpiration rate**. If the air around the plant is **dry**, the **water potential gradient** between the leaf and the air is **increased**, which increases transpiration.
4) **Wind** — the **windier** it is, the **faster** the **transpiration rate**. Lots of air movement **blows away** water molecules from around the stomata. This **increases** the water potential gradient, which increases the rate of transpiration.

A Potometer can be Used to Estimate Transpiration Rate

A **potometer** is a special piece of apparatus used to **estimate transpiration rates**. It actually measures **water uptake** by a plant, but it's **assumed** that water uptake by the plant is **directly related** to **water loss** by the **leaves**. You can use it to estimate how different factors **affect** the transpiration rate.

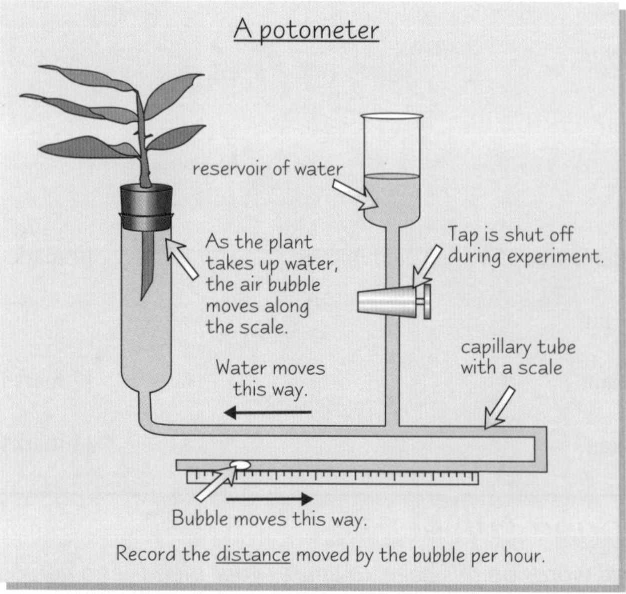

Here's what you'd do:

1) **Cut** a **shoot underwater** to prevent air from entering the xylem. Cut it at a **slant** to increase the surface area available for water uptake.
2) Check that the apparatus is **full of water** and that there are **no air bubbles**.
3) Insert the **shoot** into the apparatus **underwater**, so no air can enter.
4) Remove the potometer from the water and make sure it's **airtight** and **watertight**.
5) **Dry** the leaves, allow time for the shoot to **acclimatise** and then **shut the tap**.
6) Keep the **conditions constant** throughout the experiment, e.g. the temperature and the air humidity.
7) Record the **starting position** of the **air bubble**.
8) Start a **stopwatch** and record the **distance** moved by the bubble **per unit time**, e.g. per hour.

Transpiration

Xerophytic Plants are Adapted to Reduce Water Loss

Xerophytes are plants like **cacti**, **pine trees** and **prickly pears** (yes, the ones from the song). They're **adapted** to live in **dry climates**. Their adaptations prevent them **losing too much water** by **transpiration**. Examples of xerophytic adaptations include:

1) **Stomata** that are sunk in **pits** — so they're **sheltered from the wind**, which helps to slow transpiration down.

2) A layer of '**hairs**' on the epidermis — this **traps moist air** round the stomata, which **reduces** the water potential gradient between the leaf and the air, **slowing** transpiration down.

3) **Curled** leaves — this **traps moist air**, slowing down transpiration. This also lowers the **exposed surface area** for losing water and protects the stomata from wind.

4) **Spines** instead of leaves (e.g. cactus) — this reduces the **surface area** for water loss.

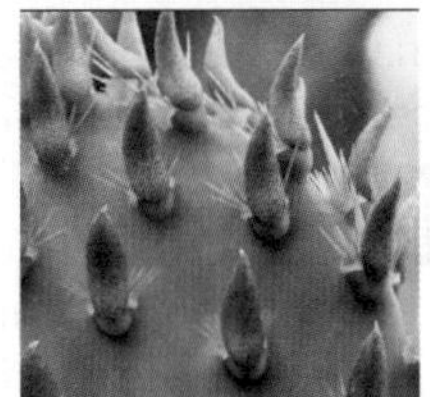

5) **Thick**, **waxy layer** on the epidermis — this **reduces** water loss by evaporation because the layer is **waterproof** (water can't move through it).

6) A reduced **number of stomata** — this means there are **fewer places** where water can be lost.

Practice Questions

Q1 Explain why transpiration is a consequence of gaseous exchange.

Q2 What piece of apparatus is used to measure transpiration?

Q3 What is a xerophyte?

Q4 Suggest three ways that xerophyte leaves are adapted to reduce water loss by transpiration.

Exam Questions

Q1 Give four conditions that increase the rate of transpiration from a plant's leaves and explain how each one increases transpiration. [8 marks]

Q2 The diagram shows a section of a leaf of a xerophytic plant. Describe and explain two ways, visible in the picture, that this leaf is adapted to reduce water loss. [4 marks]

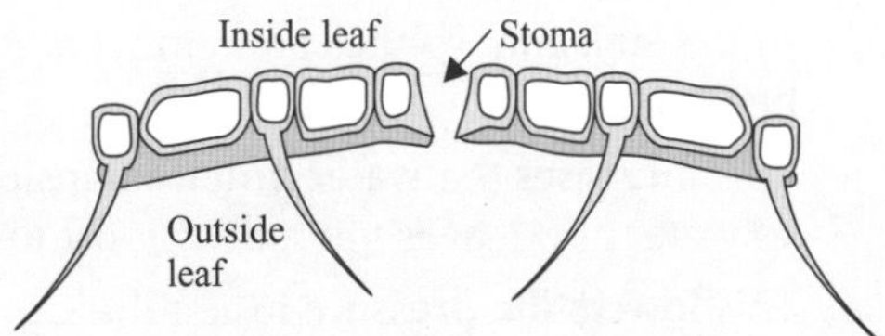

Xerophytes — an exciting word for a boring subject...

Actually, that's unfair. It's taken millions of years for plants to evolve those adaptations, and here I am slagging them off. When I've managed to develop a thicker waxy cuticle on my leaves and stems, then I can comment, and not before. Oh, and learn the rest of the stuff on this page too. It may not be thrilling — but if you know it, it could earn you vital marks.

Translocation

Translocation is the movement of dissolved solvents through a plant. Annoyingly, translocation sounds a lot like transpiration. Or is that just me? Make sure you don't get them confused.

Translocation is the *Movement* of *Dissolved Substances*

1) **Translocation** is the **movement** of dissolved substances (e.g. sugars like sucrose, and amino acids) to **where they're needed** in a plant. Dissolved substances are sometimes called **assimilates**.
2) It's an **energy-requiring** process that happens in the **phloem**.
3) Translocation moves substances from '**sources**' to '**sinks**'.
   The **source** of a substance is **where it's made** (so it's at a **high concentration** there).
   The **sink** is the area where it's **used up** (so it's at a **lower concentration** there).

See p. 45 for more on the phloem.

EXAMPLE

The **source** for **sucrose** is the **leaves** (where it's made), and the **sinks** are the **other parts** of the plant, especially the **food storage organs** and the **meristems** (areas of growth) in the roots, stems and leaves.

4) **Enzymes** maintain a **concentration gradient** from the source to the sink by **changing** the dissolved substances at the **sink** (e.g. by breaking them down or making them into something else). This makes sure there's always a **lower concentration** at the sink than at the source.

EXAMPLE

In **potatoes**, **sucrose** is converted to **starch** in the **sink** areas, so there's always a **lower concentration** of sucrose **at the sink** than inside the phloem. This makes sure a **constant supply** of new sucrose reaches the sink from the phloem.

Howard liked a bit of translocation in his spare time.

The Mass Flow Hypothesis *Best Explains* Phloem Transport

Scientists still aren't certain **exactly how** the dissolved substances (solutes) are transported from source to sink by **translocation**. The best supported theory is the **mass flow hypothesis**:

① SOURCE
low water potential,
high pressure
companion cell
pressure gradient
③
solute (e.g. sucrose)
sieve plate
② SINK
high water potential
low pressure

①

1) Active transport (see p. 18) is used to **actively load** the dissolved solutes (e.g. sucrose from photosynthesis) into the **sieve tubes** of the phloem at the **source** (e.g. the **leaves**).
2) This **lowers the water potential** inside the sieve tubes, so water enters the tubes by **osmosis**.
3) This creates a **high pressure** inside the sieve tubes at the **source end** of the phloem.

②

1) At the **sink** end, **solutes** are removed from the phloem to be used up.
2) This **increases** the **water potential** inside the sieve tubes, so water also leaves the tubes by **osmosis**.
3) This **lowers the pressure** inside the sieve tubes.

③

1) The result is a **pressure gradient** from the **source** end to the **sink** end.
2) This gradient pushes solutes along the sieve tubes to where they're needed.

Translocation

There is **Evidence** Both For and Against **Mass Flow**

Supporting evidence

1) If you remove a **ring of bark** (which includes the phloem, but not the xylem) from a woody stem a **bulge forms above** the ring. If you analyse the fluid from the bulge, you'll find it has a **higher concentration of sugars** than the fluid from below the ring — this is evidence that there's a **downward flow** of sugars.
2) You can **investigate** pressure in the phloem using **aphids** (they pierce the phloem, then their bodies are removed leaving the mouthparts behind, which allows the sap to flow out... gruesome). The sap flows out **quicker nearer the leaves** than further down the stem — this is evidence that there's a **pressure gradient**.
3) If you put a **metabolic inhibitor** (which stops ATP production) into the **phloem** then **translocation stops** — this is evidence that **active transport** is involved.
4) There's an **experimental model** for mass flow (see below).

Objections

1) Sugar travels to **many different sinks**, not just to the one with the **highest water potential**, as the model would suggest.
2) The **sieve plates** would create a **barrier** to mass flow. A **lot of pressure** would be needed for the solutes to get through at a reasonable rate.

Mass Flow Hypothesis Can be **Demonstrated** in an **Experiment**

The hypothesis can be modelled in this experiment:

1) **A** and **B** are two containers, each lined with a **selectively permeable membrane** just like cells have.
2) The **top tube** connecting A and B represents the **phloem**, and the **bottom tube** represents the **xylem**.
3) **A** represents the **source** end and contains a **concentrated sugar solution**. **B** represents the **sink** end and contains a **weak sugar solution**.
4) Water enters **A** by **osmosis**, **increasing** the pressure, which causes the sugar solution to flow along the **top tube** (phloem).
5) **Pressure** increases in **B**, forcing water out and back through the **bottom tube** (xylem), which just transports water.

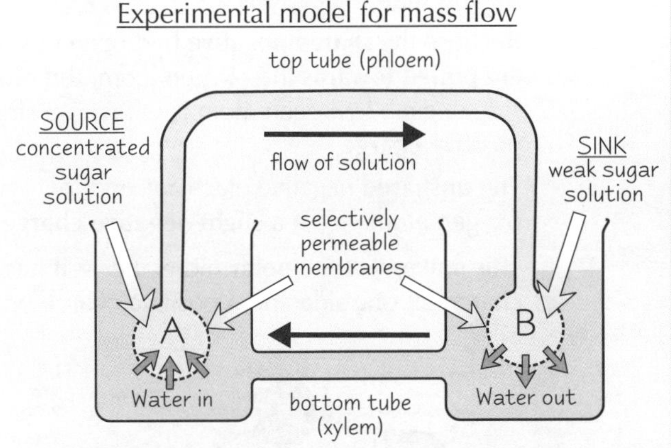

Practice Questions

Q1 Explain the terms source and sink in connection with translocation.

Q2 State two pieces of evidence that support the mass flow hypothesis for translocation.

Exam Question

Q1 The mass flow hypothesis depends on a pressure difference in the phloem sieve tubes between the source and the sink. Explain how sugars cause the pressure to increase at the source end, according to the mass flow hypothesis. [4 marks]

Human mass flow — running out of the hall at the end of an exam...

The mass flow hypothesis is just the best theory that scientists have come up with so far. If other evidence came along, a different theory could be developed based on the new findings (see p. 2). However, that doesn't mean that there's no point in learning about it — it could be in your exam. Don't look so sad — what else would you do with your time...

Water

Your body needs all sorts of different molecules to stay alive, and this section covers all the major groups. Life can't exist without water — in fact, everyday water is one of the most important substances on the planet. Funny old world.

Water is Vital to Living Organisms

Water makes up about 80% of a cell's contents. It has loads of important **functions**, inside and outside cells:

1) Water is a **reactant** in loads of important **chemical reactions**, like photosynthesis and **hydrolysis reactions** (see p. 54).
2) Water is a **solvent**, which means some substances **dissolve** in it. Most biological reactions take place **in solution**, so water's pretty essential.
3) Water **transports** substances. The fact that it's a **liquid** and a **solvent** means it can easily transport all sorts of materials, like glucose and oxygen, around plants and animals.
4) Water helps with **temperature control**. It carries away **heat energy** when it **evaporates** from a surface. This **cools** the surface and helps to **lower** the temperature.

Water Molecules have a Simple Structure

Examiners like asking you to relate **structure** to **properties** and **function**, so make sure you're clear on the structure of water.

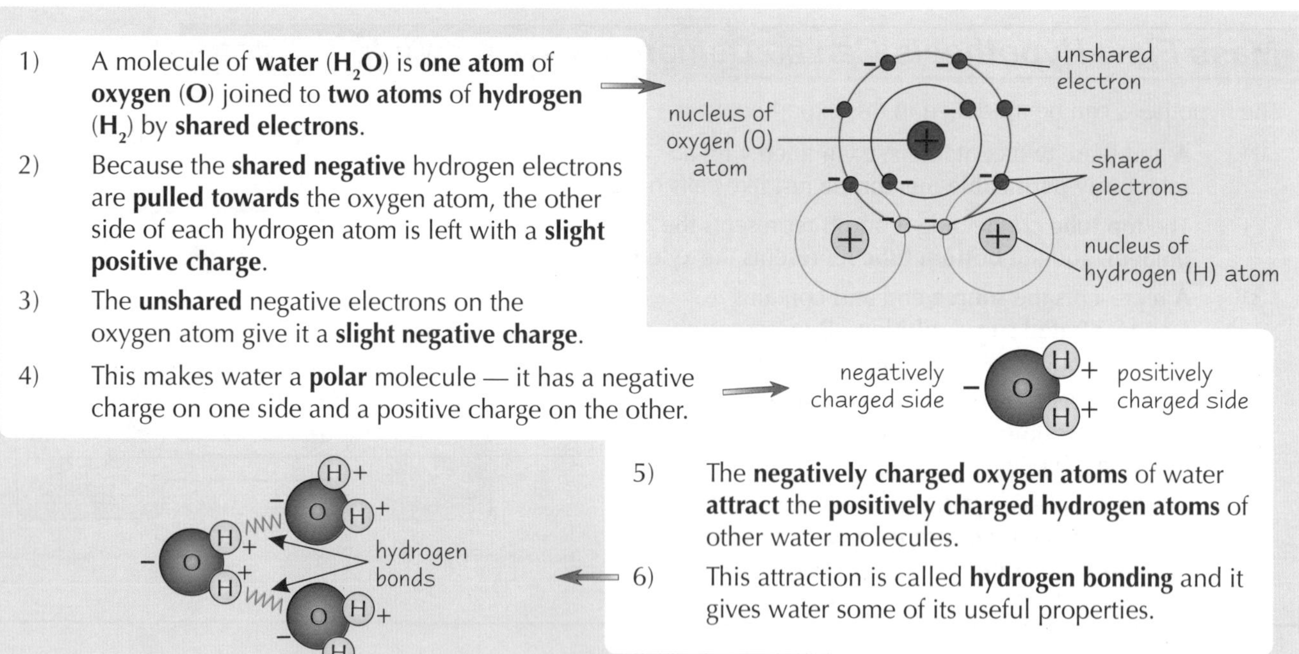

1) A molecule of **water** (**H_2O**) is **one atom** of **oxygen** (**O**) joined to **two atoms** of **hydrogen** (**H_2**) by **shared electrons**.
2) Because the **shared negative** hydrogen electrons are **pulled towards** the oxygen atom, the other side of each hydrogen atom is left with a **slight positive charge**.
3) The **unshared** negative electrons on the oxygen atom give it a **slight negative charge**.
4) This makes water a **polar** molecule — it has a negative charge on one side and a positive charge on the other.
5) The **negatively charged oxygen atoms** of water **attract** the **positively charged hydrogen atoms** of other water molecules.
6) This attraction is called **hydrogen bonding** and it gives water some of its useful properties.

Water's Structure is Related to its Properties and Functions

The **structure of a water molecule** gives it some useful **properties**, and these help to explain many of its **functions**:

Hydrogen Bonds Give Water a High Specific Heat Capacity

1) Specific heat capacity is the **energy** needed to **raise the temperature** of 1 gram of a substance by 1 °C.
2) The **hydrogen bonds** between water molecules can **absorb** a **lot** of energy.
3) So water has a **high** specific heat capacity — it takes a lot of energy to heat it up.
4) This is useful for living organisms because it **stops rapid temperature changes**, allowing them to keep their temperature **fairly stable**.

Water

Hydrogen Bonds *Also Give Water a* **High Latent Heat of Evaporation**

1) It takes a lot of **energy** (**heat**) to **break** the hydrogen bonds between water molecules.
2) So water has a **high latent heat of evaporation** — a lot of energy is used up when water **evaporates**.
3) This is useful for living organisms because it means water's great for **cooling** things.

Water's **Polarity** *Makes it* **Very Cohesive**

1) Cohesion is the **attraction** between molecules of the same type (e.g. two water molecules). Water molecules are **very cohesive** (they tend to stick together) because they're **polar**.
2) This helps water to **flow**, making it great for **transporting substances**.

Water's **Polarity** *Also Makes it a* **Good Solvent**

Remember — a molecule is polar if it has a negatively charged bit and a positively charged bit.

1) A lot of important substances in biological reactions are **ionic** (like **salt**, for example). This means they're made from **one positively charged** atom or molecule and **one negatively charged** atom or molecule (e.g. salt is made from a positive sodium ion and a negative chloride ion).
2) Because water is polar, the **positive end** of a water molecule will be attracted to the **negative ion**, and the **negative end** of a water molecule will be attracted to the **positive ion**.
3) This means the ions will get **totally surrounded** by water molecules — in other words, they'll **dissolve**.
4) So water's **polarity** makes it useful as a **solvent** for other polar molecules.

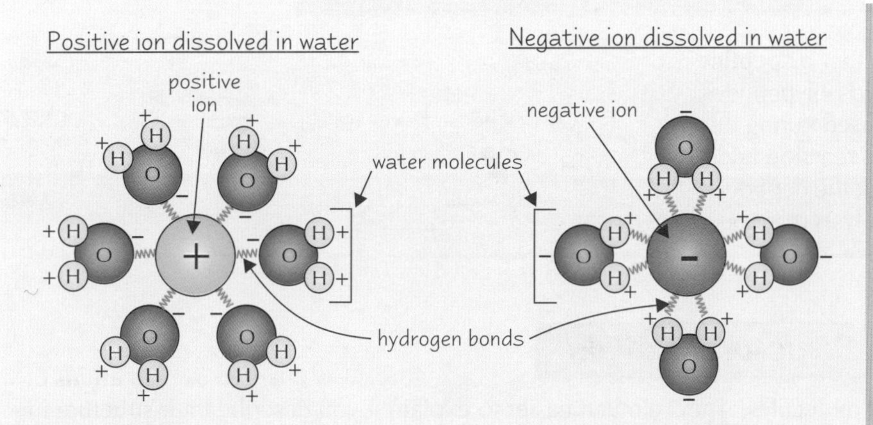

The polar nature of bears sometimes results in unexpected hydrogen bonding.

Practice Questions

Q1 State four functions of water in living organisms.

Q2 Briefly describe the structure of a water molecule.

Q3 Briefly describe what is meant by a polar molecule.

Q4 Why is water's high specific heat capacity useful for living organisms?

Exam Question

Q1 Relate the structure of the water molecule to its uses in living organisms. [15 marks]

Psssssssssssssssssssssssssssssssssssssss — need the loo yet?

Water is pretty darn useful really. It looks so, well, dull — but in fact it's scientifically amazing. It's essential for all kinds of jobs — keeping cool, transporting things, enabling reactions etc. You need to learn all of its properties and functions, and be able to say how they relate to its structure. Right, I'm off — when you gotta go, you gotta go.

Proteins

There are millions of different proteins. They're the most abundant molecules in cells, making up 50% or more of a cell's dry mass — now that's just plain greedy.

Proteins are Made from **Long Chains** of **Amino Acids**

1) A **dipeptide** is formed when **two** amino acids join together.
2) A **polypeptide** is formed when **more than two** amino acids join together.
3) **Proteins** are made up of **one or more polypeptides**.

Grant's cries of "die peptide, die" could be heard for miles around. He'd never forgiven it for sleeping with his wife.

Different Amino Acids Have **Different Variable Groups**

All amino acids have the same general structure — a **carboxyl group** (-COOH) and an **amino group** ($-NH_2$) attached to a **carbon** atom. The **difference** between different amino acids is the **variable** group (**R** on diagram) they contain.

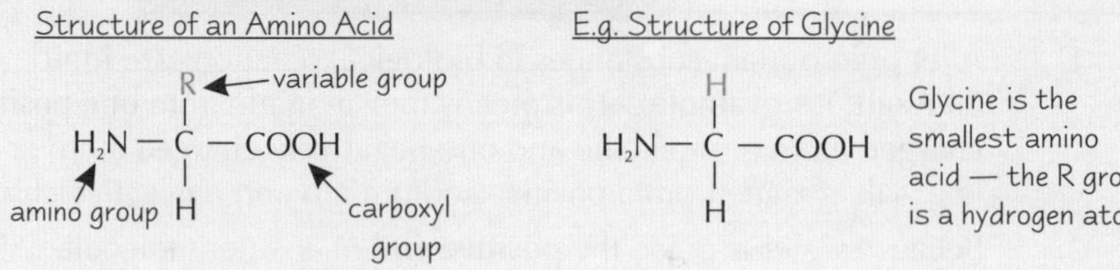

Amino Acids are Joined Together by **Peptide Bonds**

Amino acids are linked together by **peptide bonds** to form dipeptides and polypeptides. A molecule of **water** is **released** during the reaction. The **reverse** of this reaction **adds** a molecule of water to **break** the peptide bond. This is called a **hydrolysis** reaction.

amino acid 1 + amino acid 2 ⇌ dipeptide (condensation / hydrolysis)

H_2O — a molecule of water is formed during synthesis.

peptide bond

Proteins Have **Four Structural Levels**

Proteins are **big**, **complicated** molecules. They're much easier to explain if you describe their structure in four 'levels'. These levels are a protein's **primary**, **secondary**, **tertiary** and **quaternary** structures.

<u>**Primary Structure**</u> — this is the **sequence** of **amino acids** in the **polypeptide chain**.

<u>**Secondary Structure**</u> — the polypeptide chain doesn't remain flat and straight. **Hydrogen bonds** form between the amino acids in the chain. This makes it automatically **coil** into an **alpha** (α) **helix** or **fold** into a **beta** (β) **pleated sheet** — this is the secondary structure.

<u>**Tertiary Structure**</u> — the coiled or folded chain of amino acids is often **coiled** and **folded further**. **More bonds** form between different parts of the polypeptide chain. For proteins made from a **single** polypeptide chain, the tertiary structure forms their **final 3D structure**.

<u>**Quaternary Structure**</u> — some proteins are made of **several different polypeptide chains** held together by **bonds**. The **quaternary structure** is the way these polypeptide chains are assembled together. E.g. **haemoglobin** is made of **four** polypeptide chains, bonded together. For proteins made from **more than one** polypeptide chain, the quaternary structure is the protein's **final 3D structure**.

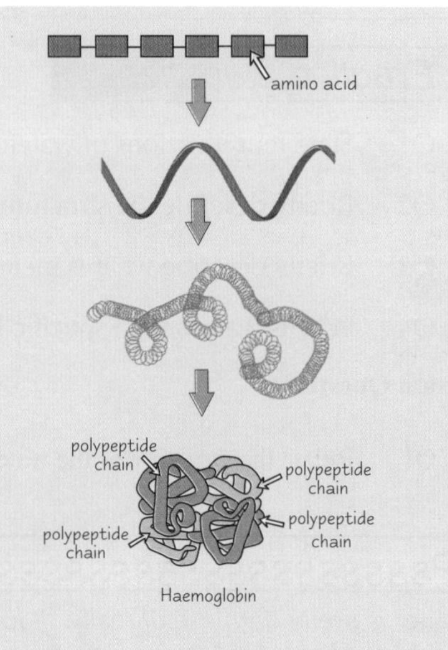

Proteins

Different Bonds Hold Different *Structural Levels* Together

The four structural levels of a protein are held together by **different kinds** of **bonds**:

1) **Primary structure** — held together by the **peptide bonds** between amino acids.
2) **Secondary structure** — held together by **hydrogen bonds** that form between nearby amino acids. These bonds create **α-helix chains** or **β-pleated sheets.**
3) **Tertiary structure** — this is affected by a few different kinds of bonds:
   - **Ionic interactions.** These are **weak attractions** between **negative** and **positive** charges on different parts of the molecule.
   - **Disulfide bonds.** Whenever two molecules of the amino acid **cysteine** come close together, the **sulfur atom** in one cysteine bonds to the sulfur in the other cysteine, forming a disulfide bond.
   - **Hydrophobic** and **hydrophilic interactions.** When **hydrophobic** (water-repelling) groups are close together in the protein, they tend to **clump together.** This means that **hydrophilic** (water-attracting) groups are more likely to be pushed to the **outside**, which affects how the protein **folds up** into its final structure.
   - **Hydrogen bonds.**
4) **Quaternary structure** — this tends to be determined by the **tertiary structure** of the individual polypeptide chains being bonded together. Because of this, it can be influenced by **all the bonds** mentioned above.

Hydrogen bonds are weak bonds between a positive hydrogen atom in one molecule and a negative atom or group in another molecule (see p. 52).

Protein Shape Relates to its *Function*

You need to learn these two **examples** of how proteins are **adapted** for their function:

1) **Collagen** is a **fibrous protein** that forms **supportive tissues** in animals, so it needs to be **strong.**
2) It's made of **three polypeptide chains** that are **tightly coiled** into a strong **triple helix.**
3) The chains are interlinked by strong **covalent bonds.**
4) **Minerals** can bind to the triple helix to **increase its rigidity.**

Fibrous proteins are tough and rope-shaped. They tend to be found in connective tissue — tendons and the like.

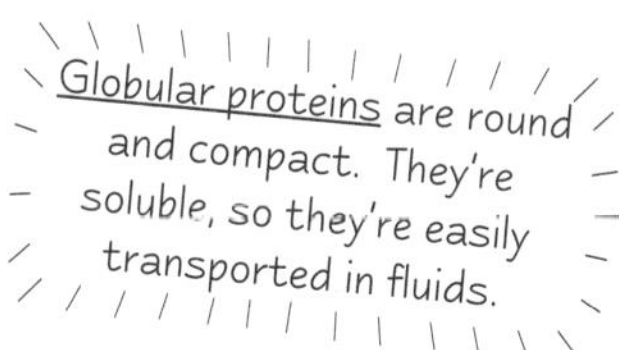

1) **Haemoglobin** is a **globular protein** with an iron-containing **haem group** that binds to **oxygen, carrying it** around the body (see p. 42).
2) Its structure is curled up so that **hydrophilic** (water-attracting) side chains are on the **outside** of the molecule and **hydrophobic** (water-repelling) side chains face **inwards.**
3) This makes haemoglobin **soluble** in water, which makes it good for **transport** in the blood.

haem group

Practice Questions

Q1 Name the two groups found in all amino acid molecules.

Q2 Name the bond that joins amino acids together in proteins.

Q3 Name four types of bond that determine the structure of a protein.

Exam Questions

Q1 Describe the structure of proteins, explaining the terms primary, secondary, tertiary and quaternary structure. [9 marks]

Q2 Describe the structure of the collagen molecule and explain how this structure relates to its function in the body. [6 marks]

The name's Bond — Peptide Bond...

Quite a lot to learn on these pages — proteins are annoyingly complicated. Not happy with one, or even two structures, they've got four of the things — and you need to learn 'em all. Remember that synthesis and hydrolysis are the reverse of each other. And as for all that nasty stuff about disulfide bonds and ionic interactions... Urgh.

Carbohydrates

Carbohydrates are dead important chemicals — for a start they're the main energy supply in living organisms, and some of them (like cellulose) have an important structural role.

Carbohydrates are Made from **Monosaccharides**

1) Most carbohydrates are **large**, complex molecules composed of **long chains** of **monosaccharides** (e.g. starch is a large carbohydrate composed of long chains of glucose).
2) **Single** monosaccharides are also called carbohydrates though.
3) **Glucose** is a monosaccharide with **six carbon** atoms in each molecule.
4) There are **two forms** of glucose — **alpha** (α) and **beta** (β):

Remember, beta-glucose has the H on the bottom as you look at the structural diagram.

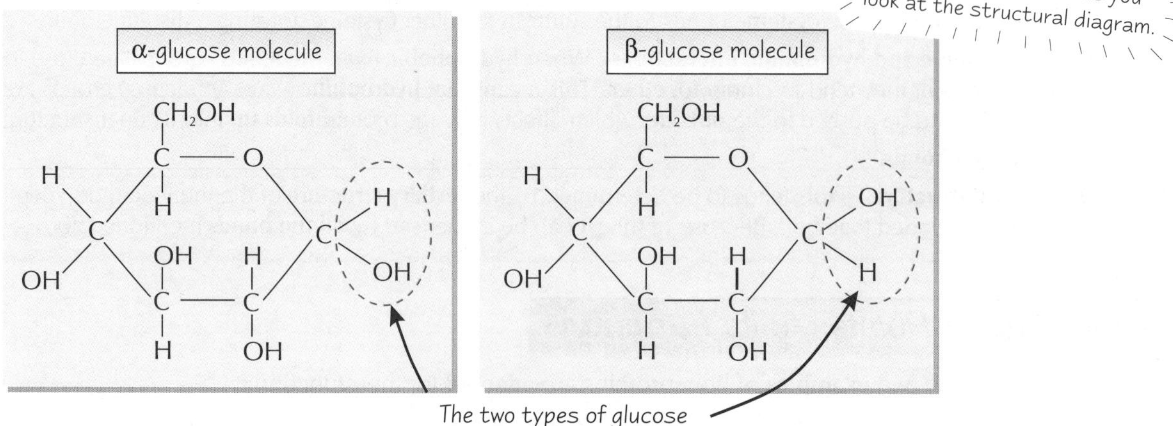

The two types of glucose have these groups reversed.

Glucose's **structure** is related to its **function** as the main **energy source** in animals and plants. Its structure makes it **soluble** so it can be **easily transported**. Its chemical bonds contain **lots of energy**.

Monosaccharides Join Together to Form **Disaccharides** and **Polysaccharides**

1) Monosaccharides are **joined together** by **glycosidic bonds**.
2) During **synthesis**, a **hydrogen** atom on one monosaccharide bonds to a **hydroxyl** (OH) group on the other, **releasing** a molecule of **water**.
3) Just like with the polypeptides on p. 54, the **reverse** of this synthesis reaction is **hydrolysis**. A molecule of water reacts with the glycosidic bond, **breaking it apart**.
4) A **disaccharide** is formed when **two monosaccharides** join together:

Sugar is a general term for monosaccharides and disaccharides.

Two **α-glucose** molecules are joined together by a **glycosidic bond** to form **maltose**.

α-glucose + α-glucose ⇌ (synthesis / hydrolysis) maltose + H_2O

H_2O is removed

glycosidic bond

5) A **polysaccharide** is formed when **more than two monosaccharides** join together:

Lots of **α-glucose** molecules are joined together by **glycosidic bonds** to form **amylose**.

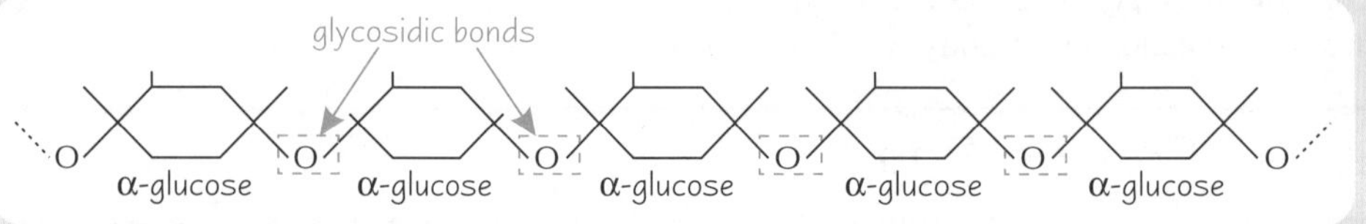

Extensive scientific research revealed an irreversible bond joining sugars to Pollyanna's gob.

Carbohydrates

You Need to Learn About Three Polysaccharides

You need to know about the relationship between the **structure** and **function** of three polysaccharides:

1) Starch — the main energy storage material in plants

1) Cells get **energy** from **glucose**. Plants **store** excess glucose as **starch** (when a plant **needs more glucose** for energy it **breaks down** starch to release the glucose).
2) Starch is a mixture of **two** polysaccharides of **alpha-glucose** — **amylose** and **amylopectin**:
   - **Amylose** — a long, **unbranched chain** of α–glucose. The angles of the glycosidic bonds give it a **coiled structure**, almost like a cylinder. This makes it **compact**, so it's really **good for storage** because you can **fit more in** to a small space.
   - **Amylopectin** — a long, **branched chain** of α–glucose. Its **side branches** allow the **enzymes** that break down the molecule to get at the **glycosidic bonds easily**. This means that the glucose can be **released quickly**.
3) Starch is **insoluble** in water, so it **doesn't** cause water to enter cells by **osmosis** (which would make them swell). This makes it good for **storage**.

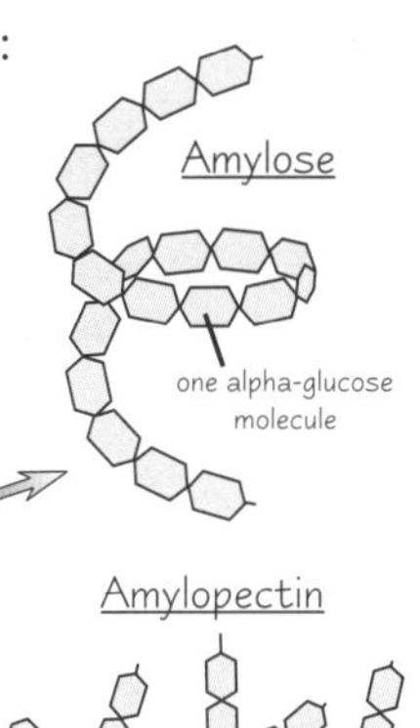

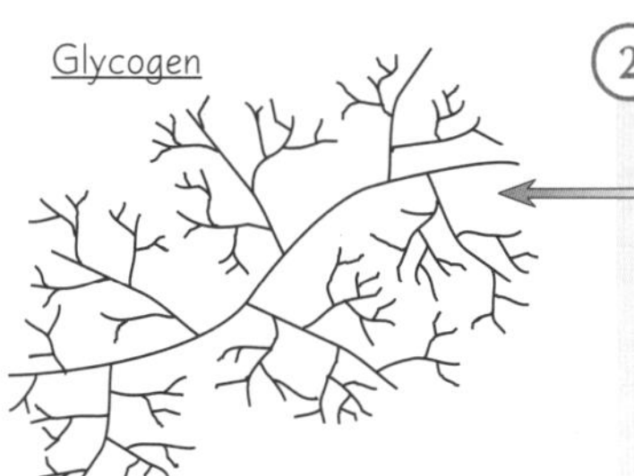

2) Glycogen — the main energy storage material in animals

1) Animal cells get **energy** from **glucose** too. But animals **store** excess glucose as **glycogen** — another polysaccharide of **alpha-glucose**.
2) Its structure is very similar to amylopectin, except that it has **loads** more **side branches** coming off it. Loads of branches means that stored glucose can be **released quickly**, which is **important for energy release** in animals.
3) It's also a very **compact** molecule, so it's good for storage.

3) Cellulose — the major component of cell walls in plants

1) Cellulose is made of **long**, **unbranched** chains of **beta-glucose**.
2) The **bonds** between the sugars are **straight**, so the cellulose chains are straight.
3) The cellulose chains are linked together by **hydrogen bonds** to form strong fibres called **microfibrils**. The strong fibres mean cellulose provides **structural support** for cells (e.g. in plant cell walls).

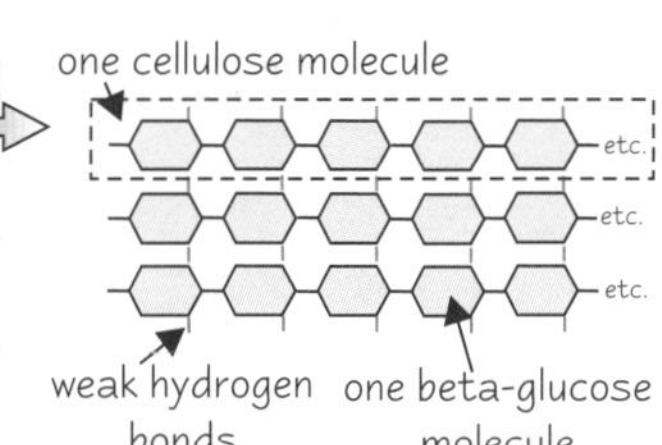

Practice Questions

Q1 What type of bonds hold monosaccharide molecules together in polysaccharides?

Q2 Briefly describe the structure of amylose.

Q3 What is the function of glycogen?

Exam Questions

Q1 Describe, with the aid of a diagram, how glycosidic bonds are formed and broken in living organisms. [7 marks]

Q2 Compare and contrast the structures of starch and cellulose, describing how each molecule's structure is linked to its function. [12 marks]

Mmmmm, starch... Tasty, tasty chips and beans... *dribble*. Ahem, sorry.

Remember that synthesis and hydrolysis reactions are the reverse of each other. You need to learn how maltose and amylose are formed and broken down by these reactions. And don't forget that starch is composed of two different polysaccharides... and that glucose exists in two forms... so many reminders, so little space...

Lipids

Right, that's proteins and carbohydrates dealt with. There's only really one more important kind of molecule in biology, and that's lipids, or 'fatty oily things' to you and me. Some of them are just straightforward fats, but others have extra bits stuck to them — you need to know what they look like and how their structures relate to their functions...

Triglycerides are a Kind of Lipid

1) A triglyceride is made of **one** molecule of **glycerol** with **three fatty acids** attached to it.
2) Fatty acid molecules have long tails made of **hydrocarbons** (carbon chains with hydrogen atoms branching off).
3) The tails are **hydrophobic** (water-repelling).
4) These tails make lipids **insoluble** in water.
5) All **fatty acids** consist of the same basic structure, but the **hydrocarbon tail varies**. The tail is shown in the diagram with the letter **R**.

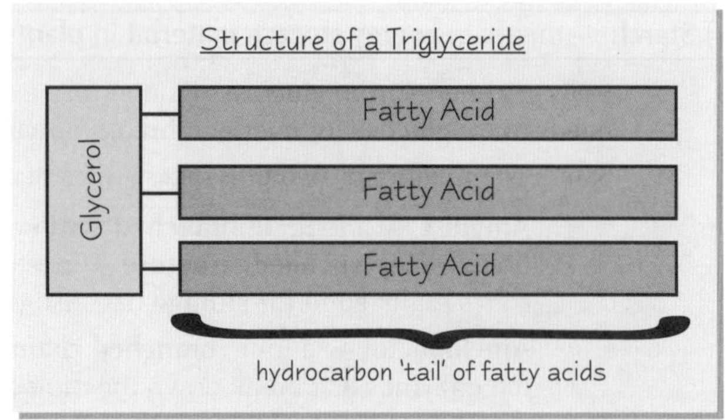

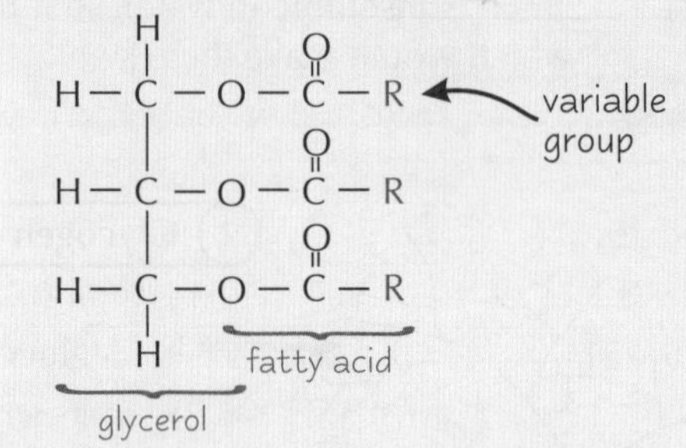

Phospholipids are Similar to Triglycerides

1) The lipids found in **cell membranes** aren't triglycerides — they're **phospholipids**.
2) Phospholipids are pretty similar to triglycerides except one of the fatty acid molecules is replaced by a **phosphate group**.
3) The phosphate group is **ionised** (electrically charged), which makes it **attract water** molecules (see p. 53).
4) So the phosphate part of the phospholipid molecule is **hydrophilic** (water-attracting) while the rest (the fatty acid **tails**) is **hydrophobic** (water-repelling).

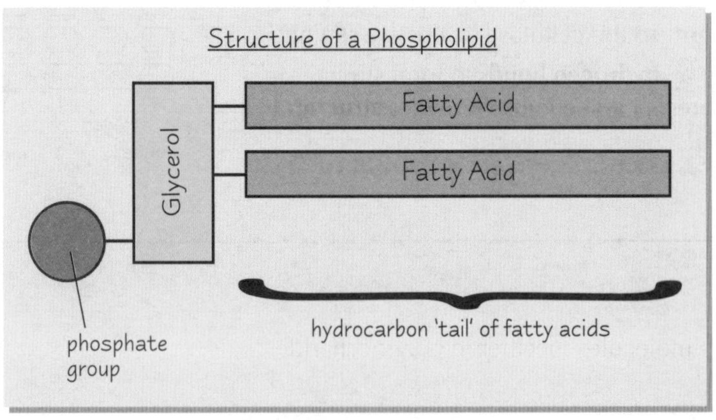

Contrary to popular belief, cows are actually hydrophilic.

Cholesterol has a Hydrocarbon Ring Structure

1) Cholesterol is a type of lipid often found in **cell membranes**. It's also used to make other things like **steroids**.
2) It has a **hydrocarbon ring** structure attached to a **hydrocarbon tail**.
3) The hydrocarbon ring has a **polar hydroxyl group** attached to it, which makes cholesterol **soluble**.

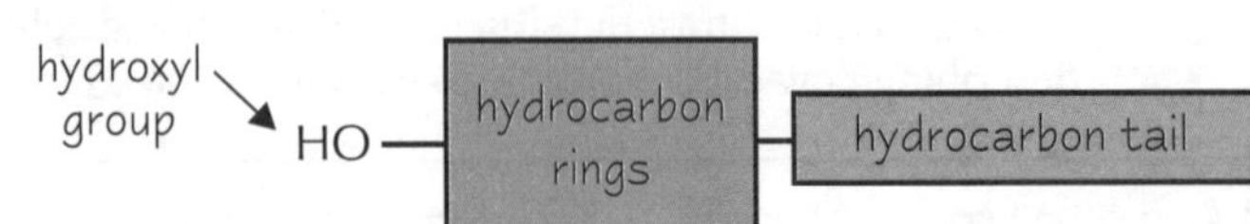

Lipids

The **Structures** of Lipids Relate to Their **Functions**

You need to know how the **structures** of triglycerides, phospholipids and cholesterol are related to their **functions**:

TRIGLYCERIDES

Triglycerides are mainly used as **energy storage molecules**. They're good for this because:

1) The **long hydrocarbon tails** of the fatty acids contain lots of **chemical energy** — a load of energy is **released** when they're **broken down**. Because of these tails, lipids contain about **twice** as much energy per gram as carbohydrates.
2) They're **insoluble**, so they don't cause water to enter the cells by **osmosis** (which would make them swell). The triglycerides bundle together as **insoluble droplets** in cells because the fatty acid tails are **hydrophobic** (water-repelling) — the tails **face inwards**, shielding themselves from water with their glycerol heads.

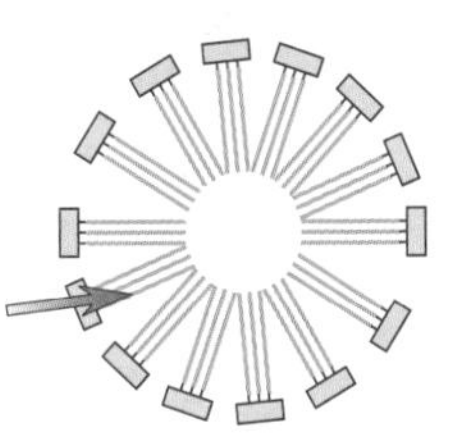

You learnt how the structure of phospholipids and cholesterol relate to their function in Unit 1: Section 2, but you need to know it for this unit too.

PHOSPHOLIPIDS

Phospholipids make up the **bilayer** of **cell membranes** (see p. 12). Cell membranes **control** what **enters and leaves a cell**.

1) Their heads are **hydrophilic** and their tails are **hydrophobic**, so they form a **double** layer with their heads facing **out** towards the water on either side.
2) The **centre** of the bilayer is **hydrophobic**, so water-soluble substances **can't** easily pass through it — the membrane acts as a **barrier** to those substances.

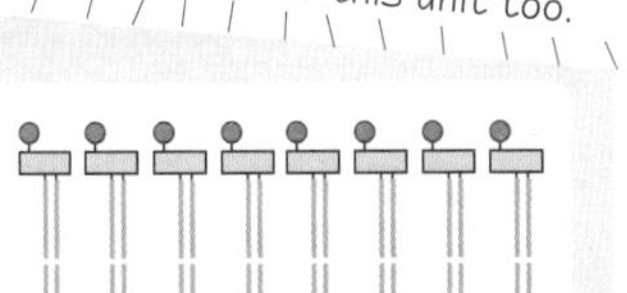

CHOLESTEROL

Cholesterol molecules help **strengthen** the cell membrane by **interacting** with the **phospholipid bilayer**.

The **small size** and **flattened shape** allows cholesterol to fit **in between** the phospholipid molecules in the membrane. They bind to the hydrophobic tails of the phospholipids, causing them to **pack more closely together**. This helps to make the membrane **less fluid** and **more rigid**.

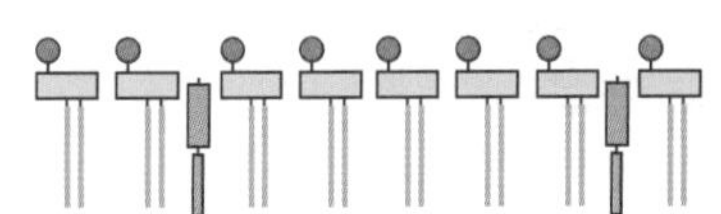

Practice Questions

Q1 What are triglycerides composed of?

Q2 Sketch the structure of a phospholipid.

Exam Questions

Q1 a) In a phospholipid, which part of the molecule is hydrophilic and which is hydrophobic? [2 marks]

b) Explain how phospholipid molecules arrange themselves in cell membranes and relate this to their structure. [3 marks]

Q2 Explain how each of these features of lipids is important for its function in living things:

a) Cholesterol molecules have a flattened shape. [2 marks]

b) Triglycerides have a hydrophobic tail. [2 marks]

Hydrocarbon tails, phospholipid bilayers... Whatever happened to plain old lard?

You don't get far in life without extensive lard knowledge, so learn all the details on this page good and proper. Lipids pop up in other sections, so make sure you know the basics about how their structure gives them some quite groovy properties. Right, all this lipids talk is making me hungry — chips time...

Biochemical Tests for Molecules

Here's a bit of light relief for you — two pages all about how you test for the different molecules you've just read about...

Use the **Benedict's Test** for **Sugars**

Sugar is a general term for **monosaccharides** and **disaccharides**. All sugars can be classified as **reducing** or **non-reducing**. To **test** for sugars you use the **Benedict's test**. The test **differs** depending on the **type** of sugar you are testing for.

REDUCING SUGARS

1) Reducing sugars include **all monosaccharides** (e.g. glucose) and **some disaccharides** (e.g. maltose).
2) You add **Benedict's reagent** (which is **blue**) to a sample and **heat it**. Make sure the solution **doesn't boil**. If the test's **positive** it will form a **coloured precipitate** (solid particles suspended in the solution).

   The colour of the precipitate changes from: **blue → green → yellow → orange → brick red**

3) The higher the concentration of reducing sugar, the further the colour change goes — you can use this to **compare** the amount of reducing sugar in different solutions. A more accurate way of doing this is to **filter** the solution and **weigh the precipitate**.

Always use an excess of Benedict's solution — this makes sure that all the sugar reacts.

NON-REDUCING SUGARS

1) To test for **non-reducing sugars**, like sucrose, first you have to break them down into monosaccharides.
2) You do this by **boiling** the test solution with **dilute hydrochloric acid** and then **neutralising** it with **sodium hydrogencarbonate**. Then just carry out the **Benedict's test** as you would for a reducing sugar.
3) Annoyingly, if the result of this test is **positive** the sugar could be reducing **or** non-reducing. To **check** it's non-reducing you need to do the **reducing sugar test** too (to rule out it being a reducing sugar).

Use the **Iodine Test** for **Starch**

Make sure you always talk about iodine in potassium iodide solution, not just iodine.

Just add **iodine dissolved in potassium iodide solution** to the test sample.

- If starch **is present**, the sample changes from **browny-orange** to a dark, **blue-black** colour.
- If there's **no starch**, it stays browny-orange.

Use the **Biuret Test** for **Proteins**

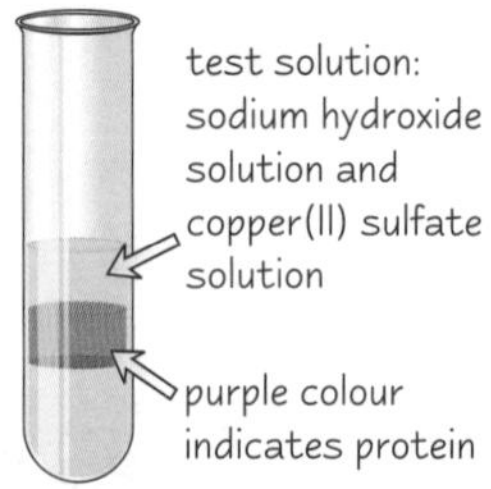

There are **two stages** to this test.

1) The test solution needs to be **alkaline**, so first you add a few drops of **sodium hydroxide solution**.
2) Then you add some **copper(II) sulfate solution**.

- If protein **is** present a **purple layer** forms.
- If there's **no protein**, the solution will **stay blue**. The colours are pale, so you need to look carefully.

Carbohydrates are polar molecules. No wait, lipids are polar molecules. No wait, I know this, I know this...

Humphrey's revision for his starch test wasn't going so well.

Use the **Emulsion Test** for **Lipids**

Shake the test substance with **ethanol** for about a minute, then **pour** the solution into **water**.

- If lipid **is present**, the solution will turn **milky**.
- The **more lipid** there is, the **more noticeable** the milky colour will be.
- If there's **no lipid**, the solution will **stay clear**.

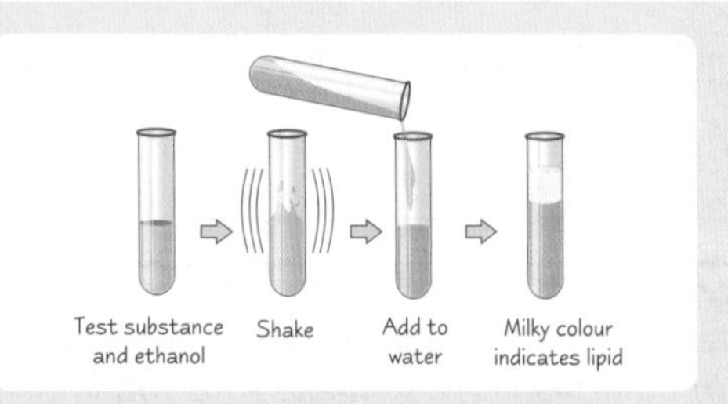

Biochemical Tests for Molecules

Colorimetry is Used to Determine the *Concentration* of a *Glucose Solution*

1) A **quantitative** version of the **Benedict's test** allows you to estimate **how much** glucose (or other **reducing sugar**) there is in a solution.
2) It uses a **colorimeter** — a device that measures the **strength** of a **coloured solution** by seeing how much **light** passes through it.
3) A colorimeter measures **absorbance** (the amount of light absorbed by the solution). The **more concentrated** the **colour** of the solution, the **higher** the **absorbance** is.

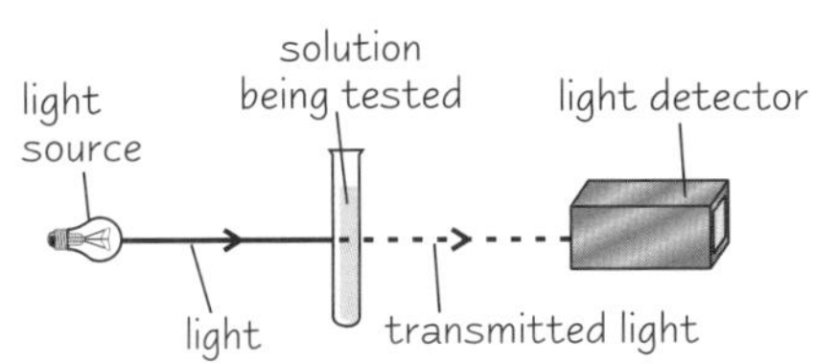

4) It's pretty difficult to measure the concentration of the coloured precipitate formed in the Benedict's test, so when you're estimating glucose concentration you measure the **concentration** of the **blue Benedict's solution** that's **left** after the test (the **paler** the solution left, the **more glucose** there was). So, the **higher** the glucose concentration, the **lower** the absorbance of the solution.

Here's how you do it:

First you need to make a **calibration curve**. To do this you need to:

1) Make up several glucose solutions of **different, known concentrations**, e.g. 10 mM, 20 mM and 30 mM. There should be the **same volume** of each.
2) Do a **Benedict's test** on each solution. Use the **same amount** of Benedict's solution in each case — it has to be a **large** enough volume to react with **all** the sugar in the strongest solution and still have some reagent **left over**.
3) **Remove** any **precipitate** from the solutions — either leave the test tubes for **24 hours** (so that the precipitate **settles out**) or **centrifuge** them.
4) Use a **colorimeter** to measure the **absorbance** of the Benedict's solution **remaining** in each tube.
5) Use the results to make the **calibration curve**, showing absorbance against glucose concentration.

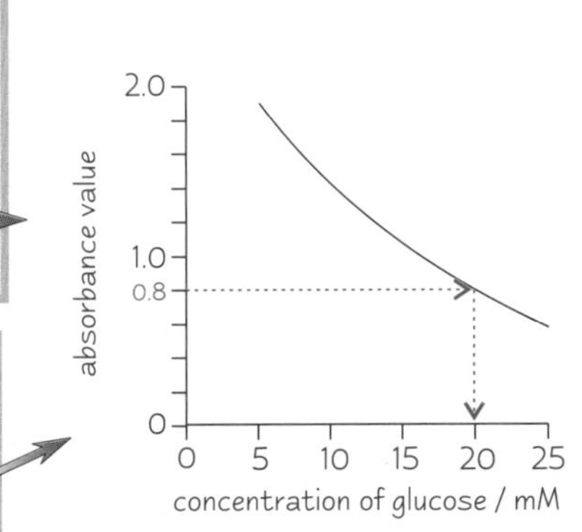

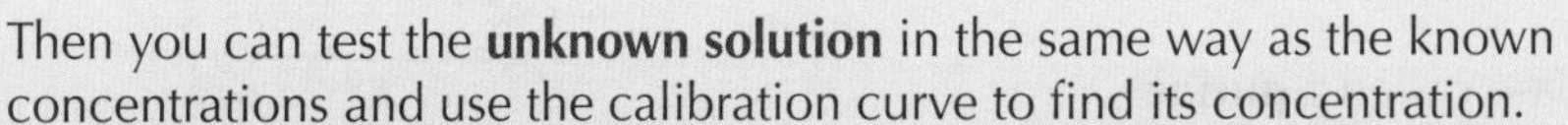

Then you can test the **unknown solution** in the same way as the known concentrations and use the calibration curve to find its concentration.

E.g. an **unknown solution** gives an absorbance value of **0.80**. Reading across the calibration graph from an absorbance value of 0.8 shows that the concentration of glucose in the unknown solution is **20 mM**.

Practice Questions

Q1 Describe how you would test a solution for starch. What result would you expect if:
a) starch was present; b) starch was not present?

Q2 Describe how you would test for lipids in a solution.

Exam Question

solution	absorbance
A	1.22
B	0.68
C	0.37

Q1 Equal volumes of three different sugar solutions (A, B and C) were each tested with the same large volume of Benedict's solution. Later, the concentrations of Benedict's solution in each test tube were compared, using a colorimeter. The table shows the absorbance of each solution.

a) Which original solution contained the highest concentration of reducing sugar? [1 mark]

b) Explain why a large volume of Benedict's solution had to be used. [1 mark]

c) Suggest two factors that should be kept constant when carrying out this test. [2 marks]

The Anger Test — annoy the test subject. If it goes red, anger is present...

A double page of biochemical tests... I literally can't think of anything worse. Well, maybe being slowly dissolved in a vat of vinegar would be worse, but it's a close one. Oh well, that's the end of this section, so good times must be on their way...

DNA and RNA

This section's all about nucleic acids — DNA and RNA. These molecules are needed to build proteins, which are required for the cells in living organisms to function. They're right handy little molecules.

DNA is Used to Store Genetic Information

1) Your DNA (deoxyribonucleic acid) contains your **genetic information** — that's **all the instructions** needed to **grow and develop** from a fertilised egg to a fully grown adult.
2) The DNA molecules are really **long** and are **coiled** up very tightly, so a lot of genetic information can fit into a **small space** in the cell nucleus.
3) DNA molecules have a **paired structure** (see below), which makes it much easier to **copy itself**. This is called **self-replication** (see p. 64). It's important for cell division (see p. 20) and for passing genetic information from **generation to generation** (see p. 23).
4) DNA contains **genes** — **sections of DNA** that code (contain the instructions) for a specific **sequence of amino acids** that forms a particular **protein**. See page 64.
5) The nucleic acid **RNA** (ribonucleic acid) is similar in structure to DNA. It's used to make **proteins** from the instructions contained within DNA (see next page).

DNA is Made of Nucleotides that Contain a Sugar, a Phosphate and a Base

1) DNA is a **polynucleotide** — it's made up of lots of **nucleotides** joined together.
2) Each nucleotide is made from a **deoxyribose sugar**, a **phosphate** group and a nitrogen-containing **base**.
3) Each nucleotide has the **same sugar and phosphate**. The **base** on each nucleotide can **vary** though.
4) There are **four** possible bases — adenine (**A**), thymine (**T**), cytosine (**C**) and guanine (**G**).
5) **A**denine and **g**uanine are a type of base called a **purine**. **C**ytosine and **t**hymine are **pyrimidines**.

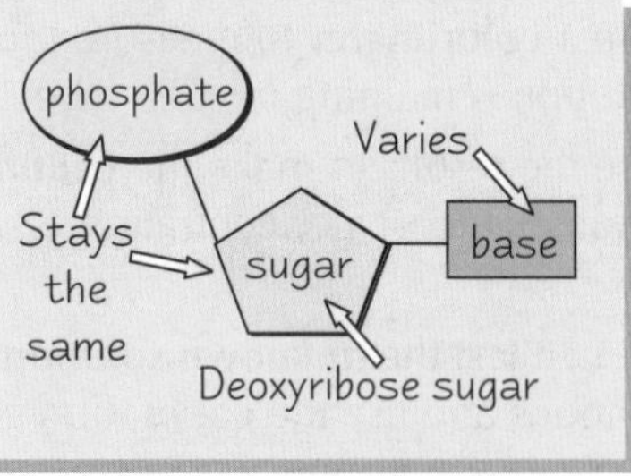

Two Polynucleotide Strands Join Together to Form a Double-Helix

1) DNA nucleotides join together to form **polynucleotide strands**.
2) The nucleotides join up between the **phosphate** group of one nucleotide and the **sugar** of another.
3) **Two** DNA polynucleotide strands join together by **hydrogen bonding** between the bases.
4) Each base can only join with one particular partner — this is called **complementary base pairing**.
5) **Adenine** always pairs with **thymine** (**A - T**) and **guanine** always pairs with **cytosine** (**G - C**). (A **purine** (A or G) always pairs with a **pyrimidine** (T or C).)
6) **Two** hydrogen bonds form between **A and T**, and **three** hydrogen bonds form between **C and G**.
7) Two **antiparallel** (running in opposite directions) polynucleotide strands **twist** to form the **DNA double-helix**.

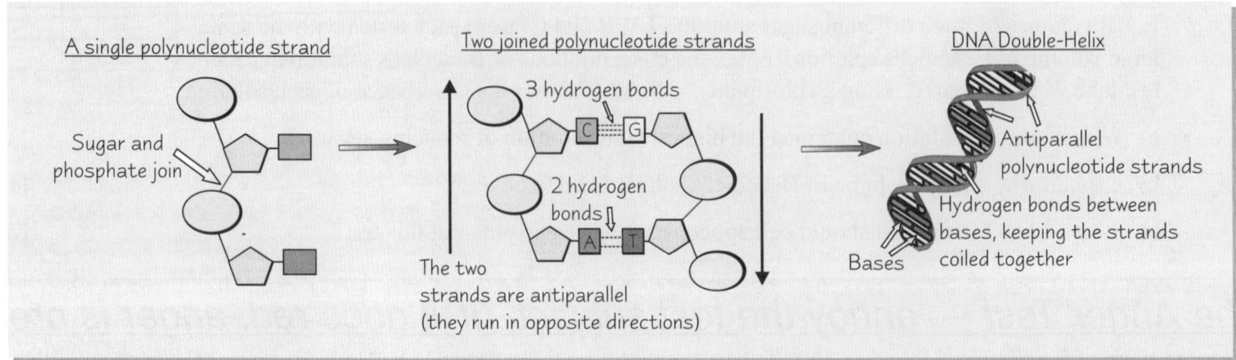

DNA and RNA

RNA is Very Similar to DNA

Mary didn't care if it was ribose or deoxyribose, she just wanted her cuppa.

1) RNA and DNA are both made from nucleotides containing **sugar**, **nitrogen-containing bases** and **phosphate**.
2) Each nucleotide in both RNA and DNA contains one of **four** different bases.
3) Also, the nucleotides form a **polynucleotide strand** that is joined up between the sugar of one nucleotide and the phosphate of another.
4) But the structure of RNA **differs** from DNA in three main ways:

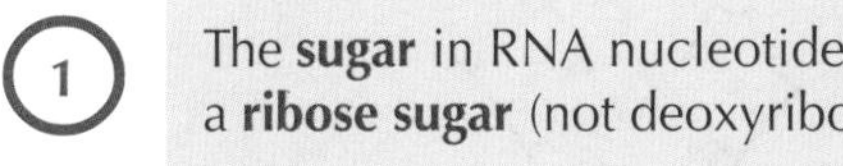

(1) The **sugar** in RNA nucleotides is a **ribose sugar** (not deoxyribose).

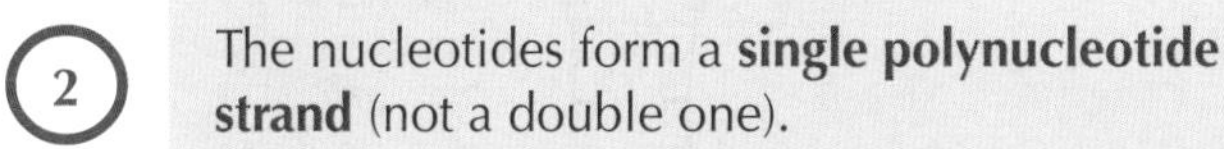

(2) The nucleotides form a **single polynucleotide strand** (not a double one).

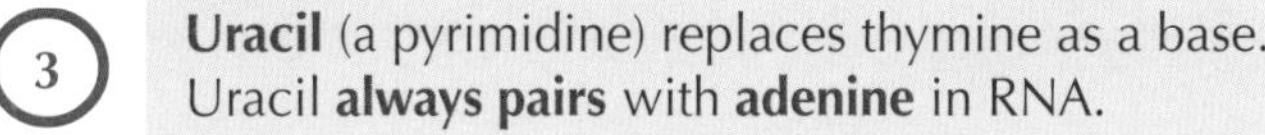

(3) **Uracil** (a pyrimidine) replaces thymine as a base. Uracil **always pairs** with **adenine** in RNA.

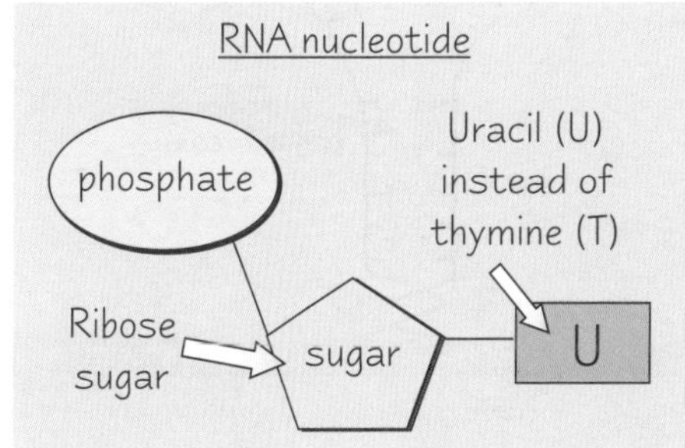

Practice Questions

Q1 What are the three main components of nucleotides?

Q2 Which bases join together in a DNA molecule?

Q3 What sugar is found in DNA nucleotides?

Q4 What type of bonds join the bases in a DNA molecule together?

Q5 Which sugar do RNA nucleotides contain?

Exam Questions

Q1 Fill in the missing nucleotides on the diagram below.

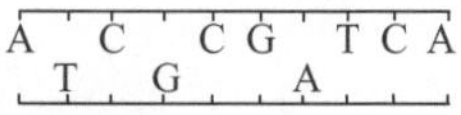

A C C G T C A
T G A

[1 mark]

Q2 a) Describe the structure of a DNA nucleotide. [3 marks]

b) Describe the main differences between DNA and RNA molecules. [3 marks]

Q3 Describe, using diagrams where appropriate, how nucleotides are joined together in DNA and how two single polynucleotide strands of DNA are joined. [4 marks]

Give me a D, give me an N, give me an A! What do you get? — very confused...

*You need to learn the structure of DNA — the polynucleotide strands, the hydrogen bonds, and don't forget the complementary base pairing. And make sure you know the three main differences between RNA and DNA — **R**NA's got **r**ibose sugar, uracil bases and it's single-stranded. You need to learn all this before moving on, or you'll struggle later.*

DNA Replication and Protein Synthesis

Here comes some truly essential stuff — DNA replication, genes, and a wee bit on protein synthesis. I'm afraid it's all horribly complicated — all I can do is keep apologising. Sorry.

DNA can Copy Itself — Self-Replication

DNA copies itself before **cell division** (see page 20) so that each new cell has the full amount of DNA.

1) The **hydrogen bonds** between the two **polynucleotide** DNA strands **break**. The helix **unzips** to form two single strands.

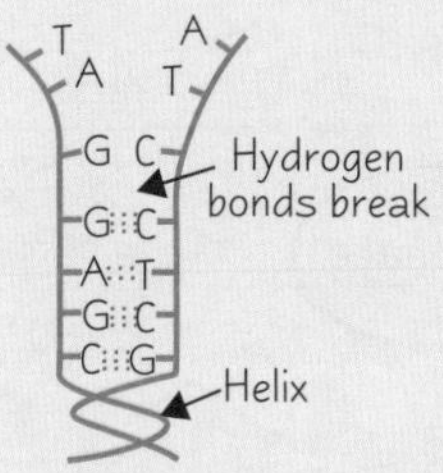

Hydrogen bonds break

Helix

2) Each **original** single strand acts as a **template** for a new strand. Free-floating DNA nucleotides join to the **exposed bases** on each original template strand by **complementary base pairing** — A with T and C with G.

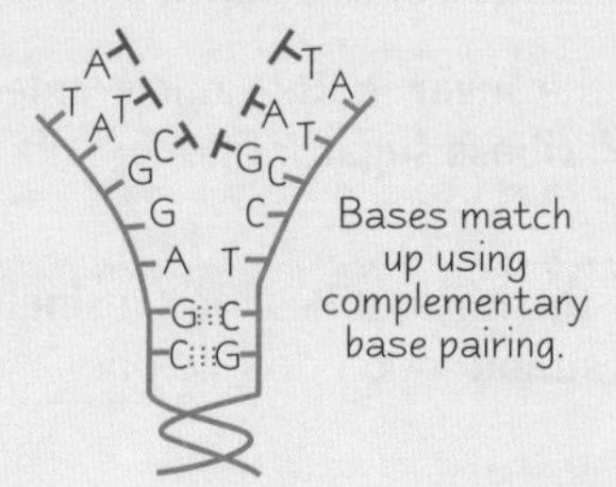

3) The nucleotides on the new strand are **joined together** by the enzyme **DNA polymerase**. **Hydrogen bonds form** between the bases on the original and new strand.

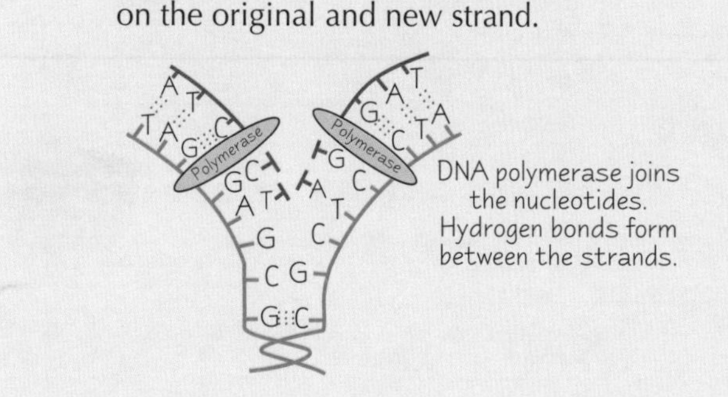

4) Each new DNA molecule contains **one strand** from the **original** DNA molecule and **one new strand.**

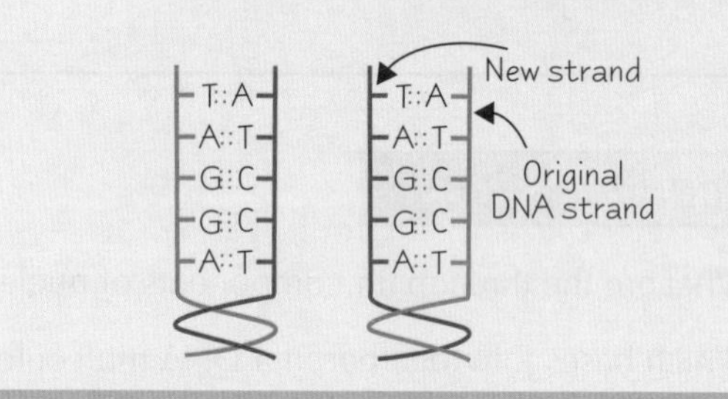

This type of copying is called **semi-conservative replication** because **half** of the new strands of DNA are from the **original** piece of DNA.

DNA Contains Genes Which are Instructions for Proteins

1) A **gene** is a **sequence** of DNA nucleotides that codes for a **protein** (polypeptide).
2) Proteins are made from **amino acids**.
3) Different proteins have a **different number** and **order** of amino acids.
4) It's the **order** of **nucleotide bases** in a gene that determines the **order of amino acids** in a particular **protein.**
5) Each amino acid is coded for by a sequence of **three bases** in a gene.
6) Different sequences of **bases** code for different **amino acids**. For example:

Polypeptide is just another word for a protein.

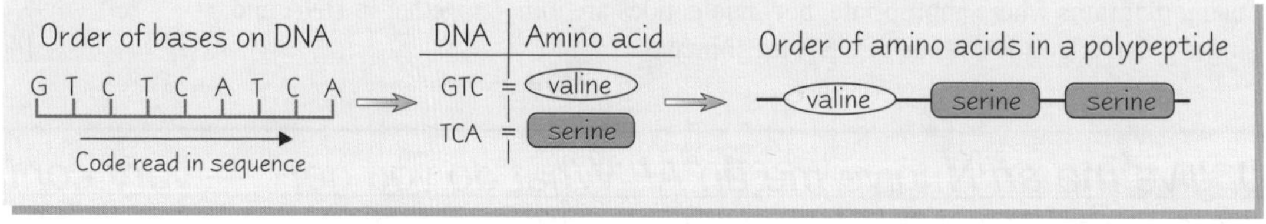

DNA Replication and Protein Synthesis

DNA is **Copied** into **RNA** for **Protein Synthesis**

1) All the reactions and **processes** in living organisms **need** proteins.
2) **DNA** carries the **instructions** to make **proteins** (as **genes**). It's found in the **nucleus**.
3) The organelles that make proteins (**ribosomes**, see p. 5) are found in the **cytoplasm**. But the DNA molecules are **too large** to move out of the nucleus.
4) Instead, sections of DNA are **copied** into **RNA**.
5) The RNA **leaves** the nucleus and joins with a ribosome in the cytoplasm, where it can be used to synthesise a protein.
6) So, DNA and RNA are **vital** for living organisms to produce proteins in order to **grow** and **develop**.

Mrs Thone knew how to synthesise some great tunes.

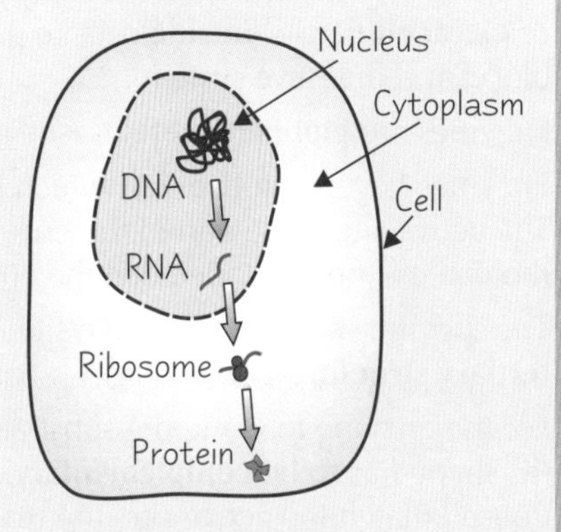

Practice Questions

Q1 Why is DNA copied before cell division?

Q2 What is the function of DNA polymerase in DNA replication?

Q3 Why is DNA replication described as semi-conservative?

Q4 Why is DNA copied into RNA?

Q5 Where is RNA formed?

Q6 Where are proteins synthesised?

Exam Questions

Q1 Describe the semi-conservative method of DNA replication. [7 marks]

Q2 Write a definition of a gene. [2 marks]

Q3 Describe the role of DNA and RNA in living organisms. [3 marks]

Genes contain instructions — wash at 40 °C...

DNA self-replication can get a bit tricky, but you need to learn what's going on. Diagrams are handy for learning stuff like this, so get drawing. And don't go forgetting about RNA — it's a really important molecule. Without it we'd have no proteins. So remember — DNA is copied into RNA, which leaves the nucleus and is used to make a protein in the cytoplasm.

Action of Enzymes

*Enzymes crop up loads in biology — they're really useful 'cos they make reactions work more quickly. So, whether you feel the need for some speed or not, read on — because you **really** need to know this basic stuff about enzymes.*

Enzymes are *Biological Catalysts*

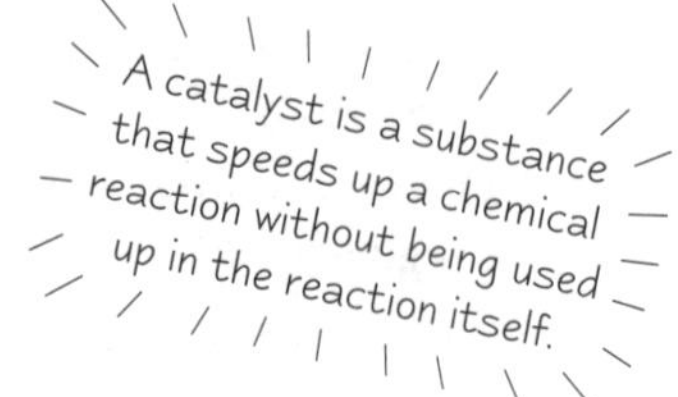

Enzymes **speed up chemical reactions** by acting as **biological catalysts**.

1) They catalyse **metabolic reactions** in your body, e.g. **digestion** and **respiration**.
2) Enzyme action can be **intracellular** — **within** cells, or **extracellular** — **outside** cells (e.g. in places like the blood and digestive system).
3) Enzymes are **globular proteins** (see p. 55).
4) Enzymes have an **active site**, which has a **specific shape**. The active site is the part of the enzyme where the **substrate** molecules (the substance that the enzyme interacts with) **bind to**.
5) The specific shape of the active site is determined by the enzyme's **tertiary structure** (see p. 54).
6) For the enzyme to work, the substrate has to **fit into** the **active site** (its shape has to be **complementary**). If the substrate shape doesn't match the active site, the reaction won't be catalysed. This means that enzymes work with very few substrates — usually only one.

Ahmed knew Sara was a lovely girl, but just couldn't get past the shape incompatibility thing.

Enzymes Reduce Activation Energy

In a chemical reaction, a certain amount of energy needs to be supplied to the chemicals before the reaction will start. This is called the **activation energy** — it's often provided as **heat**.

Enzymes **reduce** the amount of activation energy that's needed, often making reactions happen at a **lower temperature** than they could without an enzyme. This **speeds** up the **rate of reaction**.

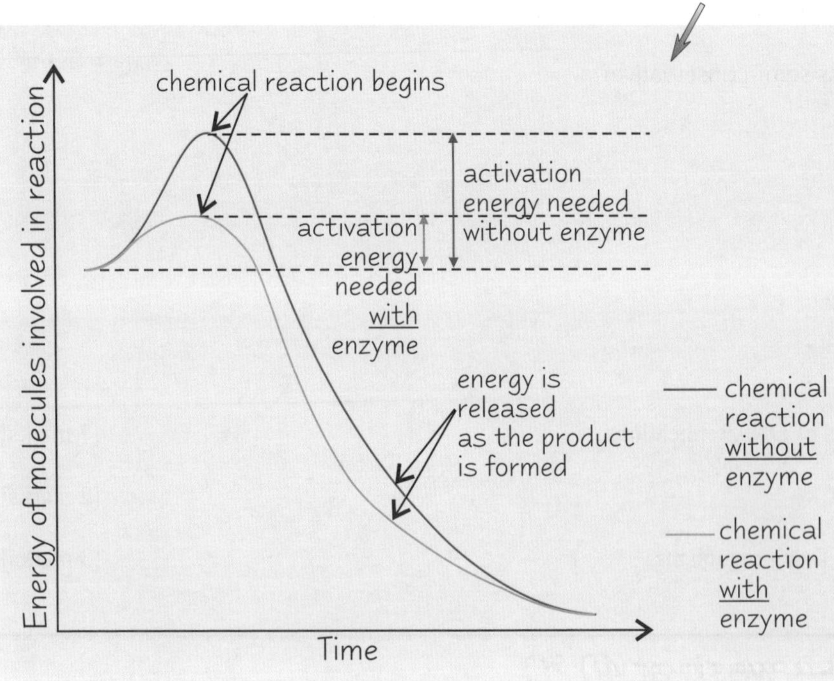

When a substance binds to an enzyme's active site, an **enzyme-substrate complex** is formed. It's the formation of the enzyme-substrate complex that **lowers** the **activation energy**. Here are two reasons why:

1) If two substrate molecules need to be **joined**, attaching to the enzyme holds them **close together**, **reducing** any **repulsion** between the molecules so they can bond more easily.
2) If the enzyme is catalysing a **breakdown reaction**, fitting into the active site puts a **strain** on bonds in the substrate. This strain means the substrate molecule **breaks up** more easily.

Action of Enzymes

The 'Lock and Key' Model is a Good Start...

Enzymes are a bit picky. They only work with **substrates** that fit their active site. Early scientists studying the action of enzymes came up with the '**lock and key**' model. This is where the **substrate fits** into the **enzyme** in the same way that a **key fits** into a **lock**.

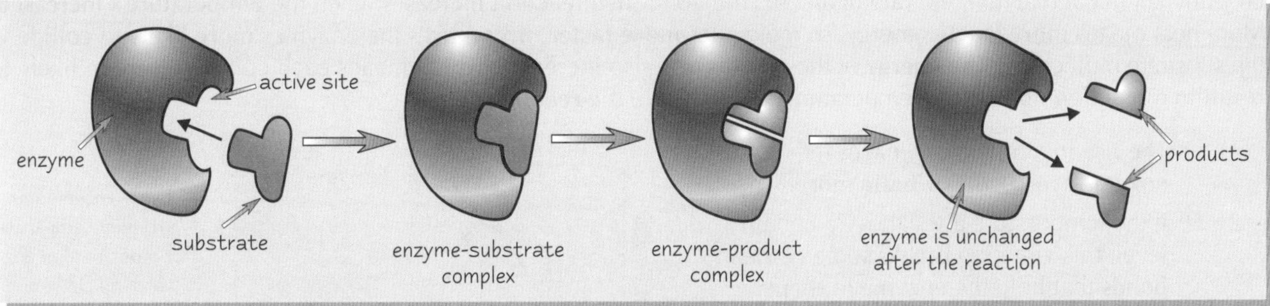

Scientists soon realised that the lock and key model didn't give the full story. The enzyme and substrate do have to fit together in the first place, but new evidence showed that the **enzyme-substrate complex changed shape** slightly to complete the fit. This **locks** the substrate even more tightly to the enzyme. Scientists modified the old lock and key model and came up with the '**induced fit**' model.

...but the 'Induced Fit' Model is a Better Theory

The '**induced fit**' model helps to explain why enzymes are so **specific** and only bond to one particular substrate.

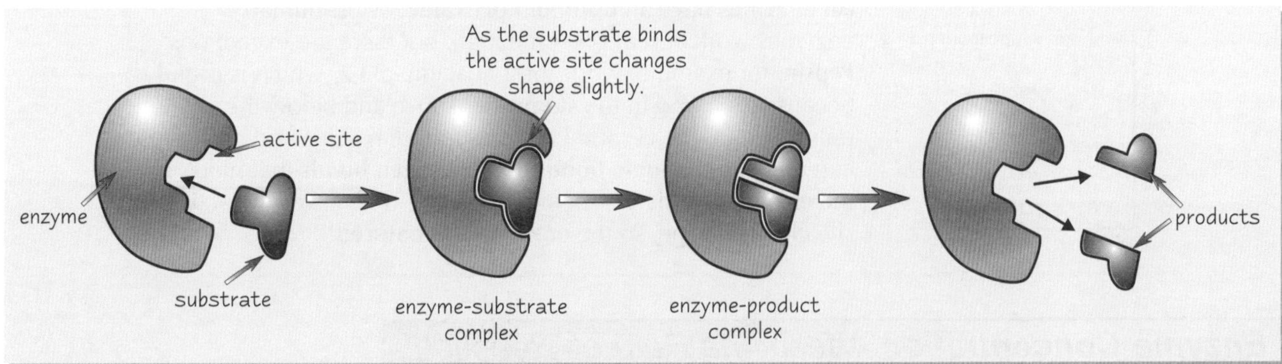

The substrate doesn't only have to be the right shape to fit the active site, it has to make the active site **change shape** in the right way as well. This is a prime example of how a widely accepted theory can **change** when **new evidence** comes along. The 'induced fit' model is still widely accepted — for now, anyway.

Practice Questions

Q1 What is an enzyme?

Q2 What is the name given to the amount of energy needed to start a reaction?

Q3 What is an enzyme-substrate complex?

Q4 Explain why enzymes are specific.

Exam Question

Q1 Describe the 'lock and key' model of enzyme action and explain how the 'induced fit' model is different. [7 marks]

But why is the enzyme-substrate complex?

OK, nothing too tricky here. The main thing to remember is that every enzyme has a specific shape, so it only works with specific substrates that fit the shape. The induced fit model is the new, trendy theory to explain this — the lock and key model is, like, ***so*** *last year. Everyone who's anyone knows that.*

Factors Affecting Enzyme Activity

Now you know what enzymes are and how they work, it's time to take a look at what makes them tick. Humans need things like money, caffeine and the newest mobile phone, but enzymes are quite content with the right temperature and pH.

Temperature has a **Big Influence** on Enzyme Activity

Like any chemical reaction, the **rate** of an enzyme-controlled reaction **increases** when the **temperature's increased**. More heat means **more kinetic energy**, so molecules **move faster**. This makes the enzymes **more likely** to **collide** with the substrate molecules. The **energy** of these collisions also **increases**, which means each collision is more likely to **result** in a **reaction**. But, if the temperature gets too high, the **reaction stops**.

1) The rise in temperature makes the enzyme's molecules **vibrate more**.
2) If the temperature goes above a certain level, this vibration **breaks** some of the **bonds** that hold the enzyme in shape.
3) The **active site changes shape** and the enzyme and substrate **no longer fit together**.
4) At this point, the enzyme is **denatured** — it no longer functions as a catalyst.

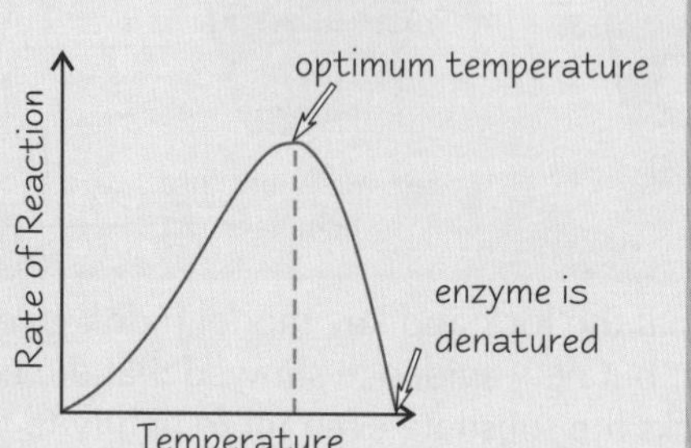

Every enzyme has an optimum temperature. For most human enzymes it's around 37 °C but some enzymes, like those used in biological washing powders, can work well at 60 °C.

pH Also Affects Enzyme Activity

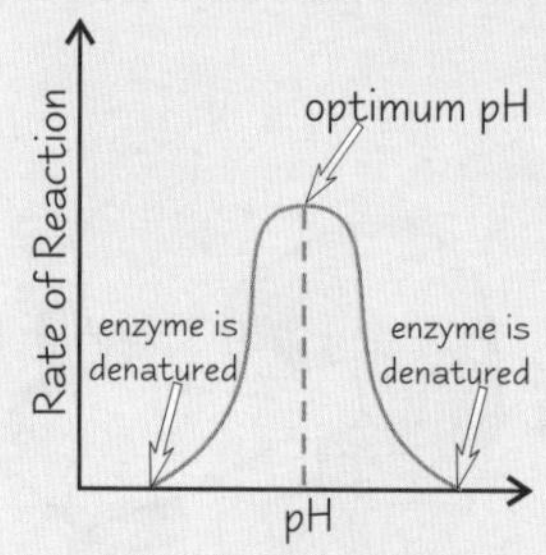

All enzymes have an **optimum pH value**. Most human enzymes work best at pH 7 (neutral), but there are exceptions. **Pepsin**, for example, works best at acidic pH 2, which is useful because it's found in the stomach. Above and below the optimum pH, the H^+ and OH^- ions found in acids and alkalis can mess up the **ionic bonds** and **hydrogen bonds** that hold the enzyme's tertiary structure in place. This makes the active site change shape, so the enzyme is **denatured**.

Enzyme Concentration Affects the Rate of Reaction

1) The **more enzyme molecules** there are in a solution, the more likely a substrate molecule is to **collide** with one and form an **enzyme-substrate complex**. So increasing the concentration of the enzyme **increases** the **rate of reaction**.
2) But, if the amount of **substrate** is **limited**, there comes a point when there's more than enough enzyme molecules to deal with all the available substrate, so adding more enzyme has **no further effect**.

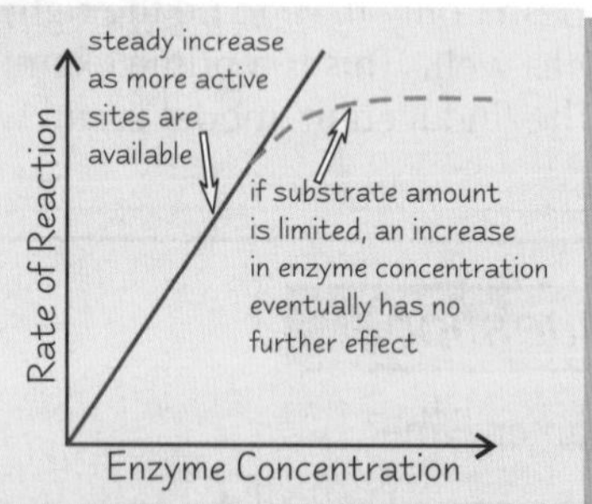

Substrate Concentration Affects the Rate of Reaction **Up to a Point**

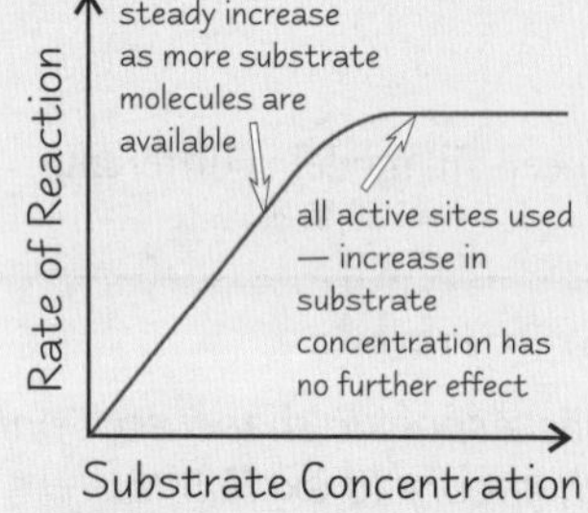

The **higher** the substrate concentration, the **faster** the reaction — more substrate molecules means a **collision** between substrate and enzyme is **more likely** and so more active sites will be used. This is only true up until a **'saturation'** point though. After that, there are so many substrate molecules that the enzymes have about as much as they can cope with (all the **active sites are full**), and adding more **makes no difference**.

Factors Affecting Enzyme Activity

*You can **Measure** the **Rate** of an **Enzyme-Controlled** Reaction*

You need to be able to **describe** how the effects of pH, temperature, enzyme concentration and substrate concentration can be investigated **experimentally**. Here are two ways of measuring the **rate** of an enzyme-controlled reaction:

Example 1

You can measure **how fast** the **product of** the reaction **appears**. The diagram on the right shows how to measure this with the enzyme **catalase**. Catalase catalyses the **breakdown** of **hydrogen peroxide** into **water** and **oxygen**. It's easy to collect the oxygen produced and measure **how fast** it's given off.

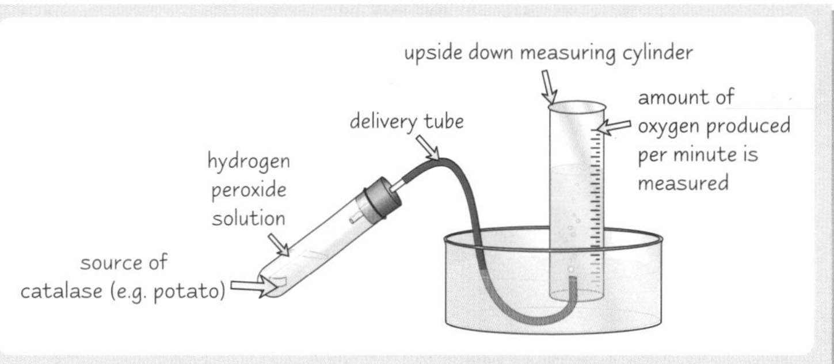

mixture sampled each minute
dropping pipette
drop of iodine in potassium iodide
starch solution and amylase enzyme
spotting tile

Time when iodine solution no longer turns blue-black is noted — starch has then been broken down.

Example 2

You can also measure the **disappearance** of the **substrate** rather than the appearance of the product and use this to **compare the rate** of reaction under different conditions. For example, the enzyme **amylase** catalyses the breakdown of **starch** to **maltose** (see p. 57). It's easy to detect starch using a solution of potassium iodide and iodine. You can **time** how long it takes for the starch to disappear by **regularly sampling** the starch solution, and use the times to compare rates between different tests.

Here are some general tips on what to include when describing an experiment:

1) Describe the **method** and the **apparatus** you'd use.
2) Say **what** you're **measuring** (the dependent variable), e.g. the volume of gas produced per minute.
3) Describe how you'd **vary** the **independent variable**, e.g. if your independent variable is **enzyme concentration** you might test **five different concentrations** of enzyme.
4) Describe what **variables** you're **keeping constant**, e.g. temperature, pH, volume of solution, substrate concentration etc.
5) Say that you need to **repeat** the experiment at least twice, to make the results **more reliable**.
6) Say that you need a **control**, e.g. a test tube containing the substrate solution but no enzyme.

Practice Questions

Q1 What does it mean if an enzyme is denatured?

Q2 Explain why increasing the concentration of an enzyme doesn't always increase the rate of reaction.

Q3 Explain the effect of increasing substrate concentration on the rate of an enzyme-catalysed reaction.

Q4 Suggest two methods of measuring the rate of an enzyme-catalysed reaction.

Exam Question

Q1 When doing an experiment on enzymes, explain why it is necessary to control the temperature and pH of the solutions involved. [8 marks]

This enzyme's not working very fast — he's out of shape...

Enzymes are pretty fussy — they'll only work best when they are nice and comfortable. So be like them — tell your teacher you'll need an optimum concentration of chocolate, a nice warm fire to sit by and... err... the right pH environment. Also, make sure you can describe how you'd investigate all those factors that affect enzyme activity.

Factors Affecting Enzyme Activity

Cofactors are substances that enzymes need to work. Enzyme inhibitors, yep you guessed it, inhibit their action. Some inhibitors are poisons, but they're not all bad — we use some of them as medicinal drugs.

Cofactors and *Coenzymes* are *Essential* for Enzymes to *Work*

Some enzymes will only work if there is another **non-protein** substance bound to them.
These non-protein substances are called **cofactors**.

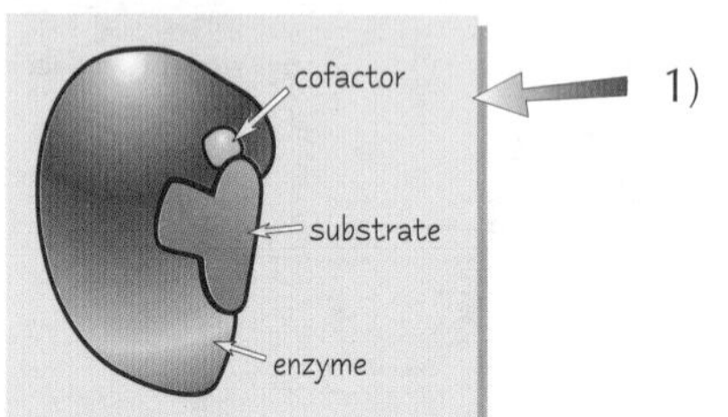

1) Some cofactors are **inorganic** molecules. They work by helping the enzyme and substrate to **bind together**. They don't directly participate in the reaction so aren't **used up** or **changed** in any way. For example, **manganese ions** are cofactors found in hydrolase (enzymes that catalyse the hydrolysis of chemical bonds).

2) Some cofactors are **organic** molecules — these are called **coenzymes**. They participate in the reaction and are **changed** by it (they're just like a second substrate, but they aren't called that). They often act as **carriers**, moving **chemical groups** between different enzymes. They're **continually recycled** during this process.

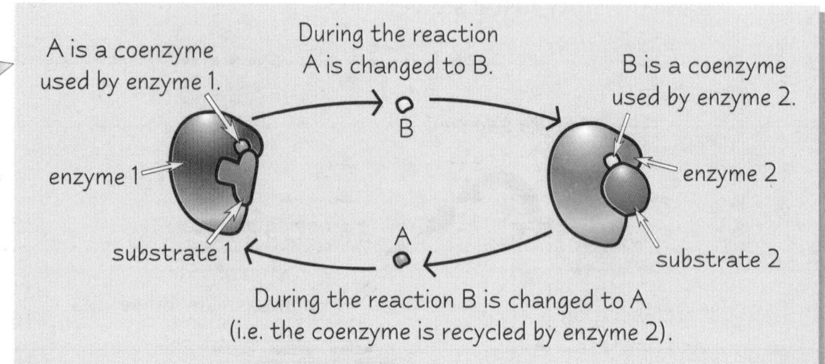

Enzyme *Activity* can be *Inhibited*

Enzyme activity can be prevented by **enzyme inhibitors** — molecules that **bind to the enzyme** that they inhibit. Inhibition can be **competitive** or **non-competitive**.

COMPETITIVE INHIBITION

1) **Competitive inhibitor** molecules have a **similar shape** to that of the **substrate** molecules.
2) They **compete** with the substrate molecules to **bind** to the **active site**, but **no reaction** takes place.
3) Instead they **block** the active site, so **no substrate** molecules can **fit** in it.
4) How much the enzyme is inhibited depends on the **relative concentrations** of the inhibitor and substrate.
5) If there's a **high concentration** of the **inhibitor**, it'll take up **nearly all** the **active sites** and hardly any of the substrate will get to the enzyme.

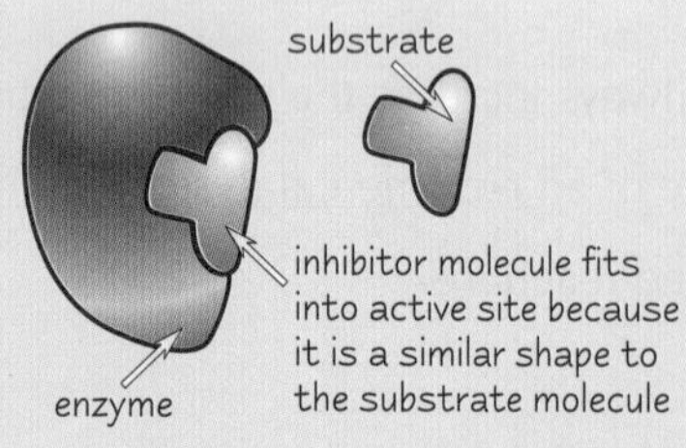

NON-COMPETITIVE INHIBITION

1) **Non-competitive inhibitor** molecules bind to the enzyme **away from its active site**.
2) This causes the active site to **change shape** so the substrate molecules can **no longer bind** to it.
3) They **don't** 'compete' with the substrate molecules to bind to the active site because they are a **different shape**.
4) **Increasing** the concentration of **substrate won't** make any difference — enzyme activity will still be inhibited.

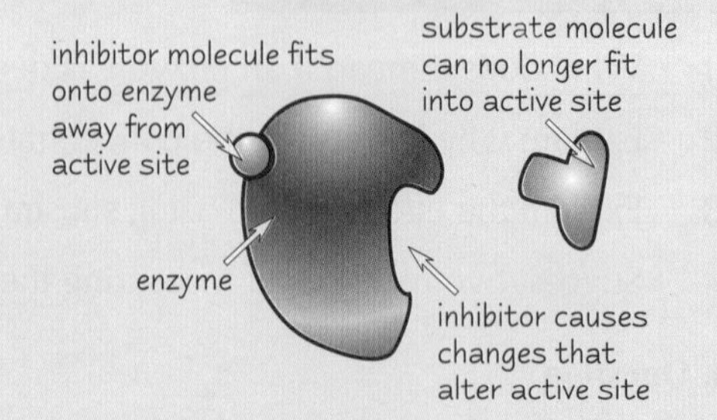

Inhibitors can be **reversible** or **non-reversible**.
Which one they are depends on the **strength of the bonds** between the enzyme and the inhibitor.

1) If they're **strong, covalent bonds**, the inhibitor can't be removed easily and the inhibition is **irreversible**.
2) If they're **weaker hydrogen bonds** or weak **ionic bonds**, the inhibitor can be removed and the inhibition is **reversible**.

Factors Affecting Enzyme Activity

Some **Metabolic Poisons** are **Enzyme Inhibitors**

Metabolic **poisons interfere** with **metabolic reactions** (the reactions that occur in cells), causing **damage**, **illness** or **death** — they're often **enzyme inhibitors**.
In the **exam** you might be asked to **describe the action** of one **named poison**, for example:

1) **Cyanide** is an **irreversible** inhibitor of **cytochrome c oxidase**, an enzyme that catalyses **respiration** reactions. Cells that can't respire **die**.
2) **Malonate** inhibits **succinate dehydrogenase** (which also catalyses respiration reactions).
3) **Arsenic** inhibits the action of **pyruvate dehydrogenase**, yet another enzyme that catalyses **respiration** reactions.

Gillian didn't think Hugo would find it quite so funny when he realised she'd spiked his food with an irreversible enzyme inhibitor. Mwah ha ha ha.

Some **Drugs** Work by **Inhibiting Enzymes**

Some **medicinal drugs** are **enzyme inhibitors**, for example:

1) Some **antiviral** drugs (drugs that stop **viruses** like **HIV**) — e.g. **reverse transcriptase inhibitors** inhibit the enzyme **reverse transcriptase**, which catalyses the **replication** of **viral DNA**. This **prevents** the virus from **replicating**.
2) Some **antibiotics** — e.g. **penicillin** inhibits the enzyme **transpeptidase**, which **catalyses** the **formation** of **proteins** in bacterial cell walls. This **weakens the cell wall** and prevents the bacterium from regulating its osmotic pressure. As a result the cell **bursts** and the bacterium is **killed**.

Practice Questions

Q1 What are cofactors and coenzymes?

Q2 What's the difference between competitive and non-competitive enzyme inhibitors?

Q3 Name one metabolic poison and describe how it works.

Q4 Describe one medicinal use of enzyme inhibitors.

Exam Questions

Q1 During an experiment hexokinase (an enzyme that catalyses reactions important in respiration) was found to work only in the presence of magnesium ions and to work slower when aluminium ions were also present.

a) Suggest a possible reason why hexokinase only works when magnesium ions are present. [2 marks]

b) Suggest a possible reason why hexokinase works slower when aluminium ions are present. [2 marks]

c) Explain why aluminium ions are a metabolic poison. [1 mark]

Q2 HIV uses protease enzymes to catalyse the breakdown of proteins. It uses the products of the reaction to replicate new viruses. Ritonavir is a drug used to treat HIV. Its molecules have a similar shape to the protein molecules which are the substrate for HIV protease. Suggest how Ritonavir will affect HIV. Explain your answer. [5 marks]

Activity — mine is usually inhibited by pizza and a movie...

Crikey, it's like a rubbish soap or something — one minute the enzymes are trying to kill us, the next they're bringing us back to life, and all the while there are some things trying to stop them, and others trying to help them — if you can follow the ins, outs, ups and downs of some crazy soap then you can follow this. Everybody needs good en-zymes...

Balanced Diet

To maintain good health you need a balanced diet containing the right amount of each essential nutrient. If you eat too much of something it can badly affect your health... and your waistline.

A **Balanced Diet** Supplies All the **Essential Nutrients**

A balanced diet gives you all the **nutrients** you need, plus **fibre** and **water**. There are **five** important nutrients — **carbohydrates**, **proteins**, **fats**, **vitamins** and **mineral salts**. Each nutrient has different functions in the body:

NUTRIENTS	FUNCTIONS
Carbohydrates	Provide energy.
Fats (lipids)	Act as an energy store, provide insulation, make up cell membranes, physically protect organs.
Proteins	Needed for growth, the repair of tissues and to make enzymes.
Vitamins	Different vitamins have different functions, e.g. vitamin D is needed for calcium absorption, vitamin K is needed for blood clotting.
Mineral salts	Different mineral salts have different functions, e.g. iron is needed to make haemoglobin in the blood, calcium is needed for bone formation.

Fibre	Aids movement of food through gut.
Water	It is used in chemical reactions. We need a constant supply to replace water lost through urinating, breathing and sweating.

Mmm... paper plates, delicious and nutritious...

Not Getting the **Right Amount** of **Each Nutrient** Causes **Malnutrition**

Basically, **malnutrition** is caused by having **too little** or **too much** of some nutrients in your diet. There are three causes:

1) Not having **enough food** — you get **too little** of **every nutrient**.
2) Having an **unbalanced diet**:
   - Getting **too little** of a nutrient can lead to all kinds of **deficiency illnesses**, e.g. getting too little **iron** in your diet causes **anaemia**.
   - Getting **too many** carbohydrates or fats can lead to **obesity**.
3) Not being able to **absorb the nutrients** from digestion into your **bloodstream** properly. E.g. coeliac disease reduces absorption of nutrients from the small intestine. This also causes **deficiency illnesses**.

Over-Nutrition and **Lack of Exercise** can Lead to **Obesity**

Obesity is a bigger problem in developed countries.

Obesity is a common **dietary condition** caused by eating **too much food**.

1) **Obesity** is defined as being **20%** (or more) **over the recommended body weight**.
2) **Too much sugary** or **fatty food** and **too little exercise** are the main causes of obesity.
3) People can also be obese due to an **underactive thyroid gland**, but this problem isn't common.
4) Obesity can increase the risk of **diabetes**, **arthritis**, **high blood pressure**, **coronary heart disease** (CHD) and even some forms of **cancer**.

Balanced Diet

An Unhealthy Diet Can Increase the Risk of Coronary Heart Disease

Coronary Heart Disease (CHD) is the result of **reduced** blood flow to the heart. It can lead to **chest pain** (angina) and **heart attacks**. It's caused by **atherosclerosis** — the narrowing and hardening of the **coronary arteries** (the blood vessels that supply the heart).

1) A diet **high** in **saturated fat** raises **blood cholesterol** level (see below). This increases the build up of **fatty deposits** in the **arteries** (called atheromas), which **causes atherosclerosis.**
2) A diet **high in salt** can cause **high blood pressure**. This can **damage artery walls**, which **causes atherosclerosis.**

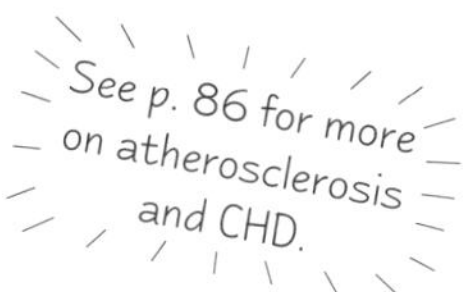
See p. 86 for more on atherosclerosis and CHD.

The Body Regulates Blood Cholesterol Level using HDLs and LDLs

1) **Cholesterol** is a **lipid** made in the body.
2) Some is **needed** for the body to **function normally**.
3) Cholesterol needs to be attached to a **protein** to be moved around, so the body forms **lipoproteins** — substances composed of both **protein** and **lipid**. There are **two types** of lipoprotein:

<u>High density lipoproteins</u> (HDLs) are **mainly protein**. They transport **cholesterol** from **body tissues** to the **liver** where it's **recycled** or **excreted**. Their function is to **reduce blood cholesterol** when the level is **too high**.

<u>Low density lipoproteins</u> (LDLs) are **mainly lipid**. They transport cholesterol from the **liver** to the **blood**, where it circulates until needed by cells. Their function is to **increase blood cholesterol** when the level is **too low**.

4) A diet **high** in **saturated fat raises LDL** level — so more cholesterol is transported **to the blood**, increasing total blood cholesterol and **increasing** the risk of CHD.
5) A diet **high** in **polyunsaturated fat raises HDL** level — so more cholesterol is transported **from the blood** to the liver, decreasing total blood cholesterol and **decreasing** the risk of CHD.

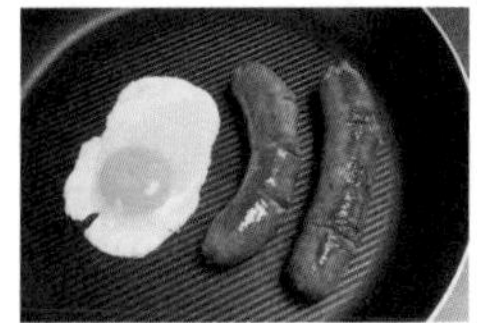
John decided to live on the edge and ordered a fry-up.

Practice Questions

Q1 Briefly describe what is meant by a balanced diet.

Q2 Give three causes of malnutrition.

Q3 Briefly describe how a diet high in salt can increase the risk of CHD.

Q4 Describe the differences between high density lipoproteins and low density lipoproteins.

Exam Questions

Q1 Explain how a diet high in saturated fat can increase the risk of coronary heart disease. [4 marks]

Q2 A patient at risk from CHD had the level of high density lipoproteins (HDLs) in his blood monitored for six months. Over this period the level of HDLs increased from 60 mg/dl to 100 mg/dl.

a) Suggest how the patient's total blood cholesterol level changed over this period. Explain your answer. [2 marks]

b) Suggest how the patient might have changed his diet to try to increase his HDL level. [1 mark]

Healthy food tastes just as good as stuff that's bad for you — yeah right...

I hate cauliflower cheese, it looks like melted brains — but a balanced diet means eating a bit of everything and not too much of anything. So when you've finished feeding your cauliflower cheese to the dog, be sure to cover the page and write out the bit about HDLs and LDLs plenty of times — it's easy to confuse them. In fact, remind me which is which...

Food Production

The ever increasing need for food has been partly met by increasing the productivity of the plants and animals we eat. There are short-term ways to do this (like using pesticides), and long-term ways to do this (like selective breeding).

Humans Ultimately **Depend** on **Plants** for Food

1) Humans **rely on plants** for **food** because plants are at the **start** of **all food chains**.
2) Plants use the **energy from sunlight** to convert **carbon dioxide** and **water** into **complex organic compounds** (such as carbohydrates).
3) **Humans**, and other **animals**, eat, digest and absorb the compounds, which they use for energy and to grow.
4) We grow plants for **direct consumption** and to **feed animals**, which we then eat.
5) Many modern farming methods aim to **maximise productivity** by **increasing** plant and animal **growth**.

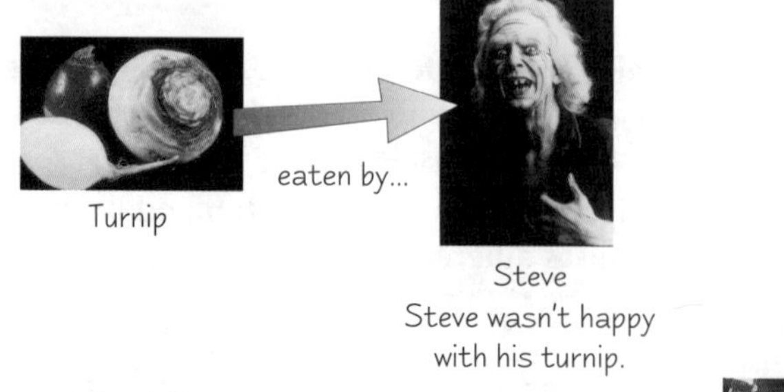

Turnip

Steve

Steve wasn't happy with his turnip.

Carrots

Moose

Helga

Helga's moose mousse went down a treat.

Fertilisers and **Pesticides Increase Food Production**

Fertilisers

1) Fertilisers are **chemicals** that **increase crop yields** by providing **minerals** (such as nitrate, phosphate and potassium) that plants need to grow.
2) Minerals in the soil are **used up** during crop growth. Fertilisers **replace** these minerals, so that a **lack** of minerals doesn't **limit** growth of the next crop.
3) Fertilisers can be **natural** — made by natural processes (e.g. compost and manure), or **artificial** — made by humans.

Pesticides

1) Pesticides are **chemicals** that **increase crop yields** by **killing pests** that feed on the crops. This means **fewer plants** are **damaged** or **destroyed**.
2) Pests include microorganisms, insects or mammals (e.g. rats).
3) Pesticides may be **specific** and kill only **one** pest species, or **broad**, and kill a **range** of different species — this could mean that some **non-pest species** are also harmed.

Animals Can be Given **Antibiotics** to **Increase Food Production**

1) Animals farmed for food are sometimes given **antibiotics** — chemicals that **kill** or **inhibit** the growth of **bacteria**.
2) Antibiotics help to treat or prevent **diseases** caused by bacteria.
3) Animals normally **use energy** fighting diseases, which reduces the amount of energy available for **growth**. Giving them antibiotics means animals can use **more energy** to grow, **increasing food production**.
4) Antibiotics also help to **promote** the growth of animals.
5) This is thought to be because the antibiotics **influence bacteria** in the animals' gut, allowing the animals to **digest** food **more efficiently**.
6) This can increase both the **growth rate** of the animal and its **size** when mature.

Food Production

Selective Breeding Increases Crop Yields...

1) Selective breeding involves **selecting** plants with **good characteristics** (e.g. high yield, disease resistance or pest resistance) to **reproduce** together in order to **increase productivity**.
2) Here's an example of how it's done:

    1) Select plants with **good characteristics** that will increase **crop yield**, e.g. a **tall** corn plant and a corn plant that produces **multiple ears**. Breed them **together**.
    2) Select the **offspring** with the best characteristics, e.g. tallest with the most ears, and breed them **together**.
    3) **Continue** this over **several generations** until a high-yielding plant is produced, e.g. **very tall** with **multiple ears** of corn.

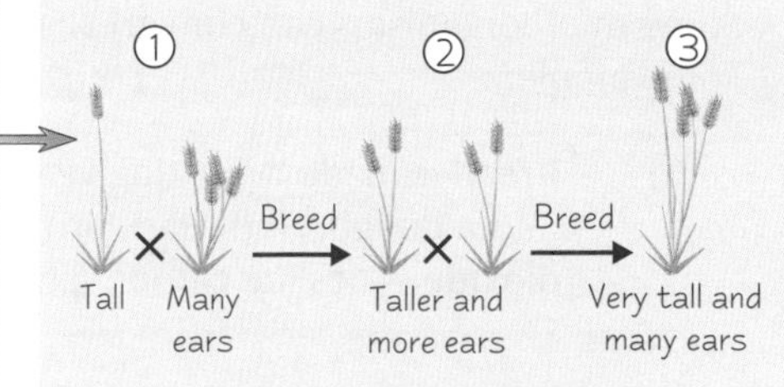

3) Selective breeding is carried out in the same way to produce plants that are **resistant to disease or pests**.

    1) Plants showing a high level of **resistance** are **bred together**.
    2) The offspring that show **most resistance** are then bred together.
    3) This continues over **several generations** to produce a crop that is disease or pest resistant.

...and the Productivity of Animals

Selective breeding can also be used to **increase** the **productivity of animals**. Useful characteristics such as **fast growth rate** and **high meat**, **milk** or **egg yields** can be developed. For example:

1) Select animals with **good characteristics** that will increase meat yield, e.g. the **largest** cows and bulls. Breed them **together**.
2) Select the **offspring** with the best characteristics, e.g. largest, and breed them **together**.
3) **Continue** this over **several generations** until cows with very high meat yields are produced, e.g. **very large cows**.

Daisy was a big cow, just like her mum — though she hadn't seen her around for a while...

Practice Questions

Q1 What type of organism is the basis of all food chains?

Q2 Briefly explain how fertilisers can increase crop yields.

Q3 Briefly explain how using antibiotics increases meat productivity.

Exam Question

Q1 Wheat is an important food crop that has been grown by farmers for over 5000 years.
Modern wheat plants have much larger grains than the wheat plants that were grown 5000 years ago.

a) Explain how selective breeding has led to wheat plants with larger grains than earlier wheat plants. [3 marks]

b) The Hessian fly is a pest of wheat crops. Describe how Hessian fly infestation would affect the wheat crop yield and suggest both a short-term and a long-term solution to the infestation. [3 marks]

Better food productivity — I'm over the moooooon...

Back in the olden days the steaks weren't as fat or the potatoes so appetising... the grass was less green too. After all this talk of food you'll need a snack — go get one and have a break. I'm having one, so you better too. Aaah, tea...

Microorganisms and Food

The waste products of some microorganisms can be harmful and contaminate food. Other microorganisms can be useful for food production though — cheese tastes delicious until you remember it's really mouldy milk.

Microorganisms can be used to *Make Food*

Microorganisms such as **bacteria**, **yeast** and other **fungi** are used in the production of many foods and drinks. Some microorganisms can **convert sugar** into other substances that humans can then use for **food production**. For example:

1) **Bread** is made by mixing **yeast** (a fungus), **sugar**, **flour** and **water** into a dough. The yeast turn the sugar into **ethanol** and **carbon dioxide** — it's the carbon dioxide that makes the bread **rise**.

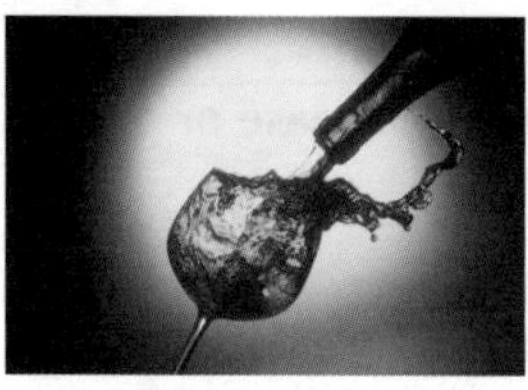

2) **Wine** is made by adding **yeast** to **grape juice**. The yeast turn the sugar in the grape juice into **ethanol** (alcohol) and **carbon dioxide**.

3) **Cheese** is made by adding **bacteria** to milk. The bacteria turn the sugar in the milk into **lactic acid**, which causes the milk to **curdle**. An enzyme is then used to turn the curdled milk into **curds** and **whey**. The curds are separated off and left to **ripen** into **cheese**. Nice.

4) **Yoghurt** is also made by adding bacteria to milk. The bacteria turn the sugar in the milk into **lactic acid**, causing the milk to **clot** and **thicken** into yoghurt.

Using Microorganisms *to* Make Food *has* Advantages...

1) Populations of microorganisms **grow rapidly** under the right **conditions**, so food can be produced **quickly**.
2) Microorganisms can **grow** on a **range** of **inexpensive** materials.
3) Their environment can be **artificially controlled** — so you can potentially **grow food anywhere** and at **any time of the year**.
4) Conditions for growth are **easy to create**.
5) Some of the food made using microorganisms often **lasts longer** in **storage** than the raw product they're made from, e.g. **cheese** can be stored for longer than **milk**.

...and Disadvantages

Being served microorganisms for tea pushed Geoff over the edge.

1) There's a **high risk** of **food contamination**. The conditions created to grow the **desirable** microorganisms are also favourable to **harmful** microorganisms. They could cause the foods produced to **spoil** (go off), or if eaten, cause illnesses such as **food poisoning**.
2) The conditions required to grow microorganisms can be simple to create, but **small changes** in temperature or pH can **easily kill** the microorganisms.

Microorganisms and Food

Food Spoilage by Microorganisms can be *Prevented*

Food spoilage can be caused by the **growth** of **unwanted microorganisms** — as the organisms grow they break down the food, **contaminating** it with **waste products**. **Preventing** food spoilage involves either **killing** the microorganisms or **depriving** the microorganisms of the conditions they need to grow — this either **slows down** or **stops** their growth.

1) Salting prevents microorganisms taking in water...

Salting is simply **adding salt** to foods. Salt **inhibits the growth** of microorganisms by interfering with their ability to **absorb water** (which they need to survive). Some **meats** are preserved by salting, and **tinned foods** are often preserved in **brine** (a mixture of salt and water).

2) ...adding sugar can have the same effect.

Adding **sugar** also **inhibits the growth** of microorganisms by interfering with their ability to **absorb water**. For example, the high sugar content of **fruit jams** reduces the growth of microorganisms, giving the jam a **long shelf life**.

3) Freezing slows the growth of microorganisms.

Freezers keep foods below –18 °C. This **slows down reactions** taking place in microorganisms and **freezes the water** in the food, so the microorganisms **can't** use it. Freezing can preserve foods for **many months**.

4) Pickling in acidic vinegar inhibits the growth of microorganisms.

Vinegar has a **low pH**, which reduces **enzyme activity** (see p. 68) in microorganisms. This means they can't function properly, **inhibiting their growth**. Vinegar is used to **pickle** foods like onions.

5) Heat treatment kills microorganisms...

Heat treatment involves heating food to a **high temperature**, which **kills** any microorganisms present. **Pasteurisation** is one form of heat treatment — it involves raising **liquids** such as **milk** to a high temperature.

6) ...and so does irradiation.

Irradiation involves exposing foods to **radiation**, e.g. **X-rays** or **gamma rays**. This treatment **kills** any microorganisms present and can **extend shelf life** considerably.

Practice Questions

Q1 Name three foods made using microorganisms.

Q2 Describe two disadvantages of using microorganisms in food production.

Q3 Describe how pickling preserves food.

Exam Question

Q1 Mycoprotein is a protein-rich food produced from an edible fungus. The fungus is grown in an environment where conditions are carefully controlled. It's then heat-treated before being processed into the final product.

a) Explain why the mycoprotein is heat-treated. [2 marks]

b) Suggest three advantages of producing protein-rich foods from fungi compared to producing protein-rich foods from cows. [3 marks]

Hmm — I believe I'll have the irradiated beef with the pickled sprouts...

Ye scurvy dogs! You see, pirates didn't just eat salted pork because they liked the taste — they knew a thing or two about food spoilage. Pity they couldn't say the same about the whole fresh fruit/scurvy/nice teeth thing. Learn the six ways of preventing food spoilage and you'll find your way to a great chest of treasure. Well, quite a few marks anyway...

Infectious Disease

Health can be affected by loads of things, especially infection with microorganisms...

Disease can be **Caused** by **Different Things**

1) In the exam you could be asked to **discuss** what **health** and **disease** mean. So here goes...
   - **Health** is a **state** of **physical**, **mental** and **social well-being**, which includes the **absence** of **disease** and **infirmity** (weakness of body or mind).
   - **Disease** is a **condition** that **impairs** the **normal functioning** of an **organism**.
2) A disease can be caused by **infection** with **pathogens** or **parasites**. You also need to be able to discuss what the terms pathogen and parasite mean, which is a little trickier:
   - A **pathogen** is an organism that can cause **damage** to the organism it **infects** (the host).
   - A **parasite** is an organism that **lives on** or **in** another organism (the host) and causes **damage** to that organism.

   A pathogen and a parasite are actually the **same** thing, but traditionally people tend to call **bacteria**, **fungi** and **viruses** pathogens, and things like **tapeworms**, **roundworms** and **fleas** parasites.
3) Diseases can also be **caused** by **genetic defects**, **nutritional deficiencies** and **environmental factors** (e.g. toxic chemicals). **Infectious diseases** are diseases that can be **passed between individuals**, e.g. malaria, HIV and TB.

Malaria is Caused by the **Parasite Plasmodium**

1) ***Plasmodium*** is a **eukaryotic**, **single-celled parasite**.
2) It's **transmitted** by **mosquitoes** — **insects** that **feed** on the **blood** of **animals**, including **humans**.
3) The mosquitoes are **vectors** — they **don't** cause the disease themselves, but they **spread** the infection by **transferring** the parasite from one host to another.
4) Mosquitoes **transfer** the *Plasmodium* parasite into an animal's blood when they **feed** on them.
5) *Plasmodium* infects the **liver** and **red blood cells**, and **disrupts** the **blood supply** to vital organs.

AIDS is Caused by the **HIV Virus**

1) The **human immunodeficiency virus** (**HIV**) infects human white blood cells.
2) HIV (and all other viruses) can only **reproduce inside** the **cells** of the organism it has infected because it doesn't have the equipment (such as enzymes and ribosomes) to replicate on its own.
3) After the virus has reproduced, it **kills** the **white blood cells** as it **leaves**.
4) HIV infection leads to **acquired immune deficiency syndrome** (**AIDS**).
5) AIDS is a condition where the **immune system deteriorates** and eventually **fails** due to the loss of white blood cells. It makes the sufferer more **vulnerable** to **other infections**, like pneumonia.
6) HIV is **transmitted** in **three** main ways:

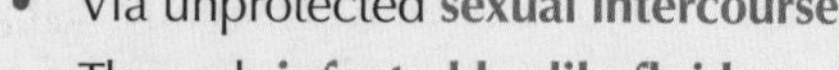

- Via unprotected **sexual intercourse**.
- Through **infected bodily fluids** (like blood), e.g. **sharing needles**, **blood transfusions**.
- From **mother to fetus** (through the placenta, breast milk or during childbirth).

Tuberculosis (TB) is Caused by a **Bacterium**

1) **Tuberculosis** (TB) is a **lung disease caused** by the **bacterium *Mycobacterium tuberculosis***.
2) TB spreads by '**droplet infection**' — when an infected person **coughs** or **sneezes**, **tiny droplets** of **saliva** and **mucus** containing the bacteria are released from their mouth and nose. These droplets are then **breathed** in by other people.
3) Many people with tuberculosis are infected but **don't show** any symptoms. But if they become **weakened**, e.g. by another disease or malnutrition, then the infection can become **active**. They'll show the symptoms and be able to pass on the infection.

Infectious Disease

Malaria, AIDS/HIV and TB Have a Global Impact

1) **Malaria**, **HIV** and **TB** are most **common** in **sub-Saharan Africa** and other **developing countries**. This is because:

- There's **limited access** to good **healthcare** — **drugs** are **not** always **available**, people are **less likely** to be **diagnosed** and **treated**, **blood donations** aren't always **screened** for infectious diseases and **surgical equipment** isn't always **sterile**.
- There's **limited health education** to inform people how to **avoid infectious diseases** — e.g. fewer people know about the **transmission** of **HIV** and that it can be **prevented** by **safe-sex** practices, e.g. using condoms.
- There's **limited equipment** to **reduce** the **spread** of infections — e.g. fewer people have **mosquito nets** to reduce the chance of infection with **malaria**.
- There are **overcrowded** conditions — this **increases** the **risk** of **TB infection** by **droplet transmission** (see previous page).

2) The **prevalence** of malaria, HIV and TB in developing countries, like sub-Saharan Africa, **slows** down **social** and **economic development** because these diseases **increase death rates**, **reduce productivity** (fewer people are able to work) and result in **high healthcare costs**.

3) **Studying** the **global distribution** of these diseases is **important** for many reasons:

- The information can be used to find out **where** people are most **at risk**.
- Any data collected can be used to **predict** where **epidemics** are most likely to occur.
- It's important for **research** (e.g. into how it's spread).
- It allows organisations to provide **aid** where it's **needed most**.

Practice Questions

Q1 Explain what is meant by the term health.

Q2 What causes malaria?

Q3 Describe how HIV can be transmitted between individuals.

Exam Questions

Q1 Africa has the highest number of deaths from tuberculosis and the USA has the lowest number of deaths.

a) State what causes tuberculosis and describe how it is transmitted between individuals. [4 marks]

b) Suggest three reasons why more deaths from tuberculosis occur in Africa than in the USA. [3 marks]

c) Suggest two reasons why it is important that other countries study the distribution of tuberculosis. [2 marks]

Q2 AIDS has killed more than 25 million people since it was first recognised in 1981.

a) Name the pathogen that causes AIDS. [1 mark]

b) Describe four ways that the spread of this pathogen can be reduced. [4 marks]

My computer has a virus — I knew I shouldn't have sneezed on it...

Malaria, AIDS and TB aren't the nicest things to learn about, but unfortunately they could pop up in the exam. Even though these diseases aren't that common in the UK (because we have free access to healthcare, good health education, low poverty, good nutrition etc.) they cause many problems in other countries across the world.

The Immune System

Well, all that stuff about disease is making me feel a bit on edge. But your body has some state-of-the-art defences to protect you against pathogens and parasites. First up, the skin and mucus membranes...

The Skin and Mucus Membranes are the Body's Primary Defences...

Your body has a number of **primary defences** that help **prevent pathogens** and **parasites** from **entering** it. These include the **skin** and **mucus membranes**:

SKIN

This acts as a **physical barrier, blocking pathogens** from **entering** the body. It also acts as a **chemical barrier** by producing **chemicals** that are **antimicrobial** and can **lower pH, inhibiting** the **growth** of pathogens.

MUCOUS MEMBRANES

They **protect body openings** that are **exposed** to the **environment** (such as the mouth, nostrils, ears, genitals and anus). Some membranes **secrete mucus** — a sticky substance that **traps pathogens** and contains **antimicrobial enzymes**.

...but if a Pathogen Gets Past Those the Immune System Responds

If a pathogen or parasite gets **past** the **primary defences** and **enters** the body, the **immune system** will respond.

An **immune response** is the body's **reaction** to a **foreign antigen**.

1) **Antigens** are **molecules** (usually proteins or polysaccharides) found on the **surface** of **cells**.
2) When a pathogen (like a bacterium) **invades** the body, the antigens on its cell surface are **identified as foreign**, which **activates** cells in the immune system.

There are Four Main Stages Involved in the Immune Response

1 Phagocytes Engulf Pathogens

A **phagocyte** (e.g. a macrophage) is a type of **white blood cell** that carries out **phagocytosis** (engulfment of pathogens). They're found in the **blood** and in **tissues** and are the **first** cells to **respond** to a pathogen inside the body. Here's how they work:

1) A phagocyte **recognises** the **antigens** on a pathogen.
2) The cytoplasm of the phagocyte moves round the pathogen, **engulfing** it.
3) The pathogen is now contained in a **phagocytic vacuole** (a bubble) in the cytoplasm of the phagocyte.
4) A **lysosome** (an organelle that contains **digestive enzymes**) **fuses** with the phagocytic vacuole. The enzymes **break down** the pathogen.
5) The phagocyte then **presents** the pathogen's antigens. It sticks the antigens on its **surface** to **activate** other immune system cells.

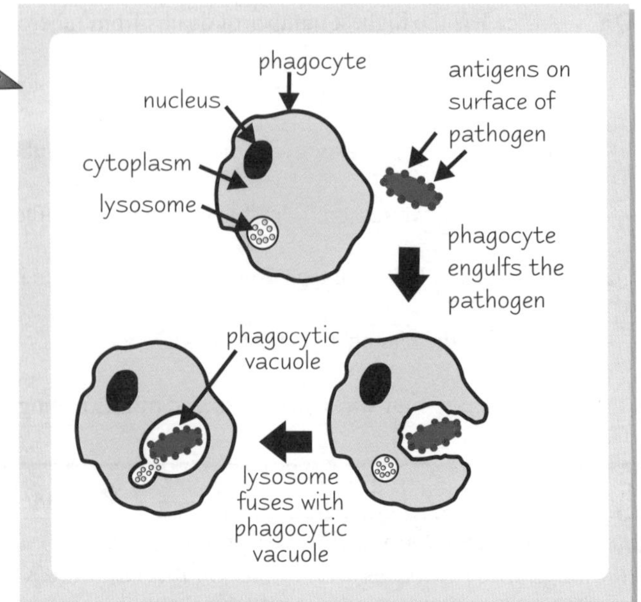

The Immune System

2) Phagocytes **Activate T lymphocytes**

1) A **T lymphocyte** is another type of **white blood cell**.
2) Their surface is covered with **receptors**.
3) The receptors **bind to antigens** presented by the phagocytes.
4) Each T lymphocyte has a **different receptor** on its surface.
5) When the receptor on the surface of a T lymphocyte meets a **complementary antigen**, it binds to it — so each T lymphocyte will bind to a **different antigen**.
6) This **activates** the T lymphocyte — it **divides** and **differentiates** into **different types** of T lymphocytes that carry out **different functions**:

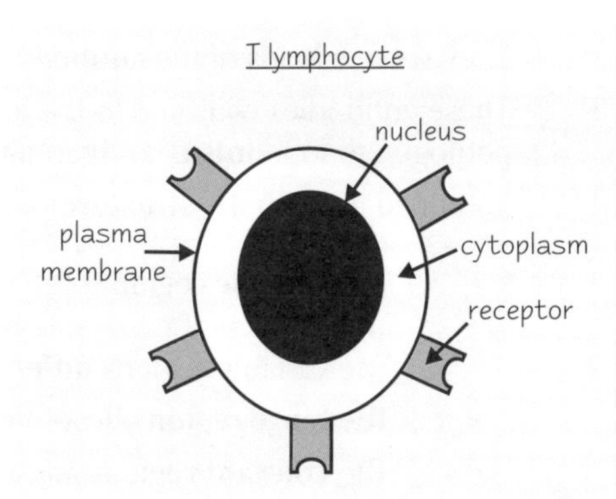

1) Some activated T lymphocytes **release substances** to **activate B lymphocytes** (see below).
2) Some **attach** to antigens on a pathogen and **kill** the cell.
3) Some become **memory cells** (see next page).

3) T lymphocytes **Activate B lymphocytes**, Which Divide Into **Plasma Cells**

1) **B lymphocytes** are another type of **white blood cell**.
2) They're covered with proteins called **antibodies**.
3) Antibodies **bind to antigens** to form an **antigen-antibody complex**.
4) Each B lymphocyte has a **different shaped antibody** on its surface.
5) When the antibody on the surface of a B lymphocyte meets a **complementary shaped antigen**, it binds to it — so each B lymphocyte will bind to a **different antigen**.
6) This, together with substances **released** from the T lymphocyte, **activates** the B lymphocyte.
7) The activated B lymphocyte **divides**, by mitosis, into **plasma cells** and **memory cells** (see next page).

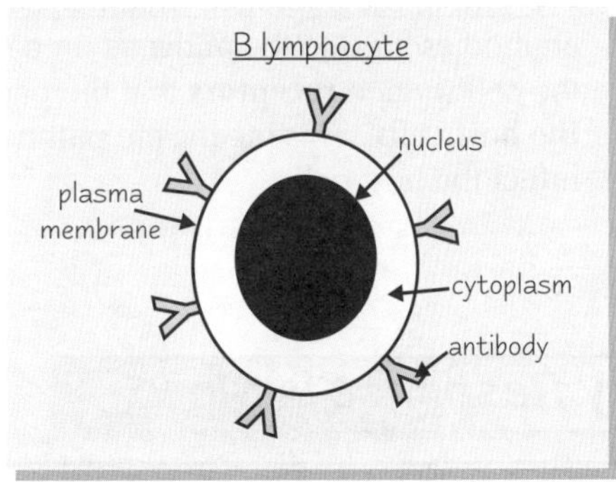

Cell Signalling

1) Cell signalling is basically how **cells communicate**.
2) A cell may **release** (or present) a **substance** that **binds to** the **receptors** on **another cell** — this causes a **response** of some kind in the other cell.
3) Cell signalling is really important in the **immune response** because it helps to **activate** all the **different types** of **white blood cells** that are needed.
4) For example, **T lymphocytes** release substances that bind to receptors on **B lymphocytes**. This **activates** the B lymphocytes — the T lymphocytes are signalling to the B lymphocytes that there's a pathogen in the body.

See p. 14 for more on cell signalling.

The Immune System

4 Plasma Cells Make More Antibodies to a Specific Antigen

1) Plasma cells are **clones** of the B lymphocyte (they're **identical** to the B lymphocyte).
2) They secrete **loads** of the **antibody**, specific to the antigen, into the blood.
3) These antibodies will bind to the antigens on the surface of the pathogen to form **lots** of **antigen-antibody complexes**.
4) You need to **learn** the **structure** of antibodies:

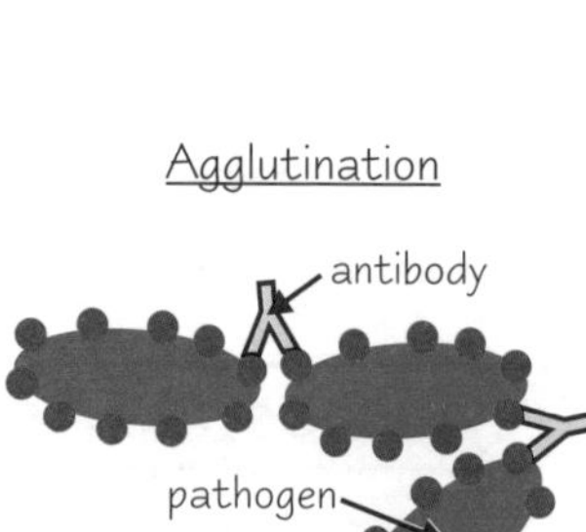

- The **variable regions** of the antibody form the **antigen binding sites**. The **shape** of the variable region is **complementary** to a particular antigen. The variable regions **differ** between antibodies.
- The **hinge region** allows **flexibility** when the antibody binds to the antigen.
- The **constant regions** allow binding to **receptors** on **immune system cells**, e.g. phagocytes. The constant region is the **same in all** antibodies.
- **Disulfide bridges** (a type of bond) hold the polypeptide chains together.

5) Antibodies **help** to **clear** an **infection** by:

1) **Agglutinating pathogens** — each antibody has **two binding sites**, so an antibody can **bind** to **two pathogens** at the **same time** — the pathogens become **clumped together**. Phagocytes then bind to the antibodies and phagocytose a lot of pathogens **all at once**.
2) **Neutralising toxins** — antibodies can **bind** to the **toxins** produced by pathogens. This **prevents** the toxins from **affecting human cells**, so the toxins are **neutralised** (inactivated). The toxin-antibody complexes are also phagocytosed.
3) **Preventing the pathogen binding to human cells** — when antibodies bind to the antigens on pathogens, they may **block** the cell surface **receptors** that the pathogens need to **bind to the host cells**. This means the pathogen **can't attach to** or **infect** the host cells.

Agglutination

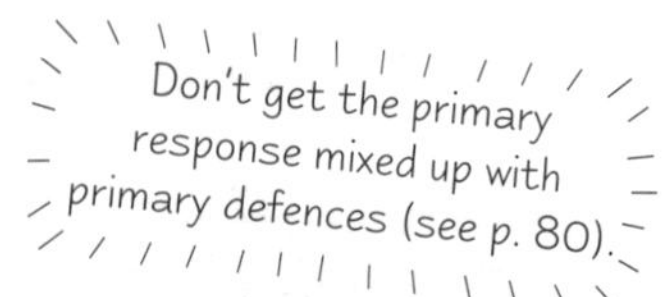

The Primary Response is Slow...

1) When a **pathogen** enters the body for the **first time** the **antigens** on its surface **activate** the **immune system**. This is called the **primary response**.
2) The primary response is **slow** because there **aren't many B lymphocytes** that can make the antibody needed to bind to it.
3) Eventually the body will produce **enough** of the right antibody to overcome the infection. Meanwhile the infected person will show **symptoms** of the disease.
4) After being exposed to an antigen, both T and B lymphocytes produce **memory cells**. These memory cells **remain in the body** for a **long** time. Memory T lymphocytes remember the **specific antigen** and will recognise it a second time round. Memory B lymphocytes record the specific **antibodies** needed to bind to the antigen.
5) The person is now **immune** — their immune system has the **ability** to respond **quickly** to a second infection.

Don't get the primary response mixed up with primary defences (see p. 80).

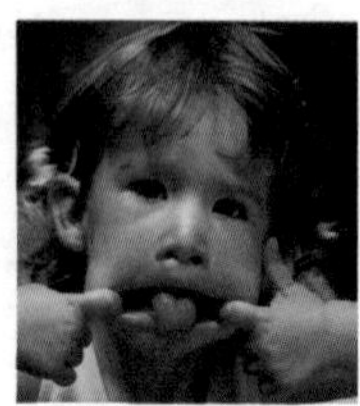

Neil's primary response — to his parents.

The Immune System

...the Secondary Response is Faster

1) If the **same pathogen** enters the body again, the immune system will produce a **quicker, stronger** immune response — the **secondary response**.
2) **Memory B lymphocytes** divide into **plasma cells** that produce the right antibody to the antigen. **Memory T lymphocytes** divide into the **correct type** of **T lymphocytes** to kill the cell carrying the antigen.
3) The secondary response often gets rid of the pathogen **before** you begin to show any **symptoms**.

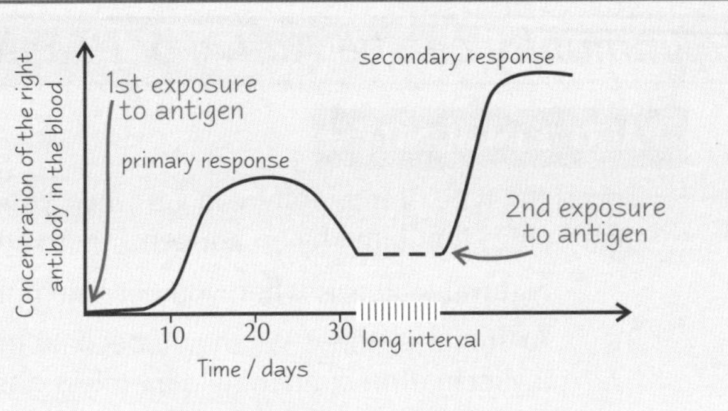

In the exam you might be asked to **compare** and **contrast** the primary and secondary immune response — basically say how they're **similar** and say how they're **different**. These are summarised in the table below:

	Primary response	Secondary response
Pathogen	Enters for 1st time	Enters for 2nd time
Speed of response	Slow	Fast
Cells activated	B and T lymphocytes	Memory cells
Symptoms	Yes	No

Practice Questions

Q1 Name two primary defences against pathogens and parasites.

Q2 Define the term immune response.

Q3 What are antigens?

Q4 What structures are found on the surface of T lymphocytes?

Q5 Draw and label the structure of a B lymphocyte.

Q6 Draw and label the structure of an antibody.

Q7 Give two differences between the primary and secondary response.

These questions cover pages 80-83.

Exam Questions

Q1 Describe how a phagocyte responds to an invading pathogen. [6 marks]

Q2 Describe the function of antibodies. [3 marks]

Q3 Emily had chickenpox as a child. She was exposed to the virus that causes it as a teenager but did not experience any symptoms. Explain why. [10 marks]

The student-revision complex — only present the night before an exam...

Memory cells are still B and T lymphocytes, but they're the ones that stick around for a long time. So if a pathogen is stupid enough to invade the body again, these cells can immediately divide into more of themselves, and release antibodies specifically against the pathogen or bind to the pathogen and destroy it. Ha ha (evil laugh).

Immunity and Vaccinations

The primary response gives you immunity against a disease, but only after you've gotten ill. If only there was a way to stimulate memory cell production without getting the disease... Well, there is — vaccination.

Immunity can be Active or Passive

ACTIVE IMMUNITY

This is the type of immunity you get when **your immune system makes its own antibodies** after being **stimulated** by an **antigen**. There are **two** different types of active immunity:

1) **Natural** — this is when you become immune after **catching a disease**.
2) **Artificial** — this is when you become immune after you've been given a **vaccination** containing a harmless dose of antigen (see below).

PASSIVE IMMUNITY

This is the type of immunity you get from being **given antibodies made by a different organism** — your immune system **doesn't** produce any antibodies of its own. Again, there are **two** types:

1) **Natural** — this is when a **baby** becomes immune due to the antibodies it receives from its **mother**, through the **placenta** and in **breast milk**.
2) **Artificial** — this is when you become immune after being **injected** with **antibodies** from **someone else**. E.g. If you contract tetanus you can be injected with antibodies against the tetanus toxin, collected from blood donations.

In the exam you might be asked to **compare** and **contrast** these types of immunity:

Active immunity	Passive immunity
Exposure to antigen	No exposure to antigen
It takes a while for protection to develop	Protection is immediate
Protection is long-term	Protection is short-term
Memory cells are produced	Memory cells aren't produced

Vaccines Help to Control Disease

1) While your B lymphocytes are busy **dividing** to build up their numbers to deal with a pathogen (i.e. the **primary response** — see p. 82), you **suffer** from the disease. **Vaccination** can help avoid this.
2) Vaccines **contain antigens** that cause your body to **produce memory cells** against a particular pathogen, **without** the pathogen **causing disease**. This means you become **immune** without getting any **symptoms**... genius.
3) If most people in a **community** are **vaccinated**, the disease becomes extremely **rare**. This means that even people who haven't been vaccinated are **unlikely** to get the disease, because there's no one to catch it from. This is called **herd immunity**.
4) Vaccines always contain antigens — these may be **free** or attached to a **dead** or **attenuated** (weakened) **pathogen**.
5) Vaccines may be **injected** or taken **orally**. The **disadvantages** of taking a vaccine orally are that it could be **broken down** by **enzymes** in the gut or the **molecules** of the vaccine may be **too large** to be **absorbed** into the blood.
6) Sometimes **booster** vaccines are given later on (e.g. after several years) to **make sure** that memory cells are produced.

Paul couldn't understand why his herd immunity wasn't working...

Immunity and Vaccinations

New Influenza Vaccines Have to be Developed Every Year

1) The **influenza virus** causes **influenza** (flu).
2) **Proteins** (**neuraminidase** and **haemagglutinin**) on the **surface** of the influenza virus act as **antigens**, **triggering** the immune system.
3) These antigens can **change regularly**, forming **new strains** of the virus.
4) **Memory cells** produced from **vaccination** with **one strain** of flu will **not recognise** other strains with **different antigens**.
5) Every year there are **different strains** of the influenza virus **circulating** in the **population**, so a **different vaccine** has to be made.
6) **Laboratories** collect **samples** of these different strains, and organisations, such as the **WHO** (World Health Organisation) and **CDC** (Centre for Disease Control), **test** the **effectiveness** of different influenza **vaccines** against them.
7) **New vaccines** are **developed** and one is chosen **every year** that is the **most effective** against the **recently** circulating influenza viruses.
8) Governments and health authorities then implement a **programme** of **vaccination** using this most **suitable** vaccine. This is a good example of how society uses science to inform **decision making**.

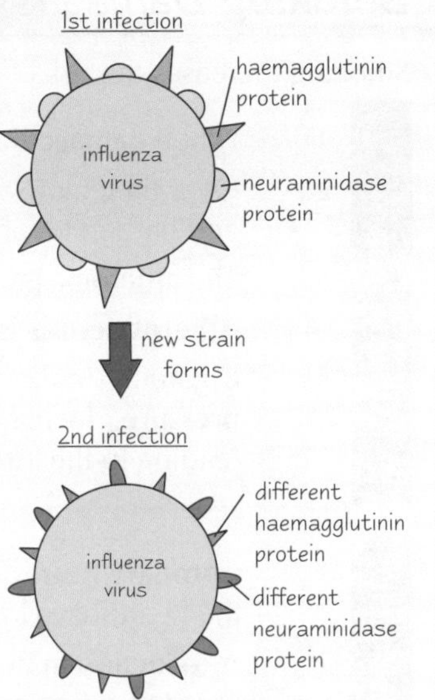

Possible Sources of Medicines Need to be Protected

1) Many **medicinal drugs** are manufactured **using natural compounds** found in **plants, animals** or **microorganisms.** E.g. **penicillin** is obtained from a **fungus**, some **cancer drugs** are made using **soil bacteria**, and **daffodils** are now grown to produce a drug used to treat **Alzheimer's disease**.
2) Only a **small proportion** of organisms have been **investigated** so far, so it's possible that plants or microorganisms **exist** that contain compounds that could be used to treat **currently incurable** diseases, such as AIDS.
3) Possible **sources of drugs** need to be **protected** by **maintaining** the **biodiversity** (the variety of different species) on Earth. If we **don't** protect them, some species could **die** out before we get a **chance** to study them.
4) Even organisms that have **already** been studied could still prove to be **useful** sources of medicines as **new techniques** are developed for identifying, purifying and testing compounds.

Practice Questions

Q1 What is the difference between active and passive immunity?

Q2 Explain the difference between natural passive immunity and artificial passive immunity.

Q3 Give two advantages of vaccination.

Q4 Why is protecting biodiversity important for the development of new medicines?

Exam Question

Q1 Influenza is caused by a virus that constantly changes its antigens.

a) Explain why a new influenza vaccine is made every year. [3 marks]

b) Describe how new influenza vaccines are chosen every year. [3 marks]

An injection of dead bugs — roll on my next vaccine...

The influenza virus is so clever that it would almost make you think it had a mind of its own. I mean, as soon as we catch up with it and develop a vaccine, off it goes and changes its surface antigens again. Influenza virus: one, humans: nil. This is one of the ways viruses have evolved to avoid your immune system. Well, clever them.

Smoking and Disease

Don't worry I won't lecture you about smoking, but you do need to know how it affects a person's health for the exam...

Smoking Damages the Cardiovascular System...

Smoking increases the risk of **atherosclerosis**, **coronary heart disease** (CHD) and **stroke**:

Atherosclerosis

1) When **damage** occurs to the **lining** of an **artery**, **white blood cells** move into the area.
2) Over time **more** white blood cells, **lipids** and **connective tissue** build up and harden to form a **fibrous plaque** at the site of damage — an **atheroma**.
3) The atheroma partially **blocks** the **lumen** of the artery and **restricts blood flow**.
4) **Atherosclerosis** is the **hardening** of **arteries** due to the formation of **atheromas**.
5) Cigarette smoke contains **nicotine**, which causes an **increase** in **blood pressure**. Increased blood pressure can cause **damage** to the arteries, leading to the formation of more **atheromas**.

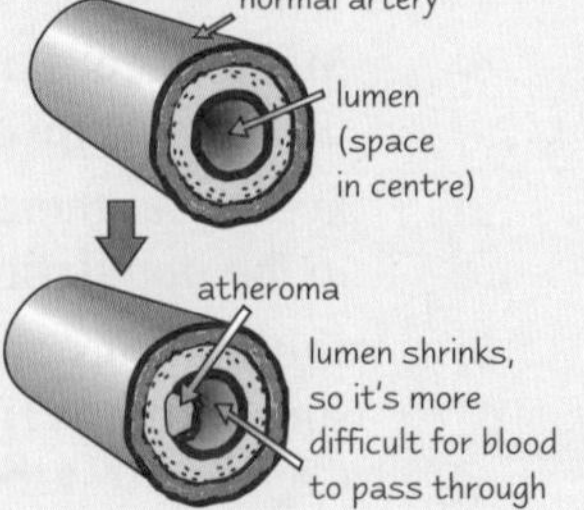

Coronary Heart Disease (CHD)

1) **Coronary heart disease** is when the **coronary arteries** (arteries that supply blood to the heart) have lots of **atheromas** in them. This **restricts blood flow** to the **heart**.
2) A reduction in blood flow **reduces** the amount of **oxygen** an area of the heart gets. This can cause **pain** (**angina**) or a **heart attack**.
3) Smoking **increases** the **risk** of CHD because **carbon monoxide** irreversibly combines with **haemoglobin**, **reducing** the amount of **oxygen** transported in the blood, which reduces the amount of oxygen available to tissues, including the **heart**.
4) Also, **nicotine** in cigarette smoke makes **platelets** (cells involved in blood clotting) **sticky**, increasing the chance of **blood clots forming**. If clotting happens in the **coronary arteries** it could cause a **heart attack**.
5) The presence of **atheromas** also increases the risk of **blood clots forming** (and smoking increases atheroma formation — see above).

CHD is a type of cardiovascular disease.

Stroke

1) A **stroke** is a **rapid loss** of **brain function** due to a **disruption** in the **blood supply** to the **brain**.
2) This can be caused by a **blood clot** in an **artery** leading to the brain, which **reduces** the amount of blood, and therefore **oxygen**, that can reach the brain.
3) Nicotine **increases** the risk of stroke because it increases the risk of **clots forming** (see above).
4) Carbon monoxide also **increases** the **risk** of stroke because it **reduces** the amount of oxygen available to the brain by combining with haemoglobin (see above).

...and the Gas Exchange System

Lung Cancer

1) Cigarette smoke contains many **carcinogens** (chemicals that can cause a cell to become cancerous).
2) These carcinogens may cause mutations in the **DNA** of **lung cells**, which could lead to **uncontrolled cell growth** and the **formation** of a **malignant** (cancerous) **tumour**.
3) Malignant tumours **grow uncontrollably**, **blocking air flow** to areas of the lung.
4) This **decreases gas exchange** and leads to a **shortness of breath** because the body is struggling to take in **enough oxygen**.
5) The tumour uses **lots** of **nutrients** and **energy** to grow, which causes **weight loss**.

Chronic Bronchitis

1) Chronic bronchitis is **inflammation** of the lungs.
2) The upper respiratory tract is lined with **goblet cells** that produce **mucus to trap microorganisms**. The tract is also lined with **cilia** that **'beat'** to move the mucus towards the **throat** so it can be **removed**.
3) Cigarette smoke **damages** the **cilia** and causes the goblet cells to produce **more mucus**.
4) The mucus **accumulates** in the lungs, which causes **increased coughing** to try and remove the mucus.
5) **Microorganisms multiply** in the mucus and cause **lung infections** that lead to **inflammation**, which **decreases gas exchange**.
6) Chronic bronchitis is a type of **chronic obstructive pulmonary disease** (COPD). COPD is a group of diseases that involve permanent airflow reduction.

Smoking and Disease

Emphysema

Emphysema is also a type of COPD.

1) Emphysema is a lung disease caused by **smoking** or long-term exposure to **air pollution** — foreign particles in the smoke (or air) become **trapped** in the alveoli.
2) This causes **inflammation**, which encourages **phagocytes** to the area. The phagocytes produce an **enzyme** that breaks down **elastin** (an elastic protein found in the **walls** of the **alveoli**).
3) The alveolar walls are **destroyed** and the **elasticity** of the lungs is **lost**.
4) This **reduces** the **surface area** of the alveoli, so the **rate** of **gaseous exchange decreases**.
5) Symptoms of emphysema include **shortness of breath** and **wheezing**. People with emphysema have an **increased breathing rate** as they try to increase the amount of air (containing oxygen) reaching their lungs.

You Might Have to ***Evaluate Evidence Linking Smoking*** *to* ***Disease*** *or* ***Death***

Here's an **example** of the kind of thing you might get:

The graph shows the results of a study involving **34 439 male British doctors**. **Questionnaires** were used to find out the smoking habits of the doctors. The number of **deaths** among the participants from ischaemic heart disease (coronary heart disease) was counted, and **adjustments** were made to account for **differences in age**.

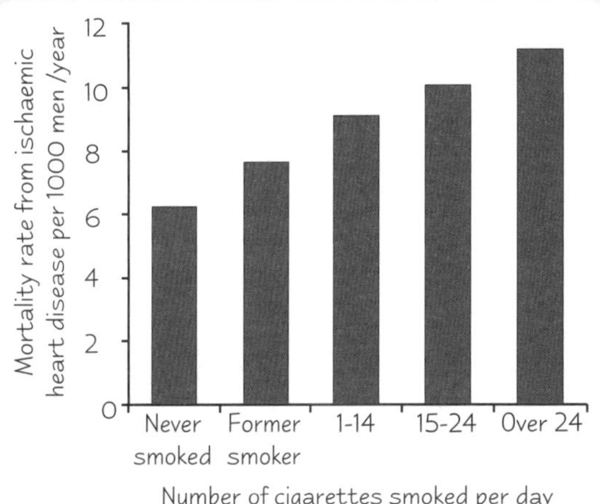

1) The graph shows that the **number** of deaths from ischaemic heart disease **increased** as the number of cigarettes smoked per day **increased. Fewer former smokers** and **non-smokers** died of ischaemic heart disease than smokers.
2) So you can conclude that there's a **positive correlation** between the number of cigarettes smoked per day by **male doctors** and the **mortality rate** from ischaemic heart disease. You **can't** say that smoking more **causes** an increased risk of dying from ischaemic heart disease though. There could be **other factors** causing the pattern, e.g. heavier smokers may **drink more alcohol** and it could be the alcohol (not smoking) that increases the risk of heart disease.
3) You might have to evaluate the study — you basically need to think about how the study **method could affect the results**. For example:
   - A **large sample size** was used — 34 439. The **bigger** the sample size the **more reliable** the results.
   - People (even doctors) can tell **porkies** on **questionnaires**, reducing the **reliability** of results.
   - The study **only** used doctors — this could have swayed the results. Doctor's might be more likely to **avoid** the other risk factors associated with cardiovascular disease (e.g. alcohol, poor diet) and so this might **bias** the data.
   - All the participants have the same job but they **weren't matched** otherwise, e.g. they might not be the same weight, or they might do different amounts of exercise a week, etc. This could have affected the results. Just like in an experiment you need to **control** as many **variables** as possible.

Practice Question

Q1 Explain how nicotine increases the risk of atheromas forming.

Exam Question

Q1 Smoking can damage the mammalian gas exchange system, causing emphysema and lung cancer. Explain how smoking can lead to each of these diseases and explain the symptoms they produce. [12 marks]

Smoky bacon — so it's okay for pigs to smoke then?

Whatever your views on smoking, you need to be objective when looking at study data. For the exam you need to make sure you can explain how smoking affects the lungs and how nicotine and carbon monoxide muck up the heart.

Studying Biodiversity

Bet you've noticed how there are loads of different living things in the world — well that's biodiversity in a nutshell.

Biodiversity is the Variety of Organisms

Before you can sink your teeth into the real meat of biodiversity, there are a few definitions you need to know:

1) **Biodiversity** — the **variety** of **living organisms** in an **area**.
2) **Species** — a group of **similar organisms** able to **reproduce** to give **fertile offspring**.
3) **Habitat** — the **area inhabited** by a species. It includes the **physical** factors, like the soil and temperature range, and the **living** (biotic) factors, like availability of food or the presence of predators.

Areas with a **high** biodiversity are those with lots of **different species**.

Pete wasn't sure that the company's new increased biodiversity policy would be good for productivity.

Biodiversity Can be Considered at Different Levels

1) **Habitat diversity** — the number of **different habitats** in an **area**. For example, a coastal area could contain many different habitats — beaches, sand dunes, mudflats, salt marshes etc.
2) **Species diversity** — the number of **different species** and the **abundance** of each species in an **area**. For example, a woodland could contain many different species of plants, insects, birds and mammals.
3) **Genetic diversity** — the variation of **alleles** within a species (or a population of a species). For example, human blood type is determined by a gene with four different alleles.

Alleles are different versions of genes.

Sampling Can be Used to Measure Biodiversity

In most cases it'd be **too time-consuming** to count every individual organism in a habitat. Instead, a **sample** of the population is taken. **Estimates** about the whole habitat are based on the sample. Here's what sampling involves:

1) **Choose** an **area** to **sample** — a small area within the habitat being studied.
2) **Count** the number of individuals of **each species**. How you do this depends on **what** you're counting, for example:
   - For plants you'd use a **quadrat** (a frame which you place on the ground).
   - For flying insects you'd use a **sweepnet** (a net on a pole).
   - For ground insects you'd use a **pitfall trap** (a small pit that insects can't get out of).
   - For aquatic animals you'd use a **net**.
3) **Repeat** the process — take as many samples as possible. This gives a better indication of the **whole habitat**.
4) Use the results to **estimate** the total number of individuals or the total number of different species in the habitat being studied.
5) When sampling **different habitats** and comparing them, always use the **same sampling technique**.

Even when randomly selecting samples, you still need to do as many repeats as possible.

The Sample Has to be Random

To avoid **bias** in your results, the sample should be random. For example:

If you were looking at plant species in a field you could pick random sample sites by dividing the field into a **grid** and using a **random number generator** to select coordinates.

Studying Biodiversity

Species Richness and Species Evenness Affect Biodiversity

The **greater** the **species richness** and **species evenness** in an area, the **higher** the biodiversity.

1) **Species richness** is the number of **different species** in an area. The **higher** the number of species, the **greater** the species richness. It's measured by taking random samples of a habitat (see previous page) and counting the number of different species.

2) **Species evenness** is a measure of the **relative abundance** of **each species** in an area. The **more similar** the **population size** of each species, the **greater** the species evenness. It's measured by taking random samples of a habitat, and counting the **number of individuals** of each different species.

Example Habitat X and habitat Y both contain **two different species** and **30 individual organisms**.

	Habitat X	Habitat Y
species 1	28	15
species 2	2	15
total	30	30

- **Species richness** in the two habitats is the **same — 2.**
- In **habitat Y** the individual organisms are **more evenly distributed** between the different species — it has **greater species evenness.**

Diversity is Measured using Simpson's Index of Diversity

1) Species present in a habitat in very **small** numbers shouldn't be treated the same as those with **bigger** populations.
2) **Simpson's Index of Diversity** takes into account both **species richness** and **species evenness**.
3) Simpson's Index of Diversity (**D**) can be calculated using this formula.
4) Simpson's Index of Diversity is always a value **between 0 and 1**. The **closer to 1** the index is, the **more diverse** the habitat. The greater the species richness and evenness, the higher the number.

$$D = 1 - \left(\sum \left(\frac{n}{N}\right)^2\right)$$

n = **Total number** of individuals of **one** species

N = **Total number** of organisms of **all** species

Σ = **'Sum of'** (i.e. added together)

Here's a simple example of the index of diversity in a field:

There are 3 different species of flower in this field — a red species, a white and a blue. There are 11 organisms altogether, so N = 11. There are 3 of the red species, 5 of the white and 3 of the blue. So the index of diversity for this field is:

$$D = 1 - \left(\left(\frac{3}{11}\right)^2 + \left(\frac{5}{11}\right)^2 + \left(\frac{3}{11}\right)^2\right) = 1 - 0.36 = 0.64$$

The field has an index of diversity of 0.64, which is fairly high.

You need to work out the $(n/N)^2$ bit for each different species then add them all together.

Practice Questions

Q1 What is meant by habitat diversity, species diversity and genetic diversity?

Q2 Why is it important that samples of a habitat are taken at random?

Exam Question

Q1 A group of students is investigating the diversity of millipedes (small ground insects) in a habitat. They want to find out the species richness and species evenness in the area.

a) Describe what is meant by species richness and species evenness. [2 marks]

b) Describe how the students could measure species evenness in the habitat. [4 marks]

Species richness — goldfish and money spiders top the list...

OK, so this isn't exactly the easiest of things to get your head around — I thought ecology was meant to be straightforward. Make sure you know the definitions of species richness and species evenness and can describe how you'd measure them. As for Simpson's Index of Diversity — well, sometimes I wish I was still a fresh-faced sixth-former, but this sure ain't one of them.

Global Biodiversity

One of the problems with this biodiversity lark is that it's really difficult to measure on a global scale — even top scientists can't seem to agree. One thing they do agree on is that climate change is affecting biodiversity...

Current Estimates *of* Global Biodiversity Vary

Global biodiversity is the **total number** of species on Earth. This includes:

1) **Named species** — scientists have named between 1.5 and 1.75 million species. This figure isn't exact because there's no central database of all species and some scientists have **different opinions** about the classification of certain species.
2) **Unnamed species** — scientists agree that a large proportion of the species on Earth **have not been named** — many species are **undiscovered**, or are known but haven't yet been named.

This strange-looking two-headed dog is among those not yet named.

Scientists **estimate** that the **total number** of species on Earth ranges from about 5 million to 100 million. Some of the most recent estimates are around 14 million. There are lots of reasons why scientists have such different ideas:

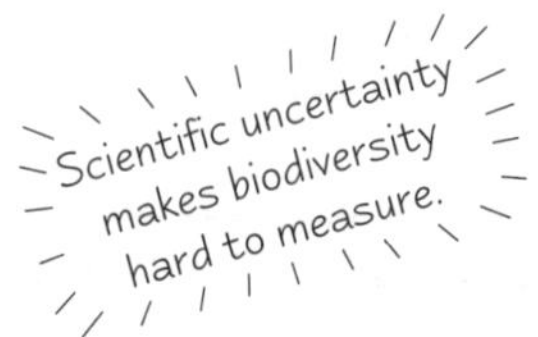

1) **Different scientists** have used **different techniques** to make their estimates.
2) Relatively **little is known** about some **groups** of organisms (e.g. bacteria and insects) — there could be **many more** than we think.
3) Biodiversity varies in **different parts** of the world — the greatest diversity is near the **equator** and it **decreases** towards the **poles**. Tropical rainforests are **largely unexplored** — this might mean current estimates of global biodiversity are **too low**.

Estimates of global biodiversity **change** as scientists find out new things — this is an example of the **tentative nature** of scientific knowledge.

Climate Change *Affects* Biodiversity*...*

1) **Climate change** is the **variation** in the Earth's climate, e.g. things like changes in **temperature** and **rainfall patterns**.
2) It occurs **naturally**, but the **scientific consensus** is that the climate change we're **experiencing at the moment** is **caused** by **humans** increasing emissions of **greenhouse gases** (such as **carbon dioxide**).
3) Greenhouse gases cause **global warming** (**increasing global average temperature**), which causes **other types** of climate change, e.g. changing rainfall patterns.
4) Climate change will affect **different areas** of the world in **different ways** — some places will get **warmer**, some **colder**, some **wetter** and others **drier**. All of these are likely to **affect global biodiversity**:

- Most species need a particular **climate** to survive.
- A change in climate may mean that an area that was previously **inhabitable** becomes **uninhabitable** (and **vice versa**).
- This may cause an **increase** or **decrease** in the **range** of some species (the area in which they live). This could increase or decrease biodiversity.
- Some species may be forced to **migrate** to a more suitable area, causing a change in **species distribution**. Migrations usually **decrease** biodiversity in the areas the species migrate from, and **increase** biodiversity in the areas they migrate to.
- If there isn't a suitable habitat to migrate to, the species is a plant and **can't migrate**, or if the change is **too fast**, the species may become **extinct**. This will **decrease** biodiversity.

Range change example

The southern **range** limit of the **Sooty Copper Butterfly** has **moved** 60 miles north in recent decades.

Extinction example

Corals die if water temperature **changes** by just one or two degrees. In 1998 a coral reef near Panama was badly damaged because the water **temperature** had **increased** — at least one species of coral became **extinct** as a result.

Global Biodiversity

...the Spread of Disease...

Changing climate may also contribute to the **spread of disease**, for example:

1) The **ranges** of some **insects** that **carry disease** might become **greater**. E.g. as areas become **warmer** and **wetter** insects like mosquitoes, which can carry **malaria**, will spread into areas that were **previously uninhabitable**, **bringing the disease** with them. This change in distribution could lead to an increase in biodiversity, though the **spread of diseases** could **reduce biodiversity** — with some species suffering population decline, or even extinction.
2) Warmer and wetter conditions may also encourage the spread of **fungal diseases**. This could also lead to an increase or decrease in biodiversity.

...and Agricultural Patterns

Changes in **temperature**, **rainfall**, the **timing of the seasons**, and the **frequency of flood** and **drought** will affect **patterns of agriculture**. This may also affect biodiversity:

1) Land that was **previously unsuitable** becomes **available** for agriculture — areas of that were previously too hot or too dry to support much biodiversity can be farmed, **increasing** the biodiversity in an area.
2) **Different crops** need **different conditions** so, as the climate in an area changes, so will the **crops grown**. This could **disrupt food chains** — some **existing species** will be left **without** a source of food, and new food sources will be provided for **other species**. This could **increase** or **decrease** biodiversity in an area.
3) **Extreme weather events** and **unexpected conditions**, such as a **flood** or a **drought** or a change in the **timing of the seasons**, might result in **crop failure**. This could **disrupt food chains** and **decrease biodiversity**.

Practice Questions

Q1 Suggest two reasons why estimates of global biodiversity vary so widely.

Q2 Explain how changing patterns of agriculture might affect biodiversity.

Exam Question

Q1 The Living Planet Index measures trends in the Earth's biodiversity. It is calculated using population data from over 1000 species. The graph below shows how the Living Planet Index changed between 1970 and 2000.

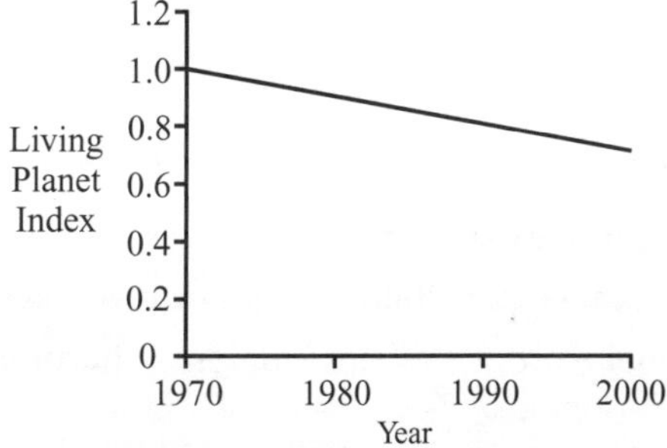

a) Suggest why the Living Planet Index does not use population data from all the species on Earth. [1 mark]

b) Describe the pattern shown on the graph. [1 mark]

c) Describe how climate change during the last 30 years could have decreased global biodiversity. [5 marks]

Mosquitoes — coming soon to a climate near you...

All of this makes the future look a bit bleak — plagues of mosquitoes in places they never used to be, half the country underwater and loads of different species dying out — I bet you thought this section was going to be all about fluffy animals. Now you know why biodiversity's at risk, it's time to take a look at why it's so important and worth saving...

Importance of Biodiversity

You're probably wondering what all this fuss about biodiversity is for. Well, biodiversity provides us with the means to make nice clothes and good food, so it's a pretty good idea not to reduce it.

Maintaining Biodiversity is Important for Economic Reasons...

Many species of animals and plants are important to the **global economy**. Products derived from plant and animal species are traded on a local and global scale. They include things like...

1) **Food** and **drink** — plants and animals are the source of almost all **food** and some **drinks**.
2) **Clothing** — a lot of **fibres** and **fabrics** are made from plants and animals (e.g. cotton from plants and leather from animals).
3) **Drugs** — many are made from compounds from plants (e.g. the painkiller **morphine** is made from **poppies**).
4) **Fuels** — we use a number of organisms to produce **renewable** fuels, including ethanol and biogas. Fossil fuels are **non-renewable** (they'll run out), so other sources are of **major economic importance**.
5) **Other industrial materials** — a huge variety of other materials are produced from plant and animal species, including **wood**, **paper**, **dyes**, **adhesives**, **oils**, **rubber** and chemicals such as **pesticides**.

It's important to conserve all the organisms we currently use to make products, as well as those we **don't currently use** — they may provide us with **new products** in the **future**, e.g. new drugs for diseases we can't yet cure.

...Ecological Reasons...

The ecological reasons for maintaining biodiversity are all down to the **complex relationships** between **organisms** and their **environments**. The loss of **just one species** can have pretty **drastic effects**, for example:

1) **Disruption** of **food chains**, e.g. some species of bear feed on salmon, which feed on herring. If the number of herring decline it can affect **both** the salmon and the bear populations.
2) **Disruption** of **nutrient cycles**, e.g. decomposers like worms improve the **quality of soil** by recycling nutrients. If worm numbers decline, soil quality will be affected. This will affect the **growth** of plants and the **amount of food** available to animals.
3) **Loss** of **habitats**, e.g. hedgerows are **wildlife corridors** — they enable organisms to move between different habitats **safely**. If they're removed species can become **isolated** and availability of **food** and **nesting sites** for many species will be **reduced**.
4) **Habitat destruction** can also affect **climate**, e.g. CO_2 is stored in trees and bogs — the destruction of forests and peat bogs is contributing to **climate change** (see p. 90).

All these ecological reasons also have knock-on economic effects.

...Ethical Reasons...

Some people believe that we should conserve species simply because it's the **right thing to do**.

1) Many believe organisms have a **right to exist** — they shouldn't become **extinct** as a result of our activities.
2) Some people believe we have a **moral responsibility** to conserve biodiversity for **future** human generations.
3) There are also **religious** and **spiritual** reasons for conservation — **harmony** with the **natural world** is important to many beliefs and philosophies.

...and Aesthetic Reasons

Others believe we should conserve biodiversity because it brings **joy** to millions of people.

1) Areas **rich** in biodiversity provide a pleasant, **attractive environment** that people can enjoy.
2) The more biodiversity in an area the more **visitors** the area is likely to **attract** — this also has economic advantages.

Importance of Biodiversity

Maintaining Biodiversity *is Important to* ***Agriculture***

In addition to all those economic, ecological, ethical and aesthetic reasons you now know all about, maintaining the biodiversity of wild plants and animals has some **benefits** for **agriculture**.

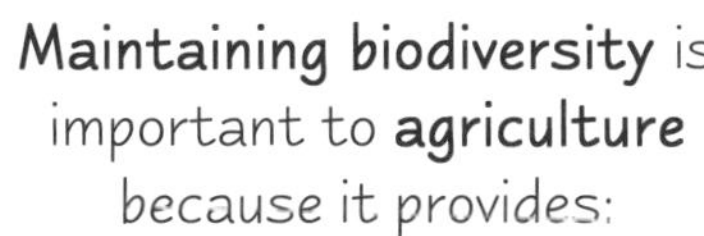

Pollinators

Many fruit and vegetable crops are **pollinated by insects** such as bees and butterflies. The higher the diversity of insects the more pollinators there are.

Protection against disasters

The majority of our food comes from **only a few species** of plants — if a disease or pest affects these few, our food supply is **at risk**. E.g. in 1845 **only two** varieties of potato were planted in Ireland. A **disease** destroyed both types of potato crop, causing **famine**. The **more** crop varieties that are used, the less chance there is that **all** the crops will be destroyed.

A source of food

Many **species** are used as **food sources** for humans and livestock. The more different species there are the more possible sources there are to **choose from**.

New varieties

Plant varieties are needed for **cross-breeding**. Wild plants can be bred with domesticated plants to produce **new varieties** with **improved characteristics**, e.g. increased disease resistance or faster growth. New varieties of crops can also be **bred** to cope with **climate change**. The more varieties of crop there are the **more characteristics** there are **to choose from**.

Pest control

A number of animals like frogs, birds and hedgehogs are **natural predators** of crop pests like slugs. The more of these organisms there are the **less pests** there will be.

Some of the wild breeds aren't too important for agriculture.

Practice Questions

Q1 Suggest why maintaining biodiversity of plants is important to the drugs industry.

Q2 Give an economic reason for the conservation of biodiversity.

Q3 Give an ethical reason for the conservation of biodiversity.

Q4 Give an aesthetic reason for the conservation of biodiversity.

Q5 Suggest two characteristics that could be improved by cross-breeding domesticated plants with wild varieties.

Exam Questions

Q1 Explain why decreasing biodiversity could have adverse ecological implications. [4 marks]

Q2 Briefly explain why maintaining biodiversity is important to the agricultural industry. [5 marks]

Hippy or not — better start hugging those trees...

So, it turns out biodiversity is pretty important. Without it, not only would your life lack its little luxuries, like toilet paper with aloe vera, and fancy designer clothes, just surviving would be tricky — there'd be nothing to eat and fewer drugs to treat you when you're ill. Make sure you learn all the reasons for maintaining biodiversity — they might just crop up in the exam.

Conservation and Biodiversity

I'm sure no animals like being snatched from the African plains and taken to live in a safari park in Kidderminster, but sometimes they just don't know what's best for them...

In Situ Conservation Keeps Species in Their **Natural Habitat**

In situ conservation means **on site** — it involves protecting species in their **natural habitat**. Conservation is important to **ensure the survival** of **endangered species** — species which are at risk of **extinction** because of a **low** population, or a **threatened habitat**. Methods of *in situ* conservation include:

1) Establishing **protected areas** such as **national parks** and **nature reserves** — habitats and species are protected in these areas by **restricting urban development, industrial development** and **farming**.
2) **Controlling** or **preventing the introduction** of species that **threaten** local biodiversity. For example, grey squirrels are not native to Britain. They **compete** with the native red squirrel and have caused a population **decline**. So they're controlled in some areas.
3) **Protecting habitats** — e.g. controlling water levels to conserve wetlands and coppicing (trimming trees) to conserve woodlands. This allows organisms to **continue living** in their **natural habitat**.
4) **Restoring damaged areas** — such as a coastline polluted by an oil spill.
5) **Promoting** particular species — this could be by protecting **food sources** or **nesting sites**.
6) Giving **legal protection** to **endangered species**, e.g. making it illegal to kill them (see next page).

Jim reckoned he'd seen the last of those red squirrels — but he hadn't counted on their friends turning up.

The advantage of *in situ* conservation is that often both the **species** and their **habitat** are conserved. **Larger populations** can be protected and it's **less disruptive** than removing organisms from their habitats. The chances of the population **recovering** are **greater** than with ***ex situ* methods** (see below). But, it can be **difficult to control** some factors that are **threatening** a species (such as poaching, predators or climate change).

Ex Situ Conservation Removes Species from Their **Natural Habitat**

Ex situ conservation means **off site** — it involves protecting a species by **removing** part of the population from a **threatened habitat** and placing it in a **new location**. *Ex situ* conservation is often a **last resort**.
Methods of *ex situ* conservation include:

1) **Relocating** an organism to a **safer area**, e.g. five white rhinos were recently relocated from the Congo to Kenya because they were in danger from **poachers** who kill them for their ivory.
2) **Breeding** organisms in **captivity** then **reintroducing** them to the wild when they are **strong enough**, e.g. sea eagles have been reintroduced to Britain through a captive breeding programme. Breeding is carried out in **animal sanctuaries** and **zoos**.
3) **Botanic gardens** are controlled environments used to grow a variety of **rare** plants for the purposes of **conservation, research, display** and **education**. **Endangered** plant species as well as species that are **extinct in the wild** can be grown and **reintroduced** into suitable habitats.
4) **Seed banks** — seeds can be frozen and stored in seed banks for over a century without losing their **fertility**. Seed banks provide a useful source of seeds if **natural reserves** are **destroyed**, for example by **disease** or other **natural disasters**.

The advantages of *ex situ* conservation are that it can be used to protect individual animals in a **controlled environment** — things like predation and hunting can be managed more easily. It can also be used to **reintroduce** species that have **left an area**. But, there are disadvantages — usually only a **small number** of individuals can be cared for. It can be **difficult** and **expensive** to create and **sustain** the **right environment**. *Ex situ* conservation is usually **less successful** than *in situ* methods — many species can't **breed successfully** in captivity, or don't **adapt** to their new environment when moved to a new location.

Conservation and Biodiversity

International Cooperation is Important in Species Conservation

Information about **threats** to biodiversity needs to be **shared** and countries need to decide on **conservation methods** and **implement them together**. Here are a couple of examples of successful international cooperation:

Rio Convention on Biodiversity

1) It aims to **develop international strategies** on the conservation of biodiversity and how to use animal and plant resources in a **sustainable** way.
2) The convention made it part of **international law** that conserving biodiversity is **everyone's responsibility**.
3) It also provides **guidance** to governments on how to conserve biodiversity.

CITES Agreement

1) CITES (**Convention** on **International Trade** in **Endangered Species**) is an agreement designed to increase **international cooperation** in **regulating trade** in wild animal and plant specimens.
2) The member countries all agreed to make it **illegal** to **kill** endangered species.
3) The agreement helps to **conserve** species by **limiting** trade through **licensing**, and by making it **illegal** to trade in products made from endangered animals (such as rhino ivory and leopard skins).
4) It's also designed to **raise awareness** of threats to biodiversity through **education**.

International cooperation is really **important** — it'd be pointless making hunting endangered species illegal in one country if poachers could just go and hunt them in another country.

Environmental Impact Assessments are Used to Inform Planning Decisions

An **Environmental Impact Assessment** (**EIA**) is an assessment of the **impact** a development project (such as building a new shopping centre or power station) might have on the environment. It involves:

1) **Estimating** biodiversity on the project site and **evaluating** how the development might **affect** biodiversity.
2) **Identifying** ways that biodiversity could be **conserved**.
3) Identifying threatened or **endangered species** on the project site and the **laws** relating to their conservation.
4) Deciding on **planning stipulations** — measures that will have to be implemented if the project proceeds, e.g. **relocating** or **protecting** endangered species.

Local authorities are often under pressure from **conservationists** who argue that developments **damage** the environment and **disturb** wildlife — they feel that habitats should be **left alone**.

Environmental impact assessments ensure that **decision makers** consider the **environmental impact** of development projects — they're used by local authorities to decide **if** and **how** projects will proceed.

Practice Questions

Q1 Describe how botanic gardens and seed banks help in the conservation of biodiversity.

Q2 What is CITES and how does it help to conserve endangered species?

Q3 Explain what environmental impact assessments are and describe how they are used.

Exam Question

Q1 The hawksbill turtle is an endangered species of sea turtle threatened by hunting and loss of nesting sites. They have slow reproductive, growth and development rates and their numbers are in rapid decline.

a) Suggest how the hawksbill turtle could be conserved by *in situ* and *ex situ* conservation methods. [5 marks]

b) Describe the disadvantages of using *ex situ* conservation methods. [4 marks]

c) Suggest why international cooperation is important to the conservation of the hawksbill turtle. [1 mark]

The path of true conservation ne'er did run smooth...

I'm sure the animals being forcibly removed from their homes are just as bemused as you are right now but I'm afraid it's another case of having to learn the facts. Plain and simple. Don't be put off by things like 'in' or 'ex' situ — that's just a way of saying 'on' or 'off' site that makes people feel clever when they say them. In fact, I'm feeling rather clever right now.

Classification Basics

For hundreds of years people have been putting organisms into groups to make it easier to recognise and name them. For example, my brother is a member of the species Idioto bigearian (Latin for idiots with big ears).

Classification is All About Grouping Together Similar Organisms

Classification is the act of **arranging organisms** into **groups** based on their **similarities** and **differences**. This makes it **easier** for scientists to **identify** them and to **study** them. **Taxonomy** is the **study** of classification. There are a few different classification systems in use, but they all involve placing organisms into groups in a **taxonomic hierarchy**:

1) There are **eight levels** of groups (called taxonomic groups) used in classification.
2) **Similar organisms** are first sorted into one of **three** very **large groups** called **domains**, e.g. animals, plants and fungi are in the Eukarya domain.
3) **Similar organisms** are then sorted into **slightly smaller groups** called **kingdoms**, e.g. all animals are in the animal kingdom.
4) **Similar** organisms from that kingdom are then grouped into a **phylum**. **Similar** organisms from each phylum are then grouped into a **class**, and **so on** down the eight levels of the taxonomic hierarchy.

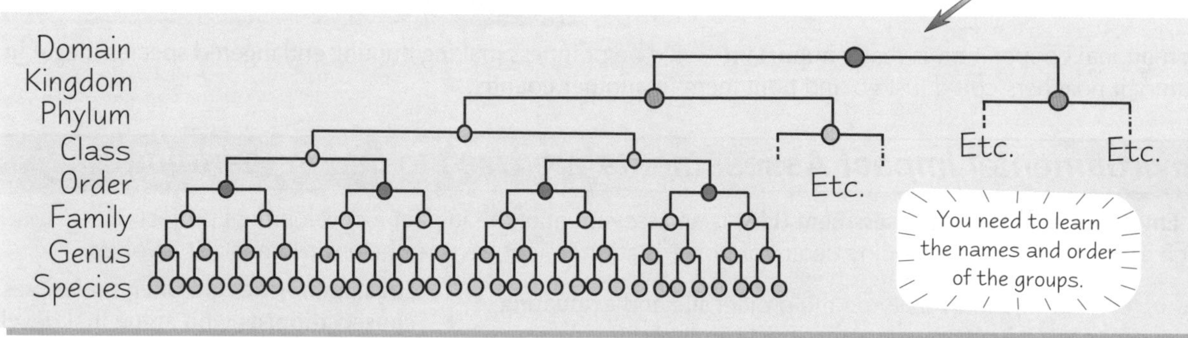

5) As you move **down** the hierarchy, there are **more groups** at each level but **fewer organisms** in each group.
6) The hierarchy **ends** with **species** — the groups that contain only **one type** of organism (e.g. humans, dog, *E. coli* and about 50 million other living species).

Organisms Can be Placed into One of Five Kingdoms

You need to **know** these five kingdoms and the **general characteristics** of the organisms in each of them:

KINGDOM	EXAMPLES	FEATURES
Prokaryotae (Monera)	bacteria	prokaryotic, unicellular (single-celled), no nucleus, less than 5 μm
Protoctista	algae, protozoa	eukaryotic cells, usually live in water, single-celled or simple multicellular organisms
Fungi	moulds, yeasts, mushrooms	eukaryotic, chitin cell wall, saprotrophic (absorb substances from dead or decaying organisms)
Plantae	mosses, ferns, flowering plants	eukaryotic, multicellular, cell walls made of cellulose, can photosynthesise, contain chlorophyll, autotrophic (produce their own food)
Animalia	nematodes (roundworms), molluscs, insects, fish, reptiles, birds, mammals	eukaryotic, multicellular, no cell walls, heterotrophic (consume plants and animals)

Classification Basics

*The **Binomial Naming System** is Used in **Classification***

1) The **nomenclature** (**naming system**) used for classification is called the **binomial system** — all organisms are given **one** internationally accepted scientific **name** in **Latin** that has **two parts**.
2) The **first part** of the name is the **genus** name and has a capital letter. The **second part** is the **species** name and begins with a lower case letter. E.g. using the binomial system humans are ***Homo sapiens***. Names are always written in ***italics*** (or they're **underlined** if they're **handwritten**).
3) The binomial system helps to avoid the **confusion** of using **common names**. E.g. over 100 different plant species are called **raspberries** and one species of buttercup has over 90 different common names.

***Phylogeny** Tells Us About the **Evolutionary History** of Organisms*

1) **Phylogeny** is the study of the **evolutionary history** of groups of **organisms**.
2) All organisms have **evolved** from shared common ancestors (**relatives**). E.g. members of the Hominidae family (great apes and humans) evolved from a common ancestor. First orangutans **diverged** (evolved to become a **different species**) from this common ancestor. Next gorillas diverged, then humans, closely followed by bonobos and chimpanzees.
3) Phylogeny tells us **who's related** to whom and how **closely related** they are.
4) Closely related species **diverged** away from each other **most recently**. E.g. the phylogenetic tree opposite shows the **Hominidae tree**. Humans and **chimpanzees** are **closely** related, as they diverged very **recently**. You can see this because their branches are **close** together. Humans and orangutans are more **distantly** related, as they diverged longer ago, so their branches are **further** apart.

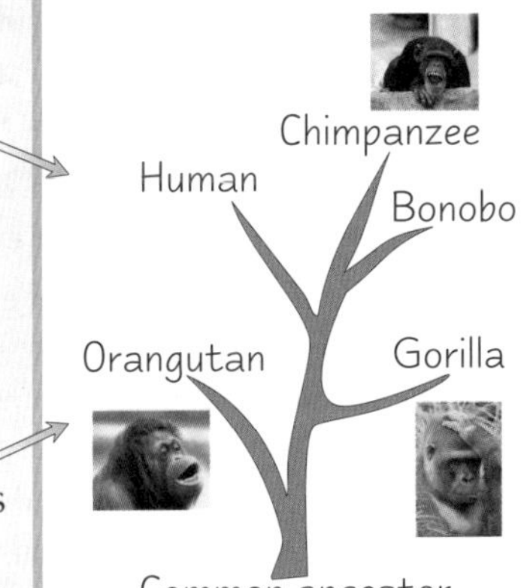

Classification systems now take into account **phylogeny** when arranging organisms into **groups**.

Practice Questions

Q1 List the taxonomic hierarchy in order, starting with the largest groups.

Q2 List two features of the kingdom Fungi.

Q3 List two features of the kingdom Animalia.

Exam Questions

Q1 Define the following terms:
a) classification [1 mark]
b) taxonomy [1 mark]
c) phylogeny [1 mark]

Q2 Describe the binomial system of naming organisms. [3 marks]

Snozcumber kingdom features — long, thin, green, filled with snot...

Make sure that you really understand all the basics on these pages before delving any deeper into this section. Remembering the order of the groups in the taxonomic hierarchy is about as easy as licking your elbow... try making up a mnemonic to help (like 'Dopey King Prawns Can't Order Fried Green Sausages' for Domain, Kingdom, Phylum, Class, Order, Family, etc.).

Evolution of Classification Systems

Classification systems and the groups organisms are placed in aren't set in stone. New technology and new evidence can lead to changes in these systems and the reclassification of organisms.

Classification Systems are now Based on a Range of Evidence

1) Early classification systems **only** used **observable features** (things you can see) to place organisms into groups, e.g. whether they lay eggs, can fly or can cook a mean chilli...
2) But this method has **problems**. Scientists don't always agree on the **relative importance** of different features and groups based **solely** on **physical features** may not show how **related** organisms are.

For example, **sharks** and **whales look** quite similar and they both **live** in the **sea**. But they're **not** actually closely related.

3) Classification systems are **now** based on observable features **along** with **other evidence**.
4) The **more similar** organisms are, the **more related** they are. We now use a wide range of evidence to see **how similar**, and therefore how related, organisms are. For example:

   1) **Molecular evidence** — the similarities in **proteins** and **DNA**. **More closely related** organisms will have **more similar** molecules. You can **compare** things like how **DNA** is **stored**, the **sequence** of DNA **bases** (see page 62) and the **sequence** of **amino acids** in **proteins** from different organisms. E.g. the **base sequence** for human and chimpanzee **DNA** is about 94% the **same**.
   2) **Embryological evidence** — the similarities in the **early stages** of an organism's **development**.
   3) **Anatomical evidence** — the similarities in **structure** and **function** of different body parts.
   4) **Behavioural evidence** — the similarities in **behaviour** and **social organisation** of organisms.

5) **New technologies** (e.g. new **DNA** techniques, better **microscopes**) can result in **new discoveries** being made.
6) Scientists can share their new discoveries in **meetings** and **scientific journals** (see p. 2). How organisms are **classified** is **continually revised** to take account of any **new findings** that scientists **discover**.

For example, skunks **were** classified in the family **Mustelidae** until **molecular evidence** revealed their **DNA sequence** was significantly different to other members of that family. So they were reclassified into the family **Mephitidae**.

Five Kingdoms Vs Three Domains

The **three domain classification system** shown on page 96 is relatively new, and was suggested because of **new evidence**:

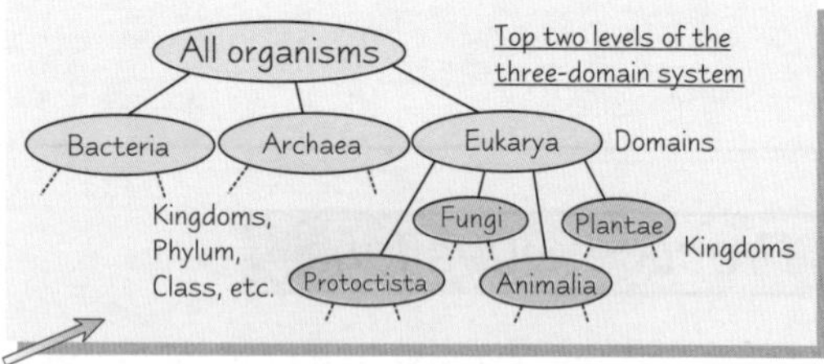

1) In the older **system** the **largest groups** were the **five kingdoms** — all organisms were placed into **one** of these groups.
2) In 1990, the three domain system was proposed. This new system has three domains — **large superkingdoms** that are **above** the kingdoms in the **taxonomic hierarchy** (see p. 96).
3) In the **three domain system**, organisms with cells that **contain a nucleus** are placed in the domain **Eukarya** (this includes four of the five kingdoms). Organisms that were in the kingdom **Prokaryotae** (which contains unicellular organisms **without a nucleus**) are separated into two domains — the **Archaea** and **Bacteria**.
4) The **lower** hierarchy stays the **same** — Kingdom, Phylum, Class, Order, Family, Genus, Species.
5) The three domain system was proposed because of **new evidence**, mainly molecular. E.g. the **Prokaryotae** were **reclassified** into **two domains** because new evidence showed **large differences** between the Archaea and Bacteria. The new evidence included:

   - **Molecular evidence** — The enzyme **RNA polymerase** (needed to make RNA) is **different** in Bacteria and Archaea. **Archaea**, but **not Bacteria**, have similar **histones** (proteins that bind to DNA) to **Eukarya**.
   - **Cell membrane evidence** — The **bonds** of the **lipids** (see p. 58) in the **cell membranes** of Bacteria and Archaea are **different**. The **development** and composition of **flagellae** (see p. 7) are also **different**.

6) Most scientists now **agree** that Archaea and Bacteria **evolved separately** and that Archaea are **more closely related** to Eukarya than Bacteria. The three-domain system reflects how **different** the Archaea and Bacteria are.

Dichotomous Keys

Dichotomous Keys can be used to Identify Organisms

1) **Dichotomous keys** provide a way to **identify organisms** based on **observable features** (e.g. colour, type of leaves).
2) They consist of a **series of questions**, each with **only two** possible answers. Each **answer** leads to the **name** of the organism or **another question**, and so on, until the organism is **identified**.
3) In the **exam** you could be asked to **use** a dichotomous key to **identify** some organisms. For example, the dichotomous key below can be used to identify **seaweeds**:

1.	Is it bright, grassy green?	Yes	Sea lettuce
		No	Go to 2.
2.	Is it reddish brown?	Yes	Irish moss
		No	Go to 3.
3.	Does it have a large, root-like structure?	Yes	Kelp
		No	Go to 4.
4.	Does it have air bladders (pockets of air) in the leaves?	Yes	Bladder wrack
		No	Go to 5.
5.	Is the leaf edge saw-toothed?	Yes	Saw wrack
		No	Go to 6.
6.	Is the leaf rolled in at the edges?	Yes	Channelled wrack
		No	Spiral wrack

Bright, grassy green? Yes. Sea lettuce? Not so sure.

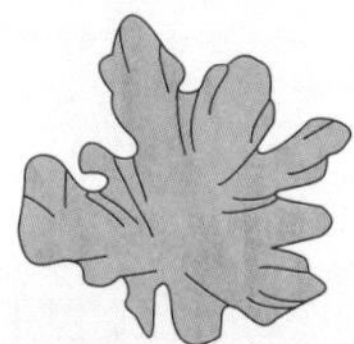

Using the **key** to identify this seaweed, the answer to question 1 is **yes** (it's **bright, grassy green**) — so it's **sea lettuce**.

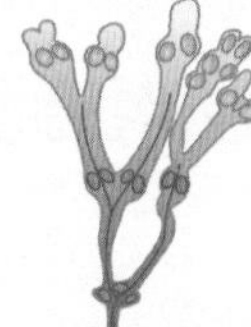

For this seaweed, the answers to questions 1, 2 and 3 are **no**. The answer to question 4 is **yes** (it has **air bladders**) — so it's **bladder wrack**.

Answer 1 is **no**, but answer 2 is yes (it's **reddish brown**) — so it's **Irish moss**.

Answers 1, 2, 3 and 4 are **no**, but 5 is **yes** (it's got **saw-toothed edges**) — so it's **saw wrack**.

Practice Questions

Q1 What evidence were the first classification systems solely based on?

Q2 What is meant by a domain?

Q3 What is a dichotomous key?

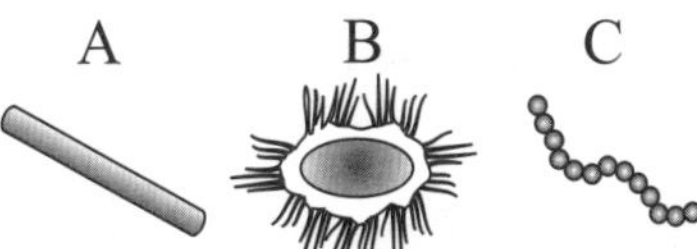

1.	Is it covered with hair-like filaments?	Yes	*Trichodesmium*
		No	Go to 2.
2.	Is it unicellular and oval shaped?	Yes	*Synechococcus*
		No	Go to 2.
3.	Is it unicellular and rod shaped?	Yes	*Lyngbya*
		No	Go to 2.
4.	Is it spiral shaped?	Yes	*Spirulina*
		No	Go to 2.
5.	Is it a long chain of spherical cells?	Yes	*Anabaena*
		No	*Dermocarpa*

Exam Question

Q1 The key above can be used to identify different types of Cyanobacteria (bacteria that can photosynthesise).

a) Use the key to identify the Cyanobacteria labelled A, B and C above. [3 marks]

b) The three domain system of classification places Cyanobacteria in the domain Bacteria. Describe three differences between organisms in the Bacteria and Archaea domains. [3 marks]

Why did the starfish blush? — because the seaweed... (classic)

So there you have it — these four little pages are all you need to learn about classification and identifying organisms. You'll be a bona fide taxonomist before you know it. Taxonomists are great fun — with their crazy little classification systems.

Variation

Ever wondered why no two people are exactly alike? No, well nor have I actually, but it's time to start thinking about it. This variation is partly genetic and partly due to differences in the environment.

Variation Exists Between **All Individuals**

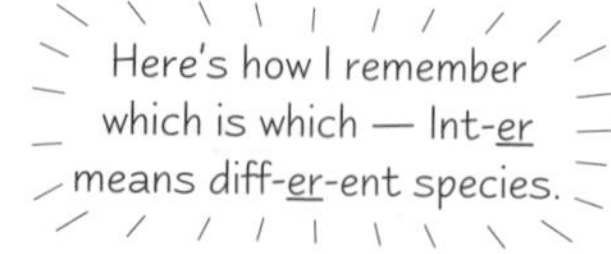

Variation is the **differences** that exist between **individuals**. Every individual organism is **unique** — even **clones** (such as identical twins) show some **variation**. It can occur:

1) **Within species** — Variation within a species is called **intraspecific** variation. For example, **individual** European robins weigh **between** 16 g and 22 g and show some variation in many other characteristics including length, wingspan, colour and beak size.
2) **Between species** — The variation between **different species** is called **interspecific** variation. For example, the **lightest** species of bird is the bee hummingbird, which weighs around 1.6 g on average. The **heaviest** species of bird is the ostrich, which can weigh up to 160 kg (100 000 times as much).

No matter what anyone said, Malcolm knew size was important.

Variation can be **Continuous...**

Continuous variation is when the **individuals** in a population vary **within a range** — there are **no distinct categories**, e.g. **humans** can be **any height** within a range (139 cm, 175 cm, 185.9 cm, etc.), **not just** tall or short. Here are some more examples:

Number of people

Height

The categories are not distinct

Animals

1) **Milk yield** — e.g. cows can produce any volume of milk within a range.
2) **Mass** — e.g. humans can be any mass within a range.

Plants

1) **Number of leaves** — e.g. a tree can have any number of leaves within a range.
2) **Mass** — e.g. the mass of the seeds from a flower head varies within a range.

Microorganisms

1) **Width** — e.g. the width of *E. coli* bacteria varies within a range.
2) **Length** — e.g. the length of the flagellum (see p. 7) can vary within a range.

...or **Discontinuous**

Discontinuous variation is when there are two or more **distinct categories** — each individual falls into **only one** of these categories, there are **no intermediates**. Here are some examples:

Animals

1) **Sex** — e.g. humans can be either male or female.
2) **Blood group** — e.g. humans can be group A, B, AB or O.

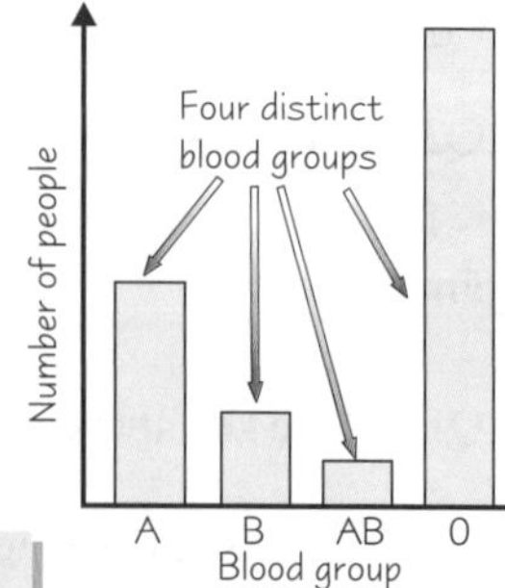

Plants

1) **Colour** — e.g. courgettes are either yellow, dark green or light green.
2) **Seed shape** — e.g. some pea plants have smooth seeds and some have wrinkled seeds.

Microorganisms

1) **Antibiotic resistance** — e.g. bacteria are either resistant or not.
2) **Pigment production** — e.g. some types of bacteria can produce a coloured pigment, some can't.

Variation

Variation can be Caused by Genes, the Environment, or Both

Variation can be caused by **genetic factors**, **environmental factors** or a combination of **both**:

(1) Genetic factors

1) **Different species** have **different genes**.
2) Individuals of the **same species** have the **same genes**, but **different versions** of them (called **alleles**).
3) The genes and alleles an organism has make up its **genotype**.
4) The differences in **genotype** result in **variation** in **phenotype** — the **characteristics** displayed by an organism.
5) Examples of variation caused **only** by genetic factors include **blood group** in humans (O, A, B or AB) and **antibiotic resistance** in bacteria.
6) You **inherit** your genes from your parents. This means variation caused by genetic factors is **inherited**.

(2) Environmental factors

1) Variation can also be caused by **differences in the environment**, e.g. climate, food, lifestyle.
2) Characteristics controlled by environmental factors can **change** over an organism's life.
3) Examples of variation caused **only** by environmental factors include **accents** and whether people have **pierced ears**.

(3) Both

Genetic factors determine the characteristics an organism's **born with**, but **environmental factors** can **influence** how some characteristics **develop**. For example:

1) **Height** — **genes** determine how tall an organism **can grow** (e.g. tall parents tend to have tall children). But **diet or nutrient availability** affect how tall an organism **actually grows**.
2) **Flagellum** — **genes** determine if a microorganism **can grow** a flagellum, but some will only **start to grow** them in **certain environments**, e.g. if metal ions are present.

Practice Questions

Q1 What is variation?

Q2 Describe what is meant by continuous variation and give one example.

Q3 Describe what is meant by discontinuous variation and give one example.

Q4 Briefly describe what is meant by variation caused by environmental factors.

Exam Question

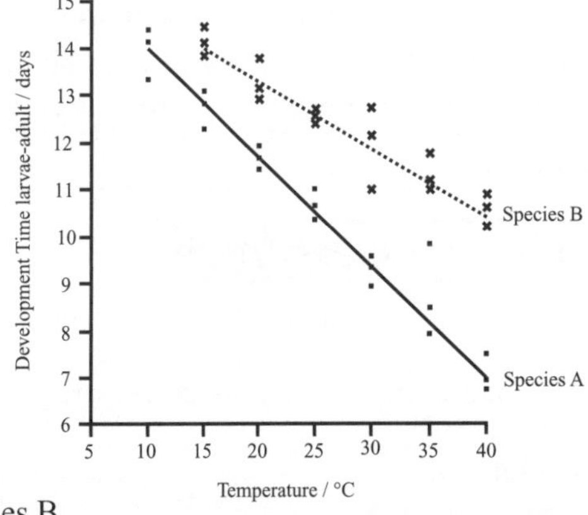

Q1 The graph shows the results of an investigation into the effects of temperature on the length of time it took for ladybird larvae to emerge as adults. Two species of ladybird were investigated, species A and species B.

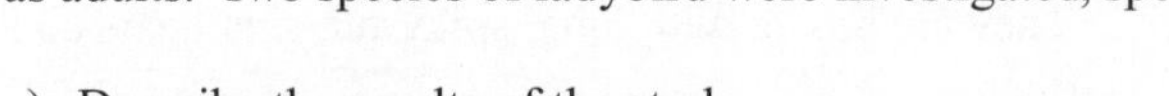

a) Describe the results of the study. [3 marks]

b) Explain what causes the variation between the species and within each species. [4 marks]

Environmental Factor — the search is on for the most talented environment...

It's amazing to think how many factors and genes influence the way we look and behave. It's the reason why every single organism is unique. My parents have often said they're glad they'll never have another child as 'unique' as me.

Adaptations

All the variation between and within species means that some organisms are better adapted to their environment than others...

Adaptations make Organisms *Well Suited* to Their *Environment*

1) Being **adapted** to an environment means an organism has features that **increase** its **chances of survival** and **reproduction**, and also the chances of its **offspring reproducing successfully**.
2) These features are called **adaptations** and can be behavioural, physiological and anatomical (see below).
3) Adaptations develop because of **evolution** by **natural selection** (see the next page).
4) In each generation, the **best-adapted individuals** are more likely to survive and reproduce — passing their adaptations on to their **offspring**. Individuals that are less well adapted are more likely to **die before reproducing**.

Adaptations can be *Behavioural, Physiological* and *Anatomical*

Behavioural adaptations

Ways an organism **acts** that increase its chance of survival. For example:

- **Possums** sometimes '**play dead**' — if they're being threatened by a **predator** they play dead to **escape attack**. This **increases** their chance of **survival**.
- **Scorpions dance** before **mating** — this makes sure they attract a mate of the **same species**, increasing the likelihood of **successful mating**.

Sid and Nancy were well adapted to hiding in candyfloss shops.

Physiological adaptations

Processes inside an organism's body that increase its chance of survival. For example:

- **Brown bears hibernate** — they **lower their metabolism** (all the chemical reactions taking place in their body) over **winter**. This **conserves energy**, so they don't need to look for **food** in the months when it's scarce — **increasing** their chance of **survival**.
- **Some bacteria** produce **antibiotics** — these **kill** other species of bacteria in the area. This means there's **less competition**, so they're **more likely** to **survive**.

Anatomical (structural) adaptations

Structural features of an organism's body that increase its chance of survival. For example:

- **Otters** have a **streamlined shape** — making it easier to **glide** through the **water**. This makes it easier for them to **catch prey** and **escape predators**, increasing their chance of **survival**.
- **Whales** have a **thick layer** of **blubber** (fat) — this helps to keep them **warm** in the cold sea. This increases their chance of survival in places where their **food** is found.

Practice Questions

Q1 What is meant by the term adaptation?

Q2 Describe the differences between behavioural, physiological and anatomical adaptations.

Exam Question

Q1 Hedgehogs are commonly found in gardens across the UK. They are brown with long, spiky fur, small ears and claws. They hibernate over winter and can roll into a ball when alarmed.

Give one behavioural, one physiological and two anatomical adaptations of hedgehogs, and suggest how each helps them to survive. [8 marks]

I'm perfectly adapted — for staying in bed...

Adaptations are features that make an organism more likely to survive and reproduce. Repetitive? Yes, but that's why it's so easy to learn. Adaptations develop because of evolution by natural selection, which is on the next page. Lucky you.

The Theory of Evolution

Evolution is the slow and continual change of organisms from one generation to the next. It explains how advantageous adaptations become common within a population of organisms...

Darwin Published his **Theory of Evolution** by **Natural Selection in 1859**

Scientists use **theories** to attempt to **explain** their **observations** — Charles Darwin was no exception. Darwin made **four** key observations about the world around him.

Observations:

1) Organisms produce **more offspring** than **survive**.
2) There's **variation** in the characteristics of members of the **same species**.
3) Some of these characteristics can be **passed on** from one generation to the next.
4) Individuals that are **best adapted** to their environment are more likely to **survive**.

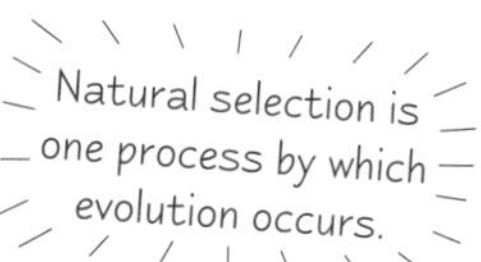

Darwin wrote his theory of **evolution by natural selection** to **explain** his observations:

Theory:

1) Individuals within a population **show variation** in their **phenotypes** (their characteristics).
2) **Predation, disease** and **competition** create a **struggle for survival.**
3) Individuals with **better adaptations** (characteristics that give a selective advantage, e.g. being able to run away from predators faster) are **more likely** to **survive, reproduce** and **pass on** their advantageous adaptations to their **offspring.**
4) Over time, the **number** of individuals with the advantageous adaptations **increases.**
5) Over generations this leads to **evolution** as the favourable adaptations become **more common** in the population.

At first, there was some **opposition** to Darwin's theory as it conflicted with some **religious beliefs**. Over time the theory has become **increasingly accepted** as more **evidence** has been found to support it and no evidence has been shown to disprove it. Evidence increases scientists' **confidence** in a theory — the more evidence there is, the more chance of something becoming an **accepted scientific explanation** (see pages 2-3).

Evolution can Lead to **Speciation**

Speciation is the **formation of a new species**:

1) A **species** is defined as a group of **similar organisms** that can **reproduce** to produce **fertile offspring**.
2) Species can exist as **one** or **more populations**, e.g. there are populations of the American black bear in parts of the USA and in parts of Canada.
3) Speciation happens when **populations** of the **same species** evolve to become so different that they can't breed with one another to produce **fertile** offspring.

Here's an example to show you **how** evolution can lead to speciation:

Darwin's finches

Darwin observed 14 species of finch on the **Galapagos Islands** — a group of islands in the Pacific Ocean. Each species of finch was unique to a single island. Although the finches were similar, the size and shape of their **beaks** differed — they were adapted to the **food sources** found on their specific island. Darwin theorised that:

1) All the species of finch had a **common ancestor**.
2) Different populations became **isolated** on different islands.
3) Each population **evolved adaptations** to their environment.
4) The populations evolved to become so different that they could no longer **breed** to produce **fertile offspring**.
5) They had evolved into **separate species**.

The Theory of Evolution

Because there's so much evidence to support the theory of evolution it's pretty much considered scientific fact now...

There's **Plenty of Evidence** to **Support Evolution**

Fossil Record Evidence

Fossils are the **remains** of organisms **preserved in rocks**.
By arranging fossils in chronological (date) order, **gradual changes** in organisms can be observed that provide **evidence** of evolution.

Example — The fossil record of the **horse** shows a **gradual change** in characteristics, including increasing **size** and **hoof** development.

DNA Evidence

1) The theory of evolution suggests that all organisms have **evolved** from shared **common ancestors.**
2) Closely related species **diverged** (evolved to become different species) **more recently.**
3) Evolution is caused by **gradual changes** in the **base sequence** of organisms' **DNA**.
4) So, organisms that diverged away from each other more recently, should have **more similar DNA,** as **less time** has passed for changes in the DNA sequence to occur. This is exactly what scientists have found.

See p. 62 for more on DNA.

Example — Humans, chimps and mice all evolved from a common ancestor. Humans and mice diverged a **long time ago**, but humans and chimps diverged **quite recently**. The **DNA base sequence** of humans and chimps is 94% the same, but human and mouse DNA is only 85% the same.

Chimps Humans
Mice
Common ancestor

Molecular Evidence

In addition to DNA, the similarities in **other molecules** provide evidence.
Scientists compare the **sequence** of **amino acids** in **proteins** (see p. 64), and compare **antibodies**.
Organisms that diverged away from each other **more recently** have **more similar molecules,** as **less time** has passed for changes in proteins and other molecules to occur.

Populations of **Bacteria** can **Evolve Resistance** to **Antibiotics**

Antibiotics are drugs that **kill or inhibit the growth** of bacteria. Scientists have observed the evolution of **antibiotic resistance** in many species of bacteria. For example, MRSA (methicillin-resistant *Staphylococcus aureus*) is a **strain** (type) of bacteria that's resistant to the antibiotic methicillin.

The **evolution** of antibiotic resistance can be explained by **natural selection**:

1) There is **variation** in a population of bacteria. **Genetic mutations** make some bacteria naturally **resistant** to an antibiotic.
2) If the population of bacteria is exposed to that antibiotic, only the individuals with resistance will **survive** to **reproduce**.
3) The **alleles** which cause the antibiotic resistance will be **passed on** to the next generation, and so the population will evolve to become resistant to the drug.

The Evolution of **Antibiotic Resistance** has **Implications** for **Humans**

1) **Infections** caused by antibiotic-resistant bacteria (such as MRSA) are **harder** to **treat** — some species of bacteria are resistant to **a lot of different antibiotics**. It takes doctors a while to figure out which antibiotics will get rid of the infection, and in that time the **patient** could become **very ill** or **die**.
2) There could come a point where a bacterium has developed resistance to **all known antibiotics**. To prevent this **new antibiotics** need to be **developed**. This takes **time** and costs a lot of **money**.

Different strains of one species of bacteria can be resistant to different antibiotics — one antibiotic won't always kill all of them.

The Theory of Evolution

Populations of Insects can Evolve Resistance to Pesticides

Pesticides are chemicals that **kill pests** (e.g. insects that damage crops). Scientists have observed the evolution of **pesticide resistance** in many species of insect. For example, some populations of **mosquito** have **evolved resistance** to the pesticide **DDT**. Some populations of **pollen beetles** (which damage the crop oilseed rape) are resistant to **pyrethroid** pesticides.

Janet was resistant to DDT but not to Malcolm's smooth talking.

The evolution of **pesticide resistance** can be explained by **natural selection**:

1) There is **variation** in a population of insects. **Genetic mutations** make some insects naturally **resistant** to a pesticide.
2) If the population of insects is exposed to that pesticide, only the individuals with resistance will **survive** to **reproduce**.
3) The **alleles** which cause the pesticide resistance will be **passed on** to the next generation, and so the population will evolve to become more resistant to the chemical.

The Evolution of Pesticide Resistance has Implications for Humans

The implications for humans are pretty similar to those for antibiotic resistance:

1) **Crop infestations** with **pesticide-resistant** insects are **harder to control** — some insects are resistant to **lots of different pesticides**. It takes farmers a while to figure out which pesticide will kill the insect and in that time **all** the crop could be **destroyed**. If the insects are resistant to specific pesticides (ones that only kill that insect), farmers might have to use **broader pesticides** (those that kill a range of insects), which could kill beneficial insects.
2) If **disease-carrying** insects (e.g. mosquitoes) become pesticide-resistant, the **spread of disease** could **increase**.
3) A population of insects could **evolve resistance** to **all** pesticides in use. To prevent this **new pesticides** need to be **produced**. This takes **time** and costs **money**.

Practice Questions

Q1 What four key observations did Darwin make?

Q2 Define speciation.

Q3 Briefly describe how fossil evidence supports the theory of evolution.

These questions cover pages 103-105.

Exam Questions

Q1 Outline Darwin's theory of evolution by natural selection. [4 marks]

Q2 The diamondback moth is a pest of many crops. In 1953 it became resistant to the pesticide DDT and by 1981 it had become resistant to 36 other pesticides.

a) Explain how the diamondback moth populations could have developed DDT resistance. [4 marks]

b) Describe two possible implications of the diamondback moth developing resistance to pesticides. [2 marks]

The fossil record — it rocks...

Evolution by natural selection isn't that bad really... just remember that any adaptation that increases the chances of an organism surviving (e.g. by avoiding being killed by antibiotics) or getting laid (no explanation required) will increase in the population due to the process of natural selection. Now I know why mullets have disappeared... so unattractive...

How to Interpret Data

Science is all about getting good evidence to test your theories... so scientists need to be able to spot a badly designed experiment a mile off, and be able to interpret the results of an experiment properly. Being the cheeky little monkeys they are, your exam board will want to make sure you can do it too. Here's a quick reference section to show you how to go about interpreting data-style questions.

You Might get **Data** to **Interpret** in the **Exam**

Here's an example of the kind of data you might get:

Experiment A

Experiment A examined the effect of temperature on the rate of an enzyme-controlled reaction. The rate of reaction for enzyme X was measured at six different temperatures (from 10 to 60 °C). All other variables were kept constant.

A negative control containing all solutions except the enzyme was included. The rate of reaction for the negative control was zero at each temperature used. The results are shown in the graph on the right.

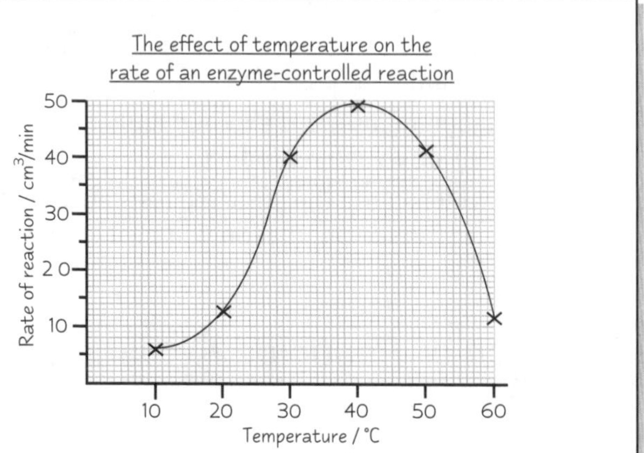

You Need to be Able to **Read Graphs**

Susie was worried by all the talk of gir-raffe paper.

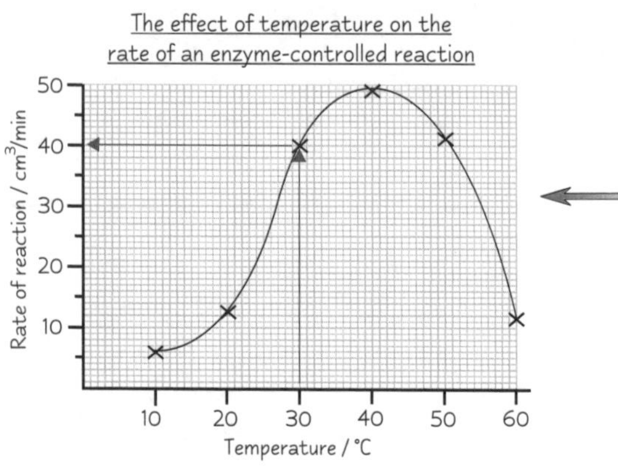

1) You should be a dab hand at **reading values off graphs** by now, but if you aren't don't worry — it's fairly easy.
2) For example, if you want to know what the rate of reaction was at **30 °C** you find 30 on the x-axis and **go up** until you hit the line — then go **across** to the y-axis and **read off the value** (40 cm^3/min).
3) Don't forget to put the **units** on your answer.

The volume of oxygen released by an enzyme-controlled reaction at 10 °C

Volume of oxygen released / cm^3 — 10, 20, 30, 40, 50 — Change in X = 10 — Change in Y = 30 — Time / s — 10, 20, 30, 40, 50, 60

A little trickier is calculating the **gradient** of the graph:

Gradient = $\frac{\text{Change in Y}}{\text{Change in X}}$ **Units** = $\frac{Y}{X}$

The x-axis is horizontal, the y-axis is vertical.

For example, if you want to know the **rate of a reaction** over the first 10 seconds:

Gradient = rate of reaction = $\frac{30}{10} = 3$ **Units** = $\frac{cm^3}{s} = cm^3/s$

The **answer** is 3 cm^3/s.

If you **aren't** told what to use (e.g. over the first 10 seconds) then use the **largest area** you can from the **straightest** part of the graph.

Reading graphs... I didn't realise they were so intelligent...

This is pretty bog-standard stuff but it's really important that you get it right — graph questions are easy marks in the exam... It can be quite easy to forget to do the simple things, like including units — make sure you don't miss them out.

How to Evaluate and Describe Experiments

Experiments Have to be *Designed Carefully*

Any experiment has to be carried out properly to get a **reliable result**. Here are the things that should be done:

1) Only one variable should change — Variables are **quantities** that have the **potential to change**, e.g. temperature. You should only ever **change one variable** in an experiment. Then you can be sure that changing that variable is the **reason** for **any effects** you see. You need to **measure** something to see if the variable is having an **effect** (e.g. volume).
   - The variable that you **change** is called the **independent variable**.
   - The variable that you **measure** is called the **dependent variable**.

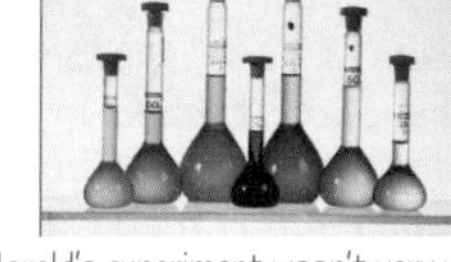
Harold's experiment wasn't very well designed, but it sure did look good.

2) All the other variables should be controlled — When you're investigating a variable you need to keep **everything else** that could affect it **constant**. This means you can be sure that **only** your independent variable is causing any effects seen.

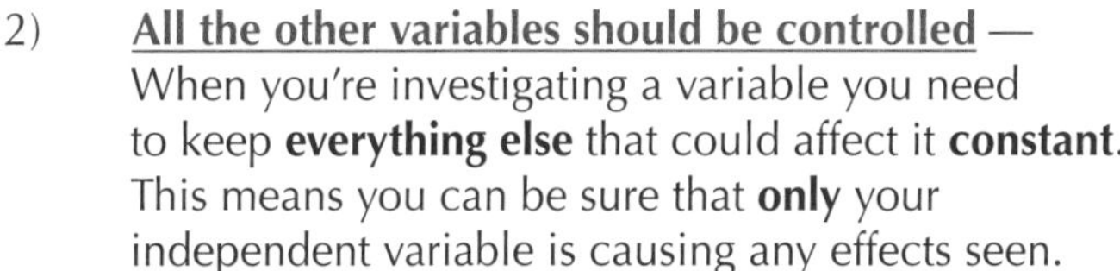

3) Experiments should be repeated — Reliable results are **reproducible**. A good experiment includes **repeated** measurements, so you can see if the results are reproducible.
4) Negative controls should be used — Negative controls are used to check that **nothing else** included in the experiment is **affecting** the thing you're measuring (the dependent variable).

EXAMPLE Investigating the effect of **temperature** on **enzyme activity**.

1) Temperature is the **independent** variable.
2) Enzyme activity is the **dependent** variable.
3) pH, volume, substrate concentration and enzyme concentration should all **stay the same**.
4) The experiment should be **repeated** at least **three times** at each temperature used.
5) A **negative control**, containing everything used **except the enzyme**, should be measured at each temperature used. No enzyme activity should be seen with these controls.

The same principles apply to **studies** — the **more people** included the better (this is a bit like having loads of repeats), as many **variables** should be **controlled** as possible, and a **control group** should be used if appropriate.

You Need to Be Able to *Describe* a *Good Experiment*

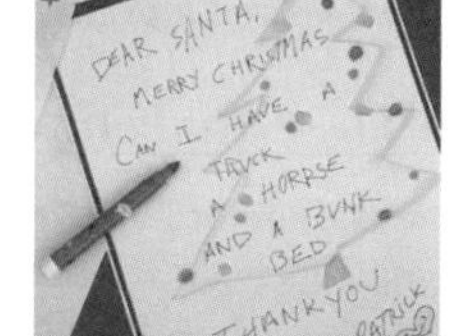

Patrick had spent ages on his plan. He wasn't convinced the examiners would like it though...

You could be asked to describe an experiment in the exam. You need to:

1) **Plan what you're going to write** before you start — roughly jot down the **sequence** of the experiment.
2) Describe the **sequence** of the experiment — what you do first, then second, then third etc. Use the **proper names** for the **equipment** and **reagents**, e.g. spectrophotometer, Benedict's reagent, etc. Don't forget to mention any **calculation steps**, e.g. finding averages. Be **specific** about what you would do.
3) If it's a **test** (e.g. a test for sugar), describe what **results** you'd expect — e.g. what **colour change** you'd expect.

Catalase catalyses the breakdown of hydrogen peroxide into water and oxygen.

EXAMPLE Investigating the effect of **temperature** on **catalase activity**.

1) Set up test tubes containing the **same concentration** of hydrogen peroxide.
2) Set up the apparatus to measure the **volume** of oxygen produced from each test tube.
3) Put each test tube in a **water bath** set to a different temperature (e.g. 10 °C, 20 °C, 30 °C and 40 °C).
4) Add the **same volume** of catalase to each test tube and **record** how much oxygen is produced in the **first minute** (60 s) of the reaction.
5) A **negative control** reaction, not containing catalase, should be carried out at each temperature.
6) **Repeat** the experiment at each temperature three times, and use the results to find an average volume.
7) **Calculate the average** rate of reaction at each temperature by dividing the volume produced by the time taken (cm^3/second).

Controls — I think I prefer the remote kind...

This page should give you a fair idea of the points to think about when describing an experiment. Just remember to take your time and make sure you've included all the main points — constants, specifics, measurements, repeats and controls.

Answers

Unit 1: Section 1 — Cell Structure

Page 7 — Eukaryotic Cells and Organelles

1 *Maximum of 4 marks available.*
*cell wall **[1 mark]**, plasmodesmata **[1 mark]**, vacuole **[1 mark]**, chloroplasts **[1 mark]**.*

2 a) i) *Maximum of 1 mark available.*
*mitochondrion **[1 mark]***
ii) *Maximum of 1 mark available.*
*Golgi apparatus **[1 mark]***
b) *Maximum of 2 marks available.*
*Mitochondria are the site of aerobic respiration **[1 mark]**.*
*The Golgi apparatus processes and packages new lipids and proteins / makes lysosomes **[1 mark]**.*

Page 9 — Prokaryotic Cells

1 a) *Maximum of 2 marks available*
*Ribosomes **[1 mark]** because this is where protein synthesis occurs **[1 mark]**.*
b) *Maximum of 3 mark available*
*The rough endoplasmic reticulum **[1 mark]**, ribosomes **[1 mark]** and some vesicles **[1 mark]**.*
c) *Maximum of 1 mark available*
*Vesicles transport substances in and out of the cell and between organelles **[1 mark]**.*

2 *Maximum of 3 marks available, from any of the 4 points below.*
*Supports the cell's organelles **[1 mark]***
*Strengthens the cell / maintains its shape **[1 mark]***
*Transports materials around the cell **[1 mark]***
*Enables cell movement **[1 mark]***

Page 11 — Studying Cells — Microscopes

1 *Maximum of 2 marks available*
Magnification = length of image ÷ length of object
*= 80 mm ÷ 0.5 mm **[1 mark]***
*= × 160 **[1 mark]***
Always remember to convert everything to the same units first — the insect is 0.5 mm long, so the length of the image needs to be changed from 8 cm to 80 mm.

2 a) *Maximum of 3 marks available*
*mitochondrion **[1 mark]** and nucleus **[1 mark]***
*The resolution of light microscopes is not good enough to show objects smaller than 0.2 μm **[1 mark]**.*
b) *Maximum of 2 marks available*
*All of the organelles in the table would be visible **[1 mark]**.*
*SEMs can resolve objects down to about 5 nm (0.005 μm) **[1 mark]**.*

Unit 1: Section 2 — Cell Membranes

Page 13 — Cell Membranes — The Basics

1 *Maximum of 2 marks available.*
*The membrane is described as fluid because the phospholipids are constantly moving **[1 mark]**. It is described as a mosaic because the proteins are scattered throughout the membrane like tiles in a mosaic **[1 mark]**.*

2 *Maximum of 1 mark available.*
*Cholesterol makes the membrane more rigid **[1 mark]**.*

Page 15 — Cell Membranes — The Basics

1 *Maximum of 3 marks available.*
*Nicotine only binds to receptors with a complementary shape **[1 mark]**. Different cells have different membrane-bound receptors **[1 mark]**. Nicotine only affects nerve cells because they have the correct receptor for nicotine **[1 mark]**.*

2 a) *Maximum of 1 mark available.*
*Tube 4 **[1 mark]**.*
b) *Maximum of 4 marks available.*
*There is a higher concentration of beetroot pigment in tube 2 than in tube 1 **[1 mark]** because the membrane is more permeable at higher temperatures **[1 mark]**. The molecules in the membrane have more energy so can move more, increasing permeability **[1 mark]**. This caused more pigment to move out of the cells into the water than in tube 1 **[1 mark]**.*
c) *Maximum of 4 marks available.*
*There is a higher concentration of beetroot pigment in tube 3 than in tube 2 **[1 mark]**. This is because the high temperature tube 3 was exposed to caused the membranes of the beetroot cells to break down **[1 mark]**, increasing their permeability **[1 mark]** and causing more pigment to move out of the cells into the water **[1 mark]**.*
For questions like this try to work out what the data in the table is telling you, using your own knowledge, before you attempt to answer the question. The table shows that the pieces of beetroot exposed to highest temperatures have released the most pigment. From your knowledge you know that very high temperatures damage cell membranes. If the cell membranes are damaged the cells become leaky, so they lose pigment.
d) *Maximum of 4 marks available*
*The absorbance reading would have been high **[1 mark]**.*
*At temperatures below 0 °C, channel proteins and carrier proteins denature **[1 mark]** and ice crystals form, which pierce the membrane **[1 mark]**. This makes the membrane highly permeable, so a lot of pigment would leak out into the solution **[1 mark]**.*

Page 17 — Transport Across Cell Membranes

1 a) *Maximum of 3 marks available.*
*The water potential of the sucrose solution was higher than the water potential of the potato **[1 mark]**. Water moves by osmosis from a solution of higher water potential to a solution of lower water potential **[1 mark]**. So water moved into the potato, increasing its mass **[1 mark]**.*
b) *Maximum of 1 mark available.*
*The water potential of the potato and the water potential of the solution was the same **[1 mark]**.*
c) *Maximum of 4 marks available.*
*– 0.4 g **[1 mark]**. The potato has a higher water potential than the solution **[1 mark]** so net movement of water is out of the potato **[1 mark]**. The difference in water potential between the solution and the potato is the same as with the 1% solution, so the mass difference should be about the same **[1 mark]**.*

Page 19 — Transport Across Cell Membranes

1 *Maximum of 6 marks available.*
*Facilitated diffusion involves channel proteins **[1 mark]**, which transport charged molecules across the membrane **[1 mark]** down their concentration gradient **[1 mark]**. It also involves carrier proteins **[1 mark]**, which transport large molecules across the membrane **[1 mark]** down their concentration gradient **[1 mark]**.*

Answers

2 *Maximum of 4 marks available.*
Endocytosis takes in substances from outside the cell ***[1 mark]*** *via vesicles formed from the plasma membrane* ***[1 mark]****.*
Exocytosis secretes substances from the cell ***[1 mark]*** *via vesicles made from the Golgi apparatus* ***[1 mark]****.*
Make sure you don't get these two processes mixed up — try to remember endo for 'in' and exo for 'out'.

Unit 1: Section 3 — Cell Division, Diversity and Organisation

Page 21 — Cell Division — Mitosis

1 a) *Maximum of 6 marks available.*
A = Metaphase ***[1 mark]****, because the chromosomes are lined up across the middle of the cell* ***[1 mark]****.*
B = Telophase ***[1 mark]****, because there are now two nuclei and the cytoplasm is dividing to form two new cells* ***[1 mark]****.*
C = Anaphase ***[1 mark]****, because the centromeres have divided and the chromatids are moving to opposite ends of the cell* ***[1 mark]****.*
If you've learned the diagrams of what happens at each stage of mitosis, this should be a breeze. That's why it'd be a total disaster if you lost three marks for forgetting to give reasons for your answers. Always read the question properly and do exactly what it tells you to do.

b) *Maximum of 3 marks available:*
X = Nuclear envelope ***[1 mark]****.*
Y = Cell membrane ***[1 mark]****.*
Z = Centriole ***[1 mark]****.*

Page 23 — Cell Division and Reproduction

1 a) *Maximum of 3 marks available.*
A bud has formed at the surface of the cell ***[1 mark]****.*
The cell has undergone interphase ***[1 mark]*** *and has started to divide by mitosis* ***[1 mark]****.*

b) *Maximum of 2 marks available.*
The bud has separated off from the parent cell ***[1 mark]****, producing a new, genetically identical yeast cell* ***[1 mark]****.*

2 *Maximum of 2 marks available.*
A pair of chromosomes, one from the mum and one from the dad ***[1 mark]****, which have the same genes but could have different versions of those genes (alleles)* ***[1 mark]****.*

Page 25 — Stem Cells and Differentiation

1 *Maximum of 4 marks available.*
It has many chloroplasts ***[1 mark]*** *to absorb light for photosynthesis* ***[1 mark]****. It has thin cell walls* ***[1 mark]****, so carbon dioxide can easily enter* ***[1 mark]****.*

2 *Maximum of 5 marks available.*
Stem cells divide to make new, specialised cells ***[1 mark]****. In animals, adult stem cells are used to replace damaged cells* ***[1 mark]****, e.g. stem cells in the bone marrow differentiate/become specialised to make erythrocytes (red blood cells)/neutrophils (white blood cells)* ***[1 mark]****. In plants, stem cells are used to make new growing parts (roots and shoots)* ***[1 mark]****, e.g. stem cells in the cambium differentiate (become specialised) to make xylem/phloem* ***[1 mark]****.*

Page 27 — Tissues, Organs and Systems

1 *Maximum of 2 marks available.*
It's best described as an organ ***[1 mark]*** *as it is made of many tissues working together to perform a particular function* ***[1 mark]****.*

2 *Maximum of 3 marks available. 1 mark for naming an organ system. 1 mark for naming each organ contained in that system, up to a maximum of 2 marks.*
E.g. respiratory system — composed of the lungs, trachea, larynx, nose, mouth and diaphragm. / Circulatory system — composed of the heart, arteries, veins and capillaries.

Unit 1: Section 4 — Exchange Surfaces and Breathing

Page 29 — Gas Exchange

1 *Maximum of 5 marks available.*
Humans are large multicellular organisms ***[1 mark]****. There is a big distance between some cells and the environment* ***[1 mark]****, so cells can't exchange substances directly quickly enough* ***[1 mark]****. Humans have a small surface area to volume ratio* ***[1 mark]****, which makes it impossible to exchange enough oxygen and carbon dioxide through their outer membranes to supply the body* ***[1 mark]****.*

2 *Maximum of 4 marks available.*
Oxygen diffuses out of the alveoli ***[1 mark]*** *across the alveolar epithelium and the capillary endothelium* ***[1 mark]*** *and into the blood* ***[1 mark]****. Carbon dioxide diffuses from the blood into the alveoli* ***[1 mark]****.*
The mark for mentioning the alveolar epithelium and capillary endothelium would also be awarded if they were mentioned in reference to the diffusion of carbon dioxide.

Page 31 — The Gaseous Exchange System

1 *Maximum of 5 marks available.*
Lungs contain many alveoli, giving a large surface area ***[1 mark]****. Each alveolus has a good blood supply, maintaining a high concentration gradient* ***[1 mark]*** *by constantly removing oxygen and delivering carbon dioxide* ***[1 mark]****. The alveoli and capillary walls are each only one cell thick, so there is a short diffusion pathway* ***[1 mark]****. Concentration gradients are also maintained by breathing in and out, which refreshes the oxygen supply and removes carbon dioxide* ***[1 mark]****.*

2 *Maximum of 10 marks available.*
Goblet cells ***[1 mark]*** *secrete mucus, which traps bacteria and dust so they don't reach the alveoli* ***[1 mark]****. Other cells have cilia* ***[1 mark]*** *which move the mucus towards the throat to be removed* ***[1 mark]****. Elastic fibres* ***[1 mark]*** *stretch when we breathe in, then recoil to help us breathe out* ***[1 mark]****. Smooth muscle tissue* ***[1 mark]*** *relaxes to make air passages wider and make breathing easier when exercising* ***[1 mark]****. Cartilage* ***[1 mark]*** *provides support and keeps the air passages open* ***[1 mark]****.*

Page 33 — Breathing

1 *Maximum of 5 marks available.*
The intercostal muscles contract ***[1 mark]****, making the ribs move up and out* ***[1 mark]****, and the diaphragm contracts/flattens* ***[1 mark]****. This increases the volume of the thorax* ***[1 mark]****, so the pressure inside decreases, drawing air into the lungs* ***[1 mark]****.*

Answers

Unit 1: Section 5 — Transport in Animals

Page 35 — The Circulatory System

1 *Maximum of 1 mark available.*
*The blood flows through the body in vessels **[1 mark]**.*

2 *Maximum of 2 marks available.*
*Insects have an open circulatory system **[1 mark]**. The blood is pumped into the body cavity where it circulates freely **[1 mark]**.*

3 a) *It is a closed system **[1 mark]**.*
b) *It is a single circulatory system, not a double one **[1 mark]**.*

Page 37 — The Heart

1 a) i) *Maximum of 1 mark available.*
*D **[1 mark]***
The semi-lunar valve will only open if the pressure in the ventricle is higher than the pressure in the aorta (or pulmonary artery, if you're looking at the right side of the heart).
ii) *Maximum of 1 mark available.*
*C **[1 mark]***
The atrioventricular valve will be forced closed when the pressure in the ventricle becomes higher than the pressure in the atrium.
b) *Maximum of 2 marks available.*
*The graph should increase and decrease at the same times as the graph for the left side (because both ventricles contract together) **[1 mark]**. The pressure should be lower than for the left side of the heart at all times **[1 mark]**.*

E.g.

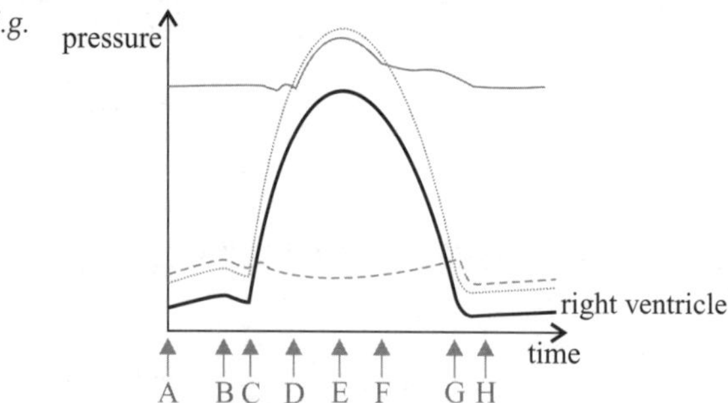

2 *Maximum of 8 marks available.*
*When the heart muscles are relaxed, blood enters the atria from the veins **[1 mark]**. The semi-lunar valves prevent blood coming back into the ventricles from the arteries **[1 mark]**. Next, the atria contract **[1 mark]**. This pushes blood from the atria into the ventricles **[1 mark]** through the atrioventricular valves **[1 mark]**. Then the ventricles contract **[1 mark]**. This pushes blood out from the ventricles into the arteries **[1 mark]**. The atrioventricular valves shut to prevent blood going back into the atria **[1 mark]**.*

Page 39 — The Heart

1 a) *Maximum of 1 mark available.*
*The sino-atrial node acts as a pacemaker/initiates heartbeats **[1 mark]**.*
b) *Maximum of 1 mark available.*
*The Purkyne tissue conducts electrical impulses through the ventricle walls **[1 mark]**.*

2 *Maximum of 2 marks available.*
*The ventricle is not contracting properly **[1 mark]**. This could be because of muscle damage / because the AVN is not conducting impulses to the ventricles properly **[1 mark]**.*

Page 41 — Blood Vessels

1 a) *Maximum of 2 marks available.*
*Elastic tissue and a thick muscle layer allow the arteries to cope with the high pressure produced when the heart beats **[1 mark]**. The folded inner lining/endothelium allows arteries to expand to cope with high pressure **[1 mark]**.*
b) *Maximum of 1 mark available.*
*Capillary walls are only one cell thick to increase diffusion **[1 mark]**.*
c) *Maximum of 1 mark available.*
*Veins have valves to stop blood flowing backwards **[1 mark]**.*

2 *Maximum of 4 marks available.*
*At the start of the capillary bed, the pressure in the capillaries is greater than the pressure in the tissue fluid outside the capillaries **[1 mark]**. This means fluid from the blood is forced out of the capillaries **[1 mark]**. Fluid loss causes the water potential of blood capillaries to become lower than that of tissue fluid **[1 mark]**. So fluid moves back into the capillaries at the vein end of the capillary bed by osmosis **[1 mark]**.*

Page 43 — Haemoglobin

1 *Maximum of 3 marks available.*
*The fetus relies on oxygen from the mother's blood **[1 mark]**. By the time it reaches the fetus, the mother's blood is not fully oxygenated **[1 mark]**. Fetal haemoglobin must therefore have a higher affinity for oxygen than its mother's blood in order to take up enough oxygen **[1 mark]**.*

2 *Maximum of 6 marks available.*
*Most of the CO_2 from respiring cells is converted to carbonic acid by the enzyme carbonic anhydrase **[1 mark]**. The carbonic acid splits up to form hydrogen ions and hydrogencarbonate ions **[1 mark]**. The hydrogencarbonate ions are transported in the blood plasma **[1 mark]**. Oxyhaemoglobin unloads some of its oxygen and binds to the hydrogen ions, forming haemoglobinic acid **[1 mark]**. At the lungs, the haemoglobin releases its hydrogen ions **[1 mark]**, which recombine with the hydrogencarbonate ions to be breathed out as carbon dioxide **[1 mark]**.*

Unit 1: Section 6 — Transport in Plants

Page 45 — Xylem and Phloem

1 *Maximum of 6 marks available.*
The distribution can be explained in words or by diagrams — whichever you find easier. In either case, these are the key points:
*In the stem, the xylem and phloem are towards the outside, with the phloem outside the xylem **[1 mark]**. This provides a scaffold for the stem to reduce bending **[1 mark]**. In the root, the xylem and phloem are in the centre, with the phloem outside the xylem **[1 mark]**. This provides support for the root as it pushes through the soil **[1 mark]**. In the leaves, the veins run throughout the leaves, with the xylem above the phloem **[1 mark]**. This provides support for the thin leaves **[1 mark]**.*

2 *Maximum of 8 marks available.*
*Xylem vessel cells have no end walls **[1 mark]**, making an uninterrupted tube that allows water to pass through easily **[1 mark]**. The vessel cells are dead and contain no cytoplasm **[1 mark]**, which allows water to pass through **[1 mark]**. Their walls are thickened with a woody substance called lignin **[1 mark]**, which helps support the xylem vessels and stop them collapsing inwards **[1 mark]**. The vessel walls have small holes called pits where there's no lignin **[1 mark]**. This allows substances to pass in and out of the vessels **[1 mark]**.*

Answers

Page 47 — Water Transport

1 Maximum of 4 marks available.
Loss of water from the leaves, due to transpiration, pulls more water into the leaves from the xylem **[1 mark]**. There are cohesive forces between water molecules **[1 mark]**. These cause water to be pulled up the xylem **[1 mark]**. Removing leaves means no transpiration occurs, so no water is pulled up the xylem **[1 mark]**.
It's pretty obvious (because there are 4 marks to get) that it's not enough just to say removing the leaves stops transpiration. You also need to explain why transpiration is so important in moving water through the xylem. It's always worth checking how many marks a question is worth — this gives you a clue about how much detail you need to include.

2 a) Maximum of 2 marks available.
In the symplast pathway, water moves through the cytoplasm **[1 mark]**. The cytoplasm of neighbouring cells is connected through plasmodesmata (small gaps in the cell walls) **[1 mark]**.

b) Maximum of 4 marks available.
In the apoplast pathway, water passes through the cell walls **[1 mark]**. The walls are very absorbent so water simply diffuses through them **[1 mark]**. In the endodermis layer of the root the Casparian strip inhibits the apoplast pathway **[1 mark]**. From here the water must take the symplast pathway **[1 mark]**.

Page 49 — Transpiration

1 Maximum of 8 marks available. 1 mark for each factor, and 1 mark for explaining each factor's effect.
Transpiration is increased when it's light **[1 mark]**, as the stomata open only when it's light **[1 mark]**. A high temperature increases transpiration **[1 mark]** because water evaporates from the cells inside the leaf faster/water diffuses out of the leaf faster **[1 mark]**. A low humidity level increases the rate of transpiration **[1 mark]** because it increases the water potential gradient between the leaf and the surrounding air **[1 mark]**. Transpiration is increased if it's windy **[1 mark]** because wind blows away water molecules from around the stomata, increasing the water potential gradient **[1 mark]**.

2 Maximum of 4 marks available.
'Hairs' on the epidermis **[1 mark]** trap moist air round the stomata, which reduces the water potential gradient and so reduces transpiration **[1 mark]**. Thick cuticle **[1 mark]** is waterproof so stops water evaporating **[1 mark]**.

Page 51 — Translocation

1 Maximum of 4 marks available.
Sugars are actively loaded into the sieve tubes at the source end **[1 mark]**. This lowers the water potential of the sieve tubes at the source end **[1 mark]**, which causes water to enter by osmosis **[1 mark]**. This causes a pressure increase inside the sieve tubes at the source end **[1 mark]**.
I think this is a pretty nasty question. If you got it all right first time you're probably a genius. If you didn't, you're probably not totally clear yet about the pressure idea. If there's a high concentration of sugar in a cell, this draws water in by osmosis, and so increases the pressure inside the cell.

Unit 2: Section 1 — Biological Molecules

Page 53 — Water

1 Maximum of 15 marks available.
Water molecules have two hydrogen atoms and one oxygen atom **[1 mark]**. The hydrogen and oxygen atoms are joined by shared electrons **[1 mark]**. Oxygen attracts the electrons more strongly than hydrogen **[1 mark]**. This makes water molecules polar **[1 mark]**. This polarity leads to the formation of hydrogen bonds between water molecules **[1 mark]**. The hydrogen bonds in water can absorb a lot of energy **[1 mark]**, giving water a high specific heat capacity **[1 mark]**. This allows living organisms to avoid rapid changes in temperature **[1 mark]**. It takes a lot of energy to break the hydrogen bonds in water **[1 mark]**, so water has a high latent heat of evaporation **[1 mark]**. This means water is good for cooling things **[1 mark]**. Water's polarity makes it very cohesive **[1 mark]**. This helps it to flow, allowing it to transport substances **[1 mark]**. Water's polarity allows it to dissolve other molecules **[1 mark]**. This allows water to act as a solvent so it can transport substances **[1 mark]**.

Page 55 — Proteins

1 Maximum of 9 marks available.
Proteins are made from amino acids **[1 mark]**. The amino acids are joined together in a long (polypeptide) chain **[1 mark]**. The sequence of amino acids is the protein's primary structure **[1 mark]**. The amino acid chain/polypeptide coils or folds in a certain way **[1 mark]**. The way it's coiled or folded is the protein's secondary structure **[1 mark]**. The coiled or folded chain is itself folded into a specific shape **[1 mark]**. This is the protein's tertiary structure **[1 mark]**. Different polypeptide chains can be joined together in the protein molecule **[1 mark]**. The way these chains are joined is the quaternary structure of the protein **[1 mark]**.

2 Maximum of 6 marks available, from any of the 7 points below.
Collagen is a fibrous protein **[1 mark]**.
For this mark, including the word 'fibrous' is essential.
It forms supportive tissues in the body, so it needs to be strong **[1 mark]**. Collagen is made of three polypeptide chains **[1 mark]**, tightly coiled to form a triple helix **[1 mark]**. The chains are interlinked by covalent bonds **[1 mark]**, which makes it strong **[1 mark]**. Minerals can bind to the triple helix, increasing its rigidity **[1 mark]**.

Page 57 — Carbohydrates

1 Maximum of 7 marks available.
Glycosidic bonds are formed when a hydrogen atom **[1 mark]** from one monosaccharide combines with a hydroxyl/OH group **[1 mark]** from another monosaccharide. This releases a molecule of water **[1 mark]**. Glycosidic bonds are broken by hydrolysis **[1 mark]**. A molecule of water reacts with the glycosidic bond to split the monosaccharide molecules apart **[1 mark]**. The last two marks are given for a diagram showing a reversible reaction with correct reactants (e.g. two glucose molecules) **[1 mark]** and correct products (e.g. water and maltose) **[1 mark]**.

α-glucose + α-glucose ⇌ (synthesis / hydrolysis) maltose + H_2O
glycosidic bond
H_2O is removed

Answers

2 Maximum of 12 marks available.
Starch is made of alpha-glucose molecules **[1 mark]** whereas cellulose is made of beta-glucose molecules **[1 mark]**. Cellulose is a single polysaccharide, whereas starch is made of two polysaccharides (amylose and amylopectin) **[1 mark]**.
The amylose in starch is unbranched and coiled **[1 mark]** and the amylopectin is branched **[1 mark]**. In contrast, cellulose is straight and unbranched **[1 mark]** and the chains are linked together by hydrogen bonds to form strong fibres/microfibrils **[1 mark]**. Starch's structure makes it a good energy storage material in plants **[1 mark]**. The branches allow enzymes access to break the glycosidic bonds and release glucose quickly **[1 mark]**. It's insoluble, so it can be stored in cells without causing water to enter by osmosis, which would cause them to swell **[1 mark]**. Cellulose's structure makes it a good supporting structure in cell walls **[1 mark]**. The fibres provide strength **[1 mark]**.
The question asks you to compare and contrast, so you need to highlight how they differ from each other.

Page 59 — Lipids

1 a) Maximum of 2 marks available.
Hydrophilic — glycerol phosphate/phosphate group **[1 mark]**.
Hydrophobic — hydrocarbon tail/fatty acids **[1 mark]**.
b) Maximum of 3 marks available.
They arrange themselves into a (phospholipid) bilayer/double layer **[1 mark]**, with fatty acid tails facing towards each other **[1 mark]**. This is because the fatty acid tails are hydrophobic (water-repelling), forcing them to face inwards, away from the water on either side of the membrane **[1 mark]**.

2 a) Maximum of 2 marks available.
The flattened shape allows them to fit in between the phospholipids, causing them to pack together more tightly **[1 mark]**, which makes the membrane less fluid and more rigid **[1 mark]**.
b) Maximum of 2 marks available.
The hydrophobic tails force them to clump together in the cytoplasm as insoluble droplets **[1 mark]**. This means they can be stored in cells without affecting the cell's water potential **[1 mark]**.

Page 61 — Biochemical Tests for Molecules

1 a) Maximum of 1 mark available.
Solution C **[1 mark]**
Solution C has the lowest absorbance. It therefore has the least amount of Benedict's reagent left — so it had the most reducing sugar before the Benedict's test.
b) Maximum of 1 mark available.
The colorimeter measures the amount of Benedict's reagent left after reacting with glucose. You therefore need to use an excessive amount of Benedict's reagent to make sure there's some left behind **[1 mark]**.
c) Maximum of 2 marks available.
The amount of Benedict's reagent used in each test tube **[1 mark]**. The concentration of Benedict's reagent used **[1 mark]**. The length of time each solution is left for **[1 mark]**.

Unit 2: Section 2 — Nucleic Acids

Page 63 — DNA and RNA

1 Maximum of 1 mark available.
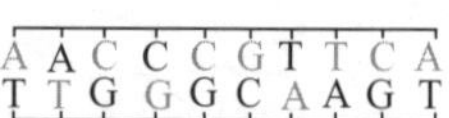

2 a) Maximum of 3 marks available, from any of the 4 points below.
DNA nucleotides consist of deoxyribose sugar **[1 mark]** joined to a phosphate group **[1 mark]** and a nitrogen-containing base **[1 mark]**. There are four possible bases in DNA — adenine (A), thymine (T), cytosine (C) or guanine (G) **[1 mark]**.
b) Maximum of 3 marks available.
RNA contains ribose sugar, not deoxyribose **[1 mark]**. RNA molecules are usually single stranded, not double stranded **[1 mark]**. The base uracil (U) is found in RNA instead of thymine (T) **[1 mark]**.

3 Maximum of 4 marks available, from any of the 6 points below.
Nucleotides are joined between the phosphate group of one nucleotide and the sugar of the next **[1 mark]**. The two polynucleotide strands join through hydrogen bonds **[1 mark]** between the base pairs **[1 mark]**. Complementary base pairing means adenine (A) always joins with thymine (T) and cytosine (C) always joins with guanine (G) **[1 mark]**. Three hydrogen bonds join C with G and two hydrogen bonds join A with T **[1 mark]**. One mark can be given for an accurate diagram showing at least one of the above points **[1 mark]**.
As the question asks for a diagram make sure you do at least one, e.g.:

sugar and phosphate join
3 hydrogen bonds
Cytosine | Guanine
2 hydrogen bonds
Adenine | Thymine

Page 65 — DNA Replication and Protein Synthesis

1 Maximum of 7 marks available.
The DNA helix unzips **[1 mark]**. Each strand acts as a template **[1 mark]**. Individual free DNA nucleotides join up along the template strand by complementary base pairing **[1 mark]**. DNA polymerase joins the individual nucleotides together **[1 mark]**.
(Students often forget to mention this enzyme in their answers — make sure you don't forget.)
Hydrogen bonds then form between the bases on each strand **[1 mark]**. Two identical DNA molecules are produced **[1 mark]**. Each of the new molecules contains a single strand from the original DNA molecule and a single new strand **[1 mark]**.

2 Maximum of 2 marks available.
A gene is a sequence of DNA nucleotides **[1 mark]** that codes for a protein/polypeptide **[1 mark]**.

3 Maximum of 3 marks available.
DNA contains the instructions for making proteins **[1 mark]**. DNA is copied into RNA **[1 mark]**, which is used to make proteins **[1 mark]**.

Unit 2: Section 3 — Enzymes

Page 67 — Action of Enzymes

1 Maximum of 7 marks available.
In the 'lock and key' model the enzyme and the substrate have to fit together at the active site of the enzyme **[1 mark]**. This creates an enzyme-substrate complex **[1 mark]**.
The active site then causes changes in the substrate **[1 mark]**.
This mark could also be gained by explaining the change (e.g. bringing molecules closer together, or putting a strain on bonds).
The change results in the substrate being broken down/joined together **[1 mark]**. The 'induced fit' model has the same basic mechanism as the 'lock and key' model **[1 mark]**.
The difference is that the substrate is thought to cause a change in the enzyme's active site shape **[1 mark]**, which enables a better fit **[1 mark]**.

Answers

Page 69 — Factors Affecting Enzyme Activity

1 *Maximum of 8 marks available, from any of the 10 points below. If the solution is too cold, the enzyme will work very slowly* ***[1 mark]****. This is because, at low temperatures, the molecules have little kinetic energy, so move slowly, making collisions between enzyme and substrate molecules less likely* ***[1 mark]****. Also, fewer of the collisions will have enough energy to result in a reaction* ***[1 mark]****.*

The marks above could also be obtained by giving the reverse argument — a higher temperature is best to use because the molecules will move fast enough to give a reasonable chance of collisions and those collisions will have more energy, so more will result in a reaction.

If the temperature gets too high, the reaction will stop ***[1 mark]****. This is because the enzyme is denatured* ***[1 mark]*** *— the active site changes shape and will no longer fit the substrate* ***[1 mark]****. Denaturation is caused by increased vibration breaking bonds in the enzyme* ***[1 mark]****. Enzymes have an optimum pH* ***[1 mark]****. pH values too far from the optimum cause denaturation* ***[1 mark]****.*

Explanation of denaturation here will get a mark only if it hasn't been explained earlier.

Denaturation by pH is caused by disruption of ionic and hydrogen bonds, which alters the enzyme's tertiary structure ***[1 mark]****.*

Page 71 — Factors Affecting Enzyme Activity

1 a) *Maximum of 2 marks available.*
Magnesium ions are a cofactor for hexokinase ***[1 mark]****. They help the enzyme and substrate bind together* ***[1 mark]****.*

b) *Maximum of 2 marks available.*
Aluminium ions are an enzyme inhibitor for hexokinase ***[1 mark]****. They bind to the enzyme and prevent the enzyme-substrate complex from forming* ***[1 mark]****.*

c) *Maximum of 1 mark available.*
Because they inhibit respiration, which is a metabolic reaction ***[1 mark]****.*

2 *Maximum of 5 marks available.*
Ritonavir will prevent the HIV virus from replicating ***[1 mark]****, because the virus will not be able to break down the proteins needed to make new viruses* ***[1 mark]****. The Ritonavir molecules are a similar shape to the protease enzyme's substrate so it will act as a competitive inhibitor* ***[1 mark]****. It will bind to the active site of the enzyme* ***[1 mark]****, and block it so the substrate cannot fit in* ***[1 mark]****.*

Unit 2: Section 4 — Diet and Food Production

Page 73 — Balanced Diet

1 *Maximum of 4 marks available.*
Saturated fat increases blood cholesterol level ***[1 mark]****, which increases the build up of fatty deposits in the arteries* ***[1 mark]****. This results in atherosclerosis/narrowing of the arteries* ***[1 mark]****, which reduces blood flow to the heart* ***[1 mark]****.*

2 a) *Maximum of 2 marks available.*
The total blood cholesterol level would have decreased ***[1 mark]*** *because there were more HDLs, which decrease blood cholesterol level by transporting cholesterol from the blood to the liver* ***[1 mark]****.*

b) *Maximum of 1 mark available.*
The patient may have increased his polyunsaturated fat intake ***[1 mark]****.*

Page 75 — Food Production

1 a) *Maximum of 3 marks available.*
Plants with large grains were bred together ***[1 mark]****. Then the offspring with the largest grains were bred together* ***[1 mark]****. This was repeated over generations* ***[1 mark]*** *to make the grains of modern wheat plants larger.*

b) *Maximum of 3 marks available.*
Hessian fly infestation would reduce the crop yield by damaging the crops ***[1 mark]****. A short-term solution would be to use a pesticide to kill the flies* ***[1 mark]****. A long-term solution would be to use selective breeding to create a wheat strain resistant to the fly* ***[1 mark]****.*

A lot of exam questions will be like this one — you have to use your knowledge and apply it to a real-life situation to show you've understood the principles. Make sure you refer to the situation the question has described.

Page 77 — Microorganisms and food

1 a) *Maximum of 2 marks available.*
It's heat-treated to kill any microorganisms ***[1 mark]****, which extends its shelf life* ***[1 mark]****.*

b) *Maximum of 3 marks available, from any of the 4 points below. The fungus can be grown faster than cows* ***[1 mark]****. The environment for growth of fungus can be more easily controlled, so they can potentially be grown anywhere* ***[1 mark]*** *and at any time of year* ***[1 mark]****. It's easier to create the right conditions for fungus to grow* ***[1 mark]****.*

Unit 2: Section 5 — Health and Disease

Page 79 — Infectious Disease

1 a) *Maximum of 4 marks available.*
It is caused by infection with Mycobacterium tuberculosis ***[1 mark]****. It is transmitted by droplet infection* ***[1 mark]****. This is where an infected person coughs or sneezes and releases tiny droplets of saliva and mucus containing the bacteria from their mouth and nose* ***[1 mark]****. These droplets are then breathed in by other people* ***[1 mark]****.*

b) *Maximum of 3 marks available, from any of the points below. Limited access to healthcare* ***[1 mark]****. Vaccinations or drugs not available* ***[1 mark]****. Less likely to be diagnosed* ***[1 mark]****. Overcrowding* ***[1 mark]****. Social disruption (which exacerbates other problems, such as access to healthcare)* ***[1 mark]****.*

c) *Maximum of 2 marks available, from any of the points below. To find out where people are most at risk* ***[1 mark]****. To predict where epidemics are most likely to occur* ***[1 mark]****. To help research* ***[1 mark]****. To allow organisations to give aid where it is needed most* ***[1 mark]****.*

2 a) *Maximum of 1 mark available.*
HIV ***[1 mark]****.*

b) *Maximum of 4 marks available, from any of the points below. Educating people about safe sex practices* ***[1 mark]****. Making condoms available* ***[1 mark]****. Quick diagnosis, so that infected people won't pass it on unknowingly* ***[1 mark]****. Screening blood from donors* ***[1 mark]****. Sterilising needles and surgical equipment* ***[1 mark]****. Making alternatives to breast-feeding available for women with HIV* ***[1 mark]****. Providing needle exchanges* ***[1 mark]****.*

If you know how a disease is transmitted you should be able to figure out how to reduce its spread. Make sure you don't put down drug treatment for HIV, as this won't reduce the spread of the virus.

Answers

Page 83 — The Immune System

1 *Maximum of 6 marks available*
*A phagocyte recognises the antigens on a pathogen **[1 mark]**. The phagocyte engulfs the pathogen **[1 mark]**. The pathogen is now contained in a phagocytic vacuole **[1 mark]**. A lysosome fuses with the phagocytic vacuole **[1 mark]** and digestive enzymes break down the pathogen **[1 mark]**. The phagocyte presents the antigens to T lymphocytes **[1 mark]**.*

2 *Maximum of 3 marks available.*
*Antibodies agglutinate pathogens, so that phagocytes can get rid of a lot of the pathogens at once **[1 mark]**. Antibodies neutralise toxins produced by pathogens **[1 mark]**. Antibodies bind to pathogens to prevent them from binding to and infecting human cells **[1 mark]**.*
There are three marks available for this question so you need to think of three different functions.

3 *Maximum of 10 marks available.*
*When Emily caught chickenpox the first time **[1 mark]** her B and T lymphocytes produced memory cells **[1 mark]**, giving her immunological memory against the virus antigens **[1 mark]**. When exposed a second time **[1 mark]** the memory B lymphocytes divided into plasma cells **[1 mark]** to produce the right antibody to the virus **[1 mark]**. The memory T lymphocytes divided into the correct type of T lymphocyte **[1 mark]** to kill the virus **[1 mark]**. The secondary response was quicker and stronger **[1 mark]** and so got rid of the pathogen before she showed any symptoms **[1 mark]**.*
This question is asking about the secondary response and the immune system memory, so no detail is needed about how the primary response got rid of the infection.

Page 85 — Immunity and Vaccinations

1 a) *Maximum of 3 marks available.*
*Different strains of the influenza virus are present in the population each year **[1 mark]**. Each different strain has different cell-surface antigens **[1 mark]**. So a new vaccine is made every year to protect against the most recently circulating strains of influenza **[1 mark]**.*

b) *Maximum of 3 marks available.*
*Samples of influenza viruses are collected by laboratories **[1 mark]**. The effectiveness of different vaccines is tested against these samples **[1 mark]** and the most effective vaccine is chosen **[1 mark]**.*

Page 87 — Smoking and Disease

1 *Maximum of 12 marks available, 6 for each disease.*
Emphysema:
*Emphysema is caused by toxic particles from cigarette smoke becoming trapped in the alveoli of the lungs **[1 mark]**. This encourages phagocytes into the area **[1 mark]**, which release an enzyme that breaks down elastin in the walls of the alveoli **[1 mark]**. This reduces the surface area and elasticity of the alveoli, decreasing the rate of gas exchange **[1 mark]**. Sufferers have a shortness of breath because they can't breathe in enough oxygen **[1 mark]**. They may breathe faster than normal/hyperventilate to try to get enough oxygen into their body **[1 mark]**. People with emphysema may have an expanded lung as some air remains trapped in the alveoli **[1 mark]**.*
Lung cancer:
*Lung cancer can be caused by the carcinogens present in cigarette smoke **[1 mark]**. These may cause mutations in the DNA of lung cells **[1 mark]**, which could lead to uncontrolled cell growth **[1 mark]**. This could cause malignant tumour growth **[1 mark]**, which would block air flow to areas of the lungs, reducing gas exchange **[1 mark]**. Lung cancer leads to a shortness of breath as sufferers struggle to take in enough oxygen **[1 mark]**. It can also cause weight loss due to the tumour using up nutrients and energy **[1 mark]**.*

Unit 2: Section 6 — Biodiversity

Page 89 — Studying Biodiversity

1 a) *Maximum of 2 marks available.*
*Species richness is the number of different species in an area **[1 mark]**. Species evenness is a measure of the relative abundance of each species in an area **[1 mark]**.*

b) *Maximum of 4 marks available.*
*They would take random samples from the area being studied **[1 mark]**. They would need to use an appropriate method to catch the millipedes, such as a pitfall trap **[1 mark]**. They would count the number of different species present **[1 mark]** and the number of individuals of each species in the sample **[1 mark]**.*

Page 91 — Global Biodiversity

1 a) *Maximum of 1 mark available, from any of the 3 points below.*
*The total number of species on Earth is not known **[1 mark]**. Some species have not been discovered yet **[1 mark]**. It would be impossible **[1 mark]**.*

b) *Maximum of 1 mark available.*
*The Living Planet Index/biodiversity of Earth has decreased from 1970 to 2000 **[1 mark]**.*

c) *Maximum of 5 marks available.*
*Climate change alters habitat conditions **[1 mark]**. Some species may be unable to survive in these conditions and become extinct, which decreases biodiversity **[1 mark]**. The ranges of some species that carry diseases may increase, which could cause population decline of other species, decreasing biodiversity **[1 mark]**. The ranges of some fungal diseases may increase, which could cause population decline of other species, decreasing biodiversity **[1 mark]**. Areas previously suitable for farming may become unsuitable, decreasing biodiversity **[1 mark]**.*
The question asks about global biodiversity so you won't get marks for mentioning anything that affects local biodiversity but not overall biodiversity, e.g. migration.

Page 93 — Importance of Biodiversity

1 *Maximum of 4 marks available.*
*If one species is removed from a food chain it can affect all organisms further up the food chain **[1 mark]**. The loss of certain organisms (such as decomposers) can affect the nutrient cycle in the area, which will affect the growth of plants and reduce the amount of food available to animals **[1 mark]**. The loss of one habitat (such as a hedgerow) would affect other habitats as they may become isolated, so availability of food/nesting sites would be reduced **[1 mark]**. The destruction of species and habitats that store CO_2, like trees and peat bogs, contributes to climate change, which is reducing biodiversity **[1 mark]**.*

Answers

2 *Maximum of 5 marks available.*
Biodiversity provides a range of species that are used as food for people and livestock ***[1 mark]****. Many crops are pollinated by a diverse range of insects* ***[1 mark]****, and other insects are used as natural predators of pest species* ***[1 mark]****. Cross-breeding with wild plants can create plants with new characteristics* ***[1 mark]****. A greater variety of crops grown means that food sources are less susceptible to disease or pests* ***[1 mark]****.*

Page 95 — Conservation and Biodiversity

1 a) *Maximum of 5 marks available.*
In situ *methods could include protecting the turtles from hunters* ***[1 mark]*** *and protecting their nesting sites* ***[1 mark]****. A national park/protected area could also be established to restrict human usage of the area* ***[1 mark]****.* Ex situ *methods could include relocating the turtles or their eggs to a safer environment* ***[1 mark]*** *or to start a captive breeding programme* ***[1 mark]****.*

b) *Maximum of 4 marks available.*
It's only possible to conserve a limited number of individuals with ex situ *methods* ***[1 mark]****. They can be very expensive* ***[1 mark]****. It may be difficult to sustain the environment for the turtle* ***[1 mark]****. They don't protect the habitat of the turtle* ***[1 mark]****.*

c) *Maximum of 1 mark available.*
International cooperation is important because it means that hunting endangered species is illegal in all countries — making hunting illegal in one country would have little use if it was legal in a neighbouring country ***[1 mark]****.*

Unit 2: Section 7 — Classification

Page 97 — Classification Basics

1 a) *Maximum of 1 mark available.*
The act of arranging organisms into groups based on their similarities and differences ***[1 mark]****.*

b) *Maximum of 1 mark available.*
The study of classification ***[1 mark]****.*

c) *Maximum of 1 mark available.*
The study of the evolutionary history/development of organisms ***[1 mark]****.*

2 *Maximum of 3 marks available.*
The binomial system gives all organisms an internationally accepted, two-word, scientific name in Latin ***[1 mark]****. The first part is a genus name* ***[1 mark]****. The second part is the species name* ***[1 mark]****.*

Page 99 — Dichotomous Keys

1 a) *Maximum of 3 marks available.*
A — Lyngbya ***[1 mark]****.*
B — Trichodesmium ***[1 mark]****.*
C — Anabaena ***[1 mark]****.*

b) *Maximum of 3 marks available, from any of the 4 points below.*
RNA polymerase is different in the Archaea and Bacteria ***[1 mark]****. Archaea, but not bacteria, have histones similar to Eukarya* ***[1 mark]****. The bonds of the lipids in the cell membranes of Archaea and Bacteria are different* ***[1 mark]****. The development and composition of flagellae are also different in the Archaea and Bacteria* ***[1 mark]****.*

Unit 2: Section 8 — Evolution

Page 101 — Variation

1 a) *Maximum of 3 marks available.*
For species A, as the temperature increases the development time decreases ***[1 mark]****. For species B the development time also decreases as the temperature increases* ***[1 mark].***
The development time of species B is less affected by temperature than species A ***[1 mark]****.*

b) *Maximum of 4 marks available.*
The variation between the species is mainly due to their different genes ***[1 mark]****. Variation within a species is caused by both genetic and environmental factors* ***[1 mark]****. Individuals have different forms of the same genes (alleles), which causes genetic differences* ***[1 mark]****. Individuals may have the same genes, but environmental factors influence how some characteristics develop* ***[1 mark]****.*

Page 102 — Adaptations

1 *Maximum of 8 marks available.*
Behavioural — It can roll into a ball when alarmed ***[1 mark]****, which increases it chance of escaping attack* ***[1 mark]****.*
Physiological — It can hibernate over winter ***[1 mark]****, which means it's more likely to survive the winter months when food is scarce* ***[1 mark]****.*
For anatomical you can get any two from the list below, to a maximum of 4 marks — 1 mark for each adaptation and 1 mark for explaining why each adaptation increases survival.
Anatomical — Brown colour ***[1 mark]****, camouflages it, so it's harder for predators to spot* ***[1 mark]****. Spiky fur* ***[1 mark]****, protects it from predators* ***[1 mark]****. Long fur* ***[1 mark]****, provides warmth* ***[1 mark]****. Small ears* ***[1 mark]****, help to reduce heat loss* ***[1 mark]****. Claws* ***[1 mark]****, are used to catch prey* ***[1 mark]****.*

Page 105 — The Theory of Evolution

1 *Maximum of 4 marks available.*
Individuals within a population show variation ***[1 mark]****. Predation, disease and competition create a struggle for survival* ***[1 mark]****. Individuals with better adaptations are more likely to survive, reproduce and pass on their advantageous adaptations to their offspring* ***[1 mark]****. Over time, the number of individuals with the advantageous adaptations increases and the adaptations become more common* ***[1 mark]****.*

2 a) *Maximum of 4 marks available.*
Genetic mutations would have resulted in some moths being resistant to DDT ***[1 mark]****. When the population was exposed to DDT, only those individuals who were resistant would survive to reproduce* ***[1 mark]****. The alleles which code for resistance would be passed on to the next generation* ***[1 mark]****. Over time, the number of individuals with DDT resistance would increase and it would become more common within the population* ***[1 mark]****.*

b) *Maximum of 2 marks available, from any of the 3 points below.*
Moth infestations would be harder to control ***[1 mark]****. Broader pesticides might be used, which could kill beneficial insects* ***[1 mark]****. New pesticides might need to be developed if the moth develops resistance to all pesticides in use* ***[1 mark]****.*

Index

Index

Index